Miniature
Orchids

MINIATURE
Orchids

JIM & BARBARA MCQUEEN

THE TEXT PUBLISHING COMPANY
MELBOURNE AUSTRALIA

The Text Publishing Company Pty Ltd
220 Clarendon Street
East Melbourne Victoria 3002
Australia

First published 1992

Printed and bound at Mandarin Offset, Hong Kong
Typeset by Bookset, Melbourne

National Library of Australia Cataloguing-in-Publication data:

McQueen, James, 1934– .
Miniature orchids.
Includes index.
ISBN 1 86372 215 7.
1. Miniature orchids. 2. Orchid culture. I. McQueen, Barbara,
1953– . II. Title. (Series: World of orchids).
635.93415

ACKNOWLEDGEMENTS

This book is dedicated to the late Jim (J.N.) Rentoul who, in his later years, encouraged us to continue growing, photographing and writing about orchids.

Our special thanks are due to our good friends Phyl and Chris Nicholas of Hobart, Tasmania, who not only allowed us to photograph a number of the plants in their extensive collection, but also supplied most of the photographs of *Masdevallia* species included in this book.

CONTENTS

INTRODUCTION   1

1 · WHAT IS AN ORCHID?   3

Distinctive features of orchids   4
Orchid seed   6
Orchids as green plants   7
  Chlorophyll and photosynthesis   7
  Inorganic elements and fertilisers   8

2 · ORCHIDS IN CULTIVATION   12

Housing orchids
  Adaptation and tolerance   13
  Altitude and the greenhouse environment   13
  Light and air   14
  Temperature   15
  Ventilation and air movement   17
Watering   18
Substrates   20
Orchids as houseplants   22
Acclimatising plants   24

3 · PLANT NAMES AND BOTANICAL LATIN   27

Taxonomy   27
  The binomial system   27
  New names and taxonomic revisions   28
Botanical Latin   29
  Pronunciation   29

ALPHABETICAL LISTING OF SPECIES   31

GLOSSARY   185
INDEX   187

INTRODUCTION

Few orchid growers, particularly those in cooler climates, ever have much growing space to spare; indeed, following a variant of Parkinson's Law, collections tend to expand to fill the available space. For this reason, if for no other, miniature orchids hold a special attraction for space-bound growers.

But there is more to miniatures than mere spatial economy. They have a charm all their own, an elegance and delicacy that is often lacking in their larger relatives. And there is much to be said for a plant that will live happily for many years in a 7 cm pot or on a small mount; ask anyone who has divided and repotted a large collection of *Cymbidium* hybrids.

There are few popular orchid genera which do not include among their number a miniature or two; while some large genera such as *Maxillaria* are composed almost entirely of miniatures and may form the basis of a specialised collection.

Miniature orchids, of course, are deservedly popular with growers who live in small apartments; provided they are given a spell out of doors in clement weather, many of them may be grown to perfection on bright windowsills or in sunny rooms. A modest collection is within the scope of anyone with even the smallest growing area. A space 30 cm square can hold as many as thirty or more true miniatures. And a carefully

chosen collection of miniatures can possess all the variety of a standard collection, while requiring only a small proportion of the time and energy needed for its maintenance.

Of course, there are miniatures and miniatures. A friend of ours who owns an orchid nursery in Brazil (the home of

This tiny and delightful African species, *Mystacidium venosum*, grows happily on its mount year after year, producing its spray of long-spurred white flowers each winter from little more than a bundle of roots

so many wonderful miniatures) maintains that some of the tiniest plants should only be sold with a magnifying glass. Well, it is true that some of the tiniest species are only for the dedicated collector. But there are many small-growing species that produce flowers every bit as large as their bigger relatives.

What exactly do we mean by the term *miniature*? Definitions vary from grower to grower, but we think of miniatures as plants that grow no taller than about 20 cm, excluding flower spike. Many of course are much smaller than this. Flower size may vary a great deal, but many species which have very small flowers compensate by producing them in quite prodigious quantity.

In this book we deal solely with species orchids. There are a few nice miniature hybrids that are worth growing, especially those with *Sophronitis* species in their background, but in general miniatures have never seriously engaged the hybridist. Again, most of the orchids covered by this book are epiphytes (although most do well in pots), as in general these are much easier to grow successfully than terrestrials. We have, however, included a few of the more easily cultivated terrestrials.

Miniature orchid species are not always easy to obtain. Most commercial nurseries tend to concentrate on a fairly narrow range of species in the more standard sizes, so some persistence is

Many desirable diminutive species, such as this *Sophronitis coccinea*, produce quite large flowers

necessary if you are to build up a comprehensive collection. But the plants, when found, are seldom excessive in price and the rewards for the hunt are high. And more and more people are coming to realise that in today's world bigger is not necessarily better.

Nowhere is this truer than in the world of orchids, where the miniature frequently outshines its larger relatives in brilliance of colour, diversity of shape, delicacy of perfume, and just plain elegance.

1 · What Is an Orchid?

Most of us, even the rankest amateurs, are able to recognise an orchid when we see one. And, from the grower's point of view, all we really need to know is that they are *green plants*. Most people, however, depending on the depth of their interest, want to know a little more about what must be one of the most popular plant families in the world.

Orchids are usually considered to have evolved from the family Liliaceae. There is a general belief among botanists that the orchid family is an old one in terms of geological time, yet for some unknown reason no fossil remains have been found. With perhaps thirty thousand species, the orchid family is one of the largest in the plant world, second only to the Compositae (the sunflower family, which includes daisies, dahlias, gazanias etc.). Orchid species far outnumber those of the Gramineae, the grass family, which has about nine thousand members. In size they vary from plants such as *Bulbophyllum globuliforme* with pseudobulbs scarcely larger than a pin head to the massive *Grammatophyllum speciosum* whose pseudobulbs may reach a height of seven metres or more.

Orchid species are widely distributed throughout the world, from the equatorial regions to the subarctic and subantarctic. Those from tropical regions tend to be mainly epiphytes or lithophytes (living on trees and rocks respectively). Those inhabiting temperate and cold regions are mostly deciduous terrestrials with underground tubers that remain dormant through freezing winters (as in Europe and North America) or through hot dry summers (as in Australia).

One of the most fascinating aspects of orchids is the diversity of their floral form. The flowers are complex and highly specialised, yet all orchids, no matter how widely separated their habitats, clearly demonstrate a common floral pattern that differentiates them from all other forms.

DISTINCTIVE FEATURES OF ORCHIDS

What **does** distinguish an orchid from other plants, then? Although we may be sure that we know an orchid when we see it, it is not always easy to arrive at a clear definition. After all, the orchid family displays almost all the known functions of plant physiology except carnivorism and parasitism. Orchids, in botanical terms, are perennial herbs, and grow on trees and sometimes on other plants such as cacti, on rocks, in the earth, under the earth, or as semi-aquatics.

There are two distinct types of vegetative growth in orchids: sympodial and monopodial. In the case of *sympodial* growth (exhibited by many epiphytes and all terrestrials), the main axis or stem stops growing at the end of a season. At the beginning of a new season a new growth axis begins, and in time the plant forms a series of successive growths. Dendrobiums and cattleyas are well-known examples of this type of growth. In plants exhibiting *monopodial* growth, on the other hand, the main axis continues to grow year after year. Vandas and phalaenopsis both exhibit monopodial growth.

The flowers of orchids, of course, are where we tend to look for the family's distinctive features. All orchid flowers are *zygomorphic* — that is, they are formed in such a way that they may be divided into two exactly similar parts by drawing a line in one particular plane only. To put it another way, an orchid flower can be divided to form mirror

Laelia dayana demonstrates sympodial habit, with new pseudobulbs being formed in front of old ones each year

Pelatantheria insectifera, an Asian miniature, shows monopodial habit, extending its main stem upward with each year's growth

images only by drawing a line vertically through the centre of the lip.

Mostly, orchid flowers are *herma-phroditic*: they have both male and female functions present in a single flower. In some species, however, plants may be *dioecious* — in which case they display both male and female flowers on the same plant — or *monoecious* — displaying male **or** female flowers on a single plant. The genera *Catasetum* and *Mormodes*, for instance, produce both male and female flowers. (Plants in bright light tend to produce female flowers, while those in shady situations tend to produce male flowers.) This situation confused early orchid botanists and taxonomists, and it took Darwin to sort matters out.

Orchids generally have *petaloid* sepals — that is, sepals in colours other than green (except, of course, in green flowers). This feature they share with non-orchids such as the iris. There are three sepals, either free or joined together, sometimes united at the base to form a *mentum* or chin, as in angraecums and many dendrobiums. Two of the three petals are regular and identical, but the third one is very much modified into a *labellum* or lip. In most species this lip — which would normally be the upper petal — is repositioned as the lowest by the twisting of the stem or ovary, a process called *resupination*. This twisting process is very noticeable in cymbidiums. The lip usually varies a great deal in size, colour and shape from other segments, and is often the most attractive and distinctive feature of the flower.

Perhaps the most distinctive feature of the orchid flower — and one which is usually obvious to the curious observer — is the fusing of the normal reproductive organs (the anther and the stigma) into a single *column*. This column varies

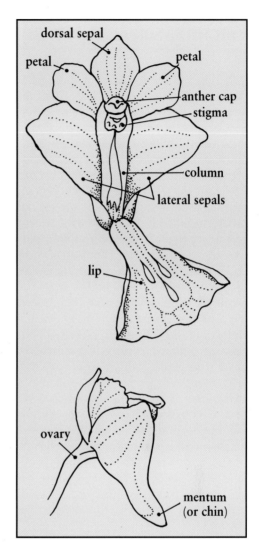

a great deal in formation from one species to another and is a valuable tool for identifying and classifying distinct species.

Despite all the fairly obvious distinctions we can note between orchids and other green plants, it was once postulated (by Pfitzer, in 1889) that the only true difference is that orchids lack an embryonic root. It is lucky for us that there are all the other, more easily recognised, criteria.

ORCHID SEED

Orchid plants produce a quite phenomenal amount of seed. An accurate count of the seed from a single pod of *Cycnoches chlorochilon* revealed a total of 3,770,000. Even species with much smaller pods produce many hundreds of thousands of seeds. Yet orchid populations, left to themselves, remain fairly stable, indicating that almost all orchid seed produced in the wild fails to germinate or, if it does germinate, fails to reach maturity. This is not difficult to understand when we consider the nature of orchid seed for, in addition to the profligacy of its production, orchid seed has a further distinction. The individual seed contains no food reserves at all, but only an embryo enclosed in a net-like cover (the *testa*, which under a low-power microscope looks a little like a string bag or fishnet). This lack of reserves in the orchid seed has very important implications for its ability to survive and germinate; this factor presented early orchid growers with enormous problems when it came to propagating orchid plants sexually (that is, by seed) rather than asexually (by division or cutting).

Many plants, including trees, have a strange partnership with various fungi. Their roots live in association with the fungi, and in fact cannot survive without them. Seeds of these plants will germinate normally and grow for some time; but unless the appropriate fungus is present, the plants will not thrive. Most orchids also live in such a symbiotic relationship with fungi, but in their case the seeds will not germinate naturally without the appropriate fungus.

This symbiotic relationship between green plants and fungi is called *mycorrhiza*, and it falls into two categories. In the first, the threads (or *mycelia*) of the fungus do not actually penetrate the green plant's root system. In this situation, the fungus probably helps the plant absorb minerals from the soil. In the second type of mycorrhiza — which involves orchids — the mycelium of the fungus actually penetrates the roots of the plant and forms groups of cells that store organic food material. These materials are utilised by the orchid for its survival. The fungus is thought to receive, in its turn, some benefit from the orchid plant; perhaps vitamins or other useful substances. The relationship is probably kept in some sort of balance by hormones produced by the orchid plants.

The seeds of almost all orchid species need the presence of the appropriate fungus in order to germinate and grow; they also need, of course, adequate and appropriate levels of humidity, light and temperature. There is still much scientific argument as to whether particular orchid species need specific fungi to grow; but this is not a matter that has any practical application for the ordinary orchid grower.

For the first century of orchid growing in Europe, the only seedlings raised artificially were those germinated by the 'symbiotic' method, that is, spreading the seed at the base of a parent plant (which was already infected with fungus about the roots), watering carefully, and hoping for the best. The great breakthrough in orchid seed-raising came in the 1920s, when Knudsen found that orchid seed could be germinated in sterile flasks on an agar gel containing various sugars and minerals. This 'asymbiotic' process has been much improved over the years, and now most epiphytic orchids and some terrestrials can be raised artificially by this method. It gave a great impetus to the creation of hybrids. However, the asymbiotic process does not work well, if at all, with many deciduous terrestrial species, including most Australian terrestrials, and pioneering work in devising methods of raising such species in symbiotic conditions (that is, in the presence of appropriate isolated fungi) is currently being done by a number of researchers.

ORCHIDS AS GREEN PLANTS

Having looked briefly at the major botanical features that distinguish orchids from other plants, we must — if we are to learn how to treat them in practice — go back to our original concept of orchids as green plants.

There are exceptions, however, even to this broad statement. There is a small number of saprophytic plants which, lacking chlorophyll, gain their nutriment directly from decaying organic matter; among these are such species as *Dipodium punctatum* and *Cymbidium macrorhizon*. Such saprophytes are extremely difficult to handle in cultivation, and rarely attempted, so for practical purposes we can disregard them and concentrate on green plants. If we understand how green plants function we will know all we need to know about how to treat our orchids.

Chlorophyll and photosynthesis
What makes plants green, of course, is the presence of chlorophyll. It is this pigment, and the way it functions, that differentiates plants from animals, from the simplest up to the most complex organism.

The sun — and it is no wonder that so many primitive people worshipped it — is the great provider of energy for our world. Its radiant energy not only heats the world, but also feeds it — through the process of photosynthesis in green plants. And this process is possible only in the presence of chlorophyll. Chlorophyll absorbs the red, orange and violet wavelengths of the sun's rays, and the resulting energy is used to combine water and carbon dioxide to produce carbohydrates such as sugar (sugar cane is a very efficient converter); in the process, oxygen is given off. **Photosynthesis thus makes green plants totally independent of outside sources of carbohydrate.** The limiting factors in the production of food by green plants for their own use are light, water and carbon dioxide.

Carbon dioxide is present as a more-or-less constant constituent in the air about us. There is usually quite a low percentage present — about 3 parts in 10,000 — but this is enough. Water, of course, is not generally a problem for plants under cultivation. Light (and its associated heat) is the factor that, as orchid growers, will probably cause us most concern. In general, the greater the amount of light present, the higher the rate of photosynthesis. There are, however, pitfalls. We might ask ourselves if we could, perhaps, give our plants around-the-clock light, and thus keep them producing sugars on a continuous basis. Unfortunately, this won't work. As well as **producing** food, plants need to **use** it. In fact, there is a very clear cyclic pattern. During daylight hours the chlorophyll acts as a catalyst in the manufacture of carbohydrates for the plants. In the hours of darkness photosynthesis stops, and a kind of reverse process takes over — the plants give off carbon dioxide and take in oxygen, releasing energy by the process of oxidation, rather the way a fire does. The energy released is used for cell multiplication. Surplus carbohydrate is stored against future need; many orchids have pseudobulbs, which are ideal for this purpose. Fats and proteins are also produced and used or stored. Fats go to build up cells, and proteins to produce protoplasm.

Inorganic elements and fertilisers

At this point, a fairly obvious question arises. If plants produce their own food entirely, why do we need to 'feed' them? Why all these packets of Aquasol and Osmocote and Bestgro and Magamp and so on? The fact is that in addition to carbohydrates and fats and proteins all plants need small quantities of *inorganic elements*.

Many pendent plants such as this Australian species, *Bulbophyllum radicans*, prefer to grow with their roots free in the air

It is possible for an orchid plant to live for quite a long time with no more sustenance than water and the tiny amounts of minerals contained in its water intake. But sooner or later, if the plant is to survive and thrive, it must have access to all the essential inorganic elements. The main ones needed are nitrogen, phosphorus and potassium; others needed in smaller amounts include calcium, sulphur, magnesium, sodium, copper, iron and boron. In nature, terrestrial plants obtain these minerals from the soil. Epiphytes obtain them from bird guano, decaying animal or vegetable matter, atmospheric dust, decomposing bark and leaves. This indicates, of course, that the quantities required are very small.

We must now revise our formula a little. To grow orchids well we need to give them light, water, carbon dioxide, and an array of minerals. Simple enough.

But is it? If it is so simple, then why the confusing array of fertilisers, the bewildering multiplicity of advice? Why does every grower, it seems, have a different and more-or-less successful formula?

The answer is not too difficult to find. The fact is that almost all the recommended fertilisers or formulae will give satisfactory results **if used under a specific set of controlled conditions**. The problem for practical hobbyists — as opposed to the research chemist or the commercial grower — is that their chances of reproducing the precise conditions needed for success with a particular fertiliser are not very high. To add to the difficulty, most hobbyists will be trying to grow a collection comprising a wide range of genera, all with slightly different requirements. And even relatively small changes in growing conditions can upset the applecart.

Like other terrestrials, this Australian species, *Pterostylis nutans*, finds all its nutrient requirements in the soil

For instance, in strong light and under optimal nutritional conditions, plant cells produce much more protein than carbohydrate; in poor light but with good conditions, protein and carbohydrate are produced in about equal quantities; while in good light with poor nutrition, some carbohydrate but more fat than protein is produced. These variations in relatively simple factors produce quite diverse effects, which have a decided influence on the growth, health and flowering potential of the plants; and, as conditions vary so much between one grower and another, between one plant and another in a mixed collection, between one end of a country and the other, between one season and another: how can an amateur grower expect to duplicate the results obtained with a particular fertiliser in a strictly controlled test?

It's impossible, of course. All that can be done is to try to strike some sort of happy medium that will give most benefit to most of the plants in a collection, and something a little less than optimum for the others.

But take heart. It is our belief that altogether too much attention is given to the matter of fertilisers — at least for the amateur grower — when it would be better directed to achieving and maintaining good growing conditions. If you have created the right environment for your plants, then a modest amount (and we **do** mean modest) of any balanced commercial fertiliser will provide your plants with all they need for satisfactory growth and flowering. What no fertiliser can ever do is offset the effects of bad growing environment or practices. Most amateurs who have been growing orchids for any length of time have probably developed an attachment to a particular fertiliser. But what is the newcomer to the game, someone who has no experience to fall back on, to do?

Well, there is first of all the option of not fertilising at all. And this is quite a valid choice. If your plants are grown in or on organic materials — bark, leaves, moss, treefern and so on — it is quite possible, even probable, that they will obtain all the minerals they need from the decaying substrates and from the water they receive. At one time, we moved a large collection of plants from one location to another, and most of the plants went unfertilised for two years without showing any sign of deficiency.

The second option is to give your plants a **light** application of any balanced fertiliser every couple of weeks during the growing season. Even if you can't see any visible improvement, you won't have done your plants any harm,

When scrambling mat-forming species such as this *Encyclia polybulbon* extend beyond their mounts, the rhizomes may be trained back onto the mount or removed and mounted as separate plants

unnecessarily. Bill Johnson, who grows orchids commercially in Victoria, has done some valuable work testing standard commercial fertilisers and adapting them to orchids. Basically this involves the addition of certain elements which most 'off-the-shelf' fertilisers lack. He found that Aquasol was the easiest to rebalance, needing fewer additives than any other, but the same rebalancing process may be applied to any commercial fertiliser. His own special formula is available commercially in Australia, but we have used the modified Aquasol with good results. Water for all our greenhouses is drawn from a single 10,000 litre tank, which is refilled as needed (twice a week in summer) with water from a creek. About every three weeks during the growing season we mix up 850 grams of Aquasol, 300 grams of magnesium sulphate and 150 grams of iron chelate, slurry it in a bucket, and pour it into the tank. This gives our plants a small but regular supply of mineral nutrients during the growing season. The solution in the tank is a very weak one and becomes increasingly diluted as the tank is refilled. In small greenhouses without an independent water supply, diluted fertiliser may be introduced as a foliar spray. The actual dilution rate is not important so long as the proportions of fertiliser, magnesium sulphate and iron chelate are maintained. This is basically an insurance program, which ensures that the plants will not lack any essential inorganic element. Most of our plants are provided with organic substrates (mount or potting material), which of course augment the supply of minerals. We believe that this program of light feeding encourages stronger plants, though sometimes slightly smaller ones, which will re-acclimatise rapidly when shifted to a new environment, an important consideration for a commer-

and you will have relieved your mind of the awful suspicion that your plants are starving.

Don't bother to fertilise when plants are not in growth; the fertiliser will be wasted as the plants will not be able to absorb it and, as watering will be limited at that time, excess mineral salts may build up about the roots and cause them to burn when new growth appears.

The third option is to take some time, read all you can on the subject, and work out a fertilising program of your own. Once you have done this you should stick to it for at least a couple of years unless your plants are obviously suffering. Don't chop and change

A number of orchid genera, including many dendrobiums such as *D. tetragonum* shown here, produce adventitious plantlets or 'keikeis', which may be detached when mature enough and grown on as separate plants

cial nursery. On the other hand, a heavily fed plant will sometimes sulk when deprived of its regular diet. So don't turn your plants into junkies.

Whatever option you choose in regard to fertilising, make sure that you give your plants a regular dose of magnesium sulphate in weak solution. Most commercial fertilisers (for reasons which escape us) are deficient in magnesium, one of the most important elements of all for plants. The chlorophyll molecule resembles, oddly enough, the haemoglobin molecule (the red blood pigment in humans and animals), except that it contains magnesium rather than iron; so give your plants an occasional dose of Epsom salts or they may become anaemic.

For as long as we can remember there has been a certain amount of controversy in the matter of organic as opposed to inorganic fertilisers. Although many growers swear by organic fertilisers, we feel that their superiority lies largely in the eye of the beholder. To our knowledge no scientific proof has ever been offered. We do feel, too, that organic fertilisers may be less consistent in their composition from batch to batch. However, if organics are your preference then use them. They probably work just as well as inorganics, as long as you avoid over-application.

There is one other factor related to fertilising that it is well to remember. Orchid plants are very economical when it comes to utilising scarce resources. They recycle minerals from old stems to new ones. So don't remove old canes or pseudobulbs until they are truly dead — until that finally happens they will be functioning as reservoirs for nutriment as well as water.

In a sense, as we have seen, we can regard orchid plants as machines. They convert sunlight and water and carbon dioxide into carbohydrates, fats and proteins for their own growth; to do this they need minute amounts of certain minerals that must come from outside their own manufacturing systems. Their needs are really quite simple, and if we satisfy them, they will never cease to reward us with their flowers.

2 · ORCHIDS IN CULTIVATION

We have seen cultivated orchids growing in all manner of odd places: in fish tanks, discarded wardrobes, derelict station wagons, old telephone boxes, converted fowl houses and aviaries, shower stalls. And a very nice collection growing happily in an old trolley bus. All this should tell us something.

First of all, of course, it tells us that there are some very ingenious people about. But it also casts a little light on a blind spot many of us have when it comes to orchids. Mention the word 'orchid' and most of us (especially if we live in a cool climate) immediately think 'greenhouse'. And if we are novices, just beginning a career of compulsive and impoverished devotion to the orchid family, we are likely to rush out and buy a greenhouse — and later find that it is quite unsuitable for our plants. Indeed, it would be true to say that with few exceptions the bulk of commercially available greenhouses are quite unsuitable for successful orchid cultivation. They are designed mostly as adjuncts to the vegetable garden, and are too bright, too hot, too badly ventilated, and above all, too small. Almost all will need substantial modifications in order to provide adequate conditions for orchids. So we should stop right away, and instead of thinking 'greenhouse', think 'environment'.

Every orchid plant that we are ever going to possess came originally — it may have been one generation ago or a hundred — from the wild. It grew there without benefit of artificial heat, hosepipes or balanced fertilisers. Its ancestors had grown that way for uncounted generations before it. It was totally acclimatised, in fact, to a particular environment, its genetic development keyed to fairly specific elements of climate, altitude, latitude, temperature, light. If we are to remove this plant, or one of its descendants, from the environment to which it has become completely attuned over thousands of years, we will have to take into account a number of factors if it is to continue growing happily.

Adaptation and tolerance

The first factor we have to rely on is what we might call the positive element in evolution — an organism's propensity to adapt, to survive in a changing environment. We are lucky here, blessed by the orchid family's fairly general tolerance of a range of conditions. This is enhanced by a very slow metabolism; uprooted, an orchid plant will, even under great stress, take quite a long time to die. So we have a small margin of time, as well as a margin of environmental tolerance.

The second factor we will depend on is our own ingenuity in approximating the plant's natural environment. And an approximation is what it will be; for there are certain further factors involved, which serve to prevent us — quite im-

placably — from re-creating exactly a specific orchid's natural environment. (That is, unless we are actually living in a similar environment already; and given the range of horticultural ambitions, this will be unlikely in respect of a mixed collection.)

Altitude and the greenhouse environment

The two factors that limit us most effectively are altitude above sea level, and the environment of a greenhouse, which influences air temperature. And both these factors interact with each other, and with other factors, to make greenhouse cultivation just that little bit more difficult.

Altitude affects the density of the air. A plant growing at a high elevation is surrounded by air of much lower density than air at sea level; not only will the air be cooler because of the altitude but, because it is less dense, it will not be able to hold as much water vapour in suspension. As air is cooled it becomes able to hold less and less water vapour, and the excess is precipitated as condensation. This is in fact dew, and in a greenhouse it is precipitated on solid surfaces such as glass, benches — and plants. At altitudes near sea level, where most of us grow orchids, this condensation from cooling air will be much heavier than it is in high mountain habitats where many orchids grow naturally. And the great majority of orchid species in cultivation come from high altitude tropical regions, a fact that is of great significance to us, particularly in winter, as we shall see.

The temperature of the air is perhaps even more significant than its density; in addition, it interacts with other conditions such as heating and cooling, ventilation and light. To understand why it is

This lovely Australian epiphyte, *Dendrobium canaliculatum,* is shown growing on its natural host *Melaleuca viridiflora,* a tree with many layers of thin papery bark that trap moisture and help the orchid survive dry periods

so important, we should examine what physics textbooks call the 'greenhouse effect'. Sunlight, from which all our energy comes, reaches the earth in the form of short-wavelength rays. Most solid objects exposed to these rays absorb them as heat; for example, our bodies become hotter when exposed to the summer sun. The darker the object, the more absorptive it is; white or shiny surfaces reflect most of the sun's rays and stay relatively cool. And some substances, in particular glass and many transparent plastic films, neither absorb nor reflect the sun's energy; it simply passes through them. The air itself acts in much the same way, allowing the sun's rays to pass **without itself becoming warm.**

If we look at a greenhouse, then, we can see that the sunlight will simply pass through the glass or plastic sheeting, and be absorbed — as heat — by the solid objects inside the greenhouse: the plants, pots, benches and so on. The factor that makes a greenhouse warmer than the outside air is just the one that also presents us with a lot of problems. All the objects that absorb heat from the sun's rays then **re-radiate the heat.** However, it is no longer composed of short-wavelength rays, but of **long**-wavelength waves that will not pass through glass or transparent plastic, and are thus trapped inside the greenhouse. And more: these long-wavelength rays also **warm the air.**

Picture for a moment an orchid plant growing high on the branch of a tree at an altitude of a thousand metres or so in the tropics. The tree may well be a deciduous one — and this is very common in South East Asia — which loses its leaves during the hot dry season. The orchid plant is thus exposed to a very high light intensity and will itself absorb quite a lot of heat. And yet it thrives. The reason it thrives, of course, is because the air about the plant does not absorb heat from the sun, but stays relatively cool. Certainly the air will be heated by radiation from the earth, tree trunks etc., but it will be much cooler than the orchid plant itself, and will cool that plant very effectively, particularly if a breeze is present.

It is obvious, then, that if that same orchid plant is removed from the tree and transferred to a closed greenhouse where it is exposed to the same amount of light it received in its natural habitat, then it will probably collapse fairly quickly because the surrounding air will be too hot to cool it effectively.

Thus we have reached our first obstacle to creating the plant's natural environment in our greenhouse, and we must make our first compromise. For, while it is technically possible to achieve a satisfactory light to temperature ratio in a greenhouse by air-conditioning and ventilation, the capital and operating costs are beyond most amateurs. Luckily, because of the adaptability of most orchids, they are also unnecessary.

Light and air

At this stage we might well ask ourselves just what that orchid plant is doing, perched high on that bare tree: a very harsh environment, to say the least.

All plants in their natural surroundings are in constant competition for light, air and water. Some opt for dim conditions and grow immense leaves to compensate for the paucity of light. Others, like epiphytic orchids, simply abandon the earth altogether, and climb high into the tree-tops. There they find light and air — indeed, perhaps too much light for their needs. Because they are far from any constant source of water, they develop heavy pseudobulbs or thick leaves for more effective water storage. And many of the pseudobulbous species shed their leaves when their host trees do, thus reducing transpiration and water loss.

We could perhaps consider whether such orchid plants might not be grateful for a somewhat more comfortable environment. After all, in seeking its high perch the orchid plant has made compromises of its own. In order to achieve an unlimited amount of light and space, it has embraced a very harsh environment. As most people who have seen epiphytic orchids in the wild will agree, it is not uncommon to find them less robust and floriferous than they are in nurseries. Some have advanced so far in their pursuit of a dry existence that they have become intolerant of water at inappropriate times and need special attention in the greenhouse; but the majority will accept less light than they receive in the wild and still grow and flower quite well.

This means, in practice, that in bright weather you may shade your greenhouse without undue fear. And this is very important, because many growers have to rely on shading as a means of controlling high summer temperatures in their greenhouses.

We live at a latitude of 42° south, close to sea level, and we have our greenhouses unshaded for only about four months in the coldest part of the year. In summer, we have a minimum of about 80 per cent shade, and during the intermediate seasons about 50 per cent shade. We achieve this by stretching a single layer of 50 per cent shadecloth over the greenhouses in early September, adding another layer to give about 80 per cent between December and February. In April the outer layer is removed,

Many orchid species, that grow in dry exposed conditions, such as the unusual *Pleurothallis teres*, develop thick succulent leaves to store and conserve moisture

and in June the inner one. We would not suggest that this is ideal for all types of orchids in all situations. But we have grown an extensive collection of many different genera for quite a number of years under these conditions with good results, and our experience may be a reasonable starting point for experiments.

Temperature

Having satisfied ourselves that we may apply a reasonable amount of shade to our plants to offset to some extent the excessive heat produced by the 'greenhouse effect', our thoughts turn naturally to the matter of temperatures in general. And it seems to us that there has always been a certain amount of confusion about this matter. Just what is 'cool'? cold? intermediate? warm? And what minimum temperatures do we need to maintain?

Much of the present confusion has arisen from the fact that for several generations most books on orchid culture have simply repeated the stipulations of the earliest English manuals. The cultural conditions developed by the authors of those works were relevant to the important orchid-growing areas of a century or more ago: Britain and central and northern Europe. The climate of these countries is characterised by long, very cold winters with extremely short day length, and short mild summers. Tasmania, where we live and grow our orchids, has probably the most severe climate of the Australian coastal belt; yet a lowland snowfall is seen here perhaps once in a generation. We have short cold winters with regular light frosts and some heavy ones; a hot dry summer with very low humidity, and extremely mild intermediate seasons. It is in fact a climate far removed from that of England and most of Europe; yet it is the most severe of the Australian littoral, where most of this country's orchid growers live. For us — even here in Tasmania — to adopt the regimen developed for a much harder climate is to harness ourselves with quite unnecessary handicaps. And it suggests that perhaps we should scrap all that irrelevant wisdom and begin to rethink things afresh for our own conditions, whatever they may be.

Orchids, like all other organisms on Earth, function adequately between certain extremes of temperature. And the orchid species from lowland tropical habitats have a different set of extremes from those originating in subtropical areas or tropical montane regions. However, a relatively small proportion of cultivated orchids originate from lowland tropical areas: most tropical species are native to mountainous areas, which are much cooler — a visit to almost any tropical country will confirm this. A large number of popular species fail to flower and gradually die once taken to lowland locations. We once asked a Thai nurseryman in Bangkok why it was so hard to obtain *Paphiopedilum appletonianum*. Were they particularly rare? Not at all, he said, it was simply that no-one could keep them alive in Bangkok because of the heat.

Let us take a bold step and discard all the minimum temperature rules set down by the traditional European books, and look instead at **average** temperatures. For many years we suspected that the ability to maintain satisfactory average temperatures was far more important than adhering slavishly to specific minima. Research in the USA has now confirmed this. In practice it means that, during hot summers when days are long, average daytime temperatures will be high, and consequently night temperatures may be allowed to drop below the levels recommended by the old rules, and so maintain an **overall average** temperature. Our own summer night temperatures occasionally drop as low as 5°C, but even warmth-loving species take no harm on these occasions. The low night temperatures last a relatively short time, and day temperatures are high.

In winter, of course, day length is shorter and nights are longer and colder. In order to maintain a reasonable overall average temperature — in the higher latitudes — it is necessary to raise night temperatures, but certainly not by as much as would be necessary in Britain or northern Europe. We have a friend who lives nearby in northern Tasmania and who grows *Phalaenopsis* species successfully with a winter minimum of 10–12°C. The truth is that in winter here we have many bright days when temperatures in the greenhouse become quite high. When we do have dull cold days, we find it is better to use artificial heat to raise daytime temperatures than try to drive night temperatures up to unrealistic levels. It is much cheaper and, in terms of overall average temperatures, the results are the same.

There must, of course, be some minimum below which a particular species will not thrive. This minimum varies to some degree from species to species according to its origins and tolerance; but the vast majority of our large collection grows and flowers well with a winter night minimum of 8–10°C. Occasionally, on very cold nights, the temperature may drop below that. We would not suggest that this figure is universally applicable, but it might serve as some sort of guideline for experiment, and it does confirm that many orchid species will tolerate minimum temperatures that are far lower than conventional wisdom suggests.

There is one point worth noting, however. Quite a few novice growers confuse 'cold-growing' species with 'cool-growing' ones. We have grown a number of species — including many Australian and South East Asian dendrobiums — with winter minima as low as 2–3°C (these are cold growing conditions). Temperatures below these approach freezing point, the point at which actual physical damage to plants can occur. There are few species among the epiphytes which will tolerate long hard frosts. Don't be misled by statements that a certain species — say, from the Organ Mountains in Brazil — is subject to regular frosts. This means, usually, that the region has light frosts lasting maybe two or three hours, which are followed by bright warm days. The kind of frosts we experience here in Tasmania destroy plant cells and can usually kill all but the hardiest of orchid plants. We believe that among the generally cultivated epiphytes there are very few that are not happier with a winter night minimum above 5° or 6°C.

There is one other point to be made in relation to the formulae for temperature ranges that have been handed down by those British and European growers of last century. Their formulae focus almost solely on winter minima, seldom considering summer maxima. Thus the preoccupation still seems to be with winter lows, and the danger of summer highs may be forgotten. Even with shading, ventilation, damping down, extra watering, we are often unable to keep our summer daytime greenhouse temperatures below 35°C, which is far too high for most of the plants we grow. Ideally, we would like to see it always below 28°C. But we can't, and we note nearly every year that we have two well-defined growing seasons: one in spring, one in autumn. The high daytime temperatures in midsummer often push the plants into a period of stress that temporarily halts growth.

Ventilation and air movement

Plants grown in a closed environment such as a greenhouse are obviously deprived of one of the main benefits they receive as a matter of course in their natural habitat: the free movement of air. Air movement both cools the plant in hot weather and prevents the formation of fungal infections when conditions are cool and damp. How are we to reproduce this condition in our greenhouses?

We cannot, without great expense and difficulty. Outside tropical coastal areas, orchid houses are constructed to create an artificially warm environment. And we cannot, in cold weather, admit much outside air without losing a great deal of that warmth. Similarly, in warm weather doors and vents are often inadequate to achieve sufficient cooling.

Once again we have to compromise. Obviously, we admit as much outside air as we can in **all** seasons without risking disastrous falls in temperature. But in prolonged cold weather we can admit very little. What we **can** do is to provide air movement and, if adequate, this is quite a good substitute. Electric fans are a godsend to the orchid grower in winter; you can use large ceiling fans, oscillating household fans, it doesn't really matter. Position them to give maximum coverage, move them around if necessary, and err, if you must err, on the generous side. Gentle air movement is not enough: the air movement should be positive and vigorous.

In summer, in exceptionally hot weather, fans may be inadequate to cool a greenhouse. If this is a regular problem in your greenhouse, consider a solar chimney, which is a simple device with no moving parts. It consists of a 'chimney' made of metal or hardboard, either square or circular in section, about 25–50 cm in diameter and as tall as is consistent with stability. The chimney is mounted on top of the greenhouse with a hatch, which can be opened in hot weather, at the base. The chimney is painted flat black, and absorbs a great deal of heat from the sun. The heated air inside the chimney rises, creating a draught which sucks fresh air into the greenhouse through doors and vents. The system is self-regulating; when the sun disappears the chimney cools and the draught ceases. Used in conjunction with misting or spraying to create evaporative cooling inside the greenhouse, this is in practice the only cheap and efficient cooling system for greenhouses during very hot summer weather.

It is worth remembering that air movement is one of the greatest aids to orchid growing. Apart from cooling plants and introducing an adequate supply of carbon dioxide for photosynthesis, it prevents outbreaks of fungal diseases. If your orchid house has adequate ventilation and air movement you can usually forget about fungicides.

WATERING

Perhaps the factor that causes most problems for new growers relates to watering. How often should we water? How heavily?

The easy answer, of course, is: water when your plants need it. But when **do** they need it? They need it when they are carrying out photosynthesis; they need it when they are in active growth; they need it when they are transpiring heavily.

First of all, we should say that in our experience and in our conditions — always provided that plants have adequate drainage — it is impossible to overwater in summer; conversely, it is almost impossible to underwater in winter. The exceptions are the relatively few tropical lowland species that are in more-or-less constant growth all year round. Since they need heating through the winter, they will dry out fairly quickly and thus will need more water.

The seasons that present us with a problem, then, are spring and autumn. In spring, a good indicator of watering needs is the condition of the root-tips. If you can see green beyond the white layer of velamen, then it is time to begin regular watering. If the roots are not active,

Wooden slat baskets are ideal for plants with extensive root systems like this miniature *Laelia* species

Translucent green root tips visible at the end of the white velamen-covered root of this *Cattleya intermedia* indicate that the plant is in active growth

the plants will in any case not be able to absorb much water. In such cases water can do no good and may in fact rot the roots and set the plant back. In addition, excess water at this time of the year may encourage fungal diseases.

In autumn, as the days shorten and the nights grow longer, most of the plants we grow move slowly into dormancy. A decrease in watering helps to induce the dormancy. Watering from this time on should be restricted, and no more water given than will prevent plants from shrivelling.

Actual frequency of watering depends to a very great degree on the material used for potting or mounting, the size of the containers, the positioning of the plant in regard to warmth and light. A fine potting mixture retains more moisture than a coarse open one, a cork mount drains more quickly than one of treefern, a small container dries out more quickly than a larger one, plants suspended near the roof need more water than those in a cooler shadier position. It is all really just a matter of commonsense.

It is something of a paradox that the further we are from the tropics, the more moisture retentive the planting medium must be. This is due to the fact that humidity is much lower in higher latitudes. In the tropical lowlands plants may be grown in open wooden baskets with no medium at all about the roots, and still thrive with infrequent waterings because of the constant high humidity. (This is the way most vandaceous species are cultivated in places like Bangkok and Singapore.) In our latitude we experience low humidity all year, and so must compensate by using the more moisture-retentive materials and more frequent waterings.

During warm weather in summer, when the air is extremely dry, we often need to water our plants twice a day. In winter once a week may be adequate, or even once a fortnight; between the waterings, however, we often mist the plants — particularly those hung high in the greenhouses — on bright sunny mornings. This increases the humidity about the plants without actually soaking them.

We do not use automatic watering systems, but water all year round with a hose and nozzle, allowing us a certain selectivity: not all plants may need water. If you suspect you might be a little heavy handed with water in winter time, we suggest that you may care to do as we do in our quarantine greenhouse (which is often crowded and slow to dry out); at the beginning of winter, or even earlier, we change the standard nozzle on the hose for a fogging nozzle that delivers a very fine spray, which raises the humidity without soaking the plants.

Experienced orchid growers are usually able to tell by their nose when a greenhouse is sufficiently humid; it has a particular smell, almost a feel, to it; the old books called it a 'buoyant atmosphere'. There is no substitute for experience in this. Until your 'nose' develops, you should be especially attentive when visiting the greenhouses of other growers to the smell or feel of the atmosphere; often you can learn more this way than by looking at the actual plants.

Most new growers are faced with almost permanent low humidity in their greenhouses, simply because they have few plants and lots of bare spaces. Consequently the atmosphere is usually too dry and the light too bright. If you are faced with this situation, then try to fill your greenhouse — at least temporarily — with any plants you can lay your hands on: ferns, houseplants, philodendrons, small shrubs ...; bromeliads are excellent as most have leaf-vases which hold quite a lot of water and thus raise the humidity significantly.

Some points to bear in mind are that no two greenhouses are identical, that all growers treat their plants at least a little differently, and that what works for one situation may not work in another. There is an enormous number of variables involved: geographical situation, size, type and orientation of the greenhouse, type of substrates used, variety of plants, frequency of watering, variations in fertilising, amount of light and heat, and so on. Temperature, humidity and light in varying combinations can produce a wide range of results. Don't follow other people's advice slavishly, and don't be afraid to experiment.

SUBSTRATES

Many new orchid growers are a little confused by the old dilemma: should a plant be potted or mounted?

First determine whether the plant in question is a terrestrial or an epiphyte. If it is a true terrestrial — such as a *Calanthe* or a *Habenaria* — then it should certainly be potted. If it is an epiphyte, then you can be sure that it will grow well if mounted. However, many epiphytes happily accommodate themselves to pots; for instance, many of the epiphytic dendrochilums will do equally well potted or mounted, as will many of the *Sophronitis* species. On the other hand, a number of epiphytes will sulk and decline if potted. *Dendrobium aemulum* must be mounted, as should most *Barkeria* species and *Constantia cipoensis*. Many species grow well enough in pots, but because of extended rhizomes they soon sprawl out of their

Not all species are adaptable to pot culture. *Dendrobium aemulum*, an attractive Australian species, sulks in a pot and must be mounted

Many miniature orchids such as this *Neolehmannia porpax* have such a rambling habit that they are difficult to cultivate in pots and should be mounted on some appropriate mount such as cork

containers and so are better if mounted; many bulbophyllums are in this category. And, of course, there are many small mat-forming species, such as *Encyclia polybulbon* and *Neolehmannia porpax*, which are uncomfortable in pots and look their best only when displayed on a mount.

And what materials should be used for potting and mounting? It doesn't really matter too much. It is obviously sensible to use materials which are cheap and readily available locally. Bear in mind that the higher the latitude in which you live, the more moisture retentive the materials should be. We mostly use treefern for mounts, and chunks of treefern and fresh sphagnum moss for potting as well as sheoak *(Casuarina)* needles and seed capsules. The latter are excellent for coarse-

Small amounts of sawn treefern fibre make ideal mounts for such miniatures as *Pleurothallis grobyi*, which prefer a substrate that retains moisture

rooted species such as vandas and aerides, as they retain some moisture but provide air gaps in the pot. We use paperbark (*Melaleuca* species) branches or trunks sawn into sections for many mat-forming species. *Melaleuca* is common where we live, and one of the finest of all mounts, if a little heavy. In our conditions it makes an excellent mount for *Sophronitella violacea*, a species which sometimes can be a little fussy. We also use natural cork bark for epiphytes that prefer drier conditions, such as *Cattleya aclandiae*.

In fact, after trying many of the new mixes and materials which have come into vogue in the last quarter of a century we have reverted very much to the type of substrates used by British growers more than a century ago. It is no coincidence, of course, that of all Australian conditions ours in Tasmania are closest to those of England and Europe. Growers living closer to the Equator will find themselves gravitating to more open potting mixes and slabs of cork and hard bark. Make your own choice. The most important thing to remember is that the type of substrates you use will often dictate the frequency and intensity of watering.

Finally, of course, it is well to remember that orchid plants are phototropic — that is, they grow towards the light — and it is important to plant them the right way up. A certain gentleman, who had best remain nameless, once visited our nursery and asked to be shown some *Stanhopea* species (which, as most of us know, send their flower spikes downward, often through the bottom of a basket, rather than upward). When shown some stanhopeas growing happily in their wire baskets, he gazed on them for a minute or two in a pensive fashion.

At last he spoke. "They grow upside down, don't they?"

We explained carefully that while the flower spikes grew downward, the plant did — like all well-mannered plants — grow upwards towards the light.

"Well," said our gentleman, "I don't want to buy one, I just wanted to look. I've got one already."

But there was still something on his mind.

"I'd better go home," he said at last, "and turn it up the other way. I've had it for two years, but I think I've planted it upside down."

The vision of that poor *Stanhopea* has haunted us for a long time. When it comes down to it, orchid growing, like so much else in life, is really just a matter of commonsense.

ORCHIDS AS HOUSEPLANTS

In countries that experience extremely severe winter conditions, such as northern Europe and parts of north America, ordinary greenhouse cultivation of orchids becomes both difficult and expensive. The problem is compounded for city dwellers by lack of outdoor space. Many growers have converted a room or basement of their homes to a growing area with an almost completely artificial environment, utilising artificial heating, lighting, air movement. This is a viable alternative for the keen grower in any inclement climate, and there are many excellent books available on the subject.

Similarly, the Wardian cases, which were favourites in Victorian times, have made something of a comeback. Today aquaria and fish tanks are often modified and pressed into service for this purpose. They are in fact merely smaller versions of the 'orchid room' described in the previous paragraph, and again provide a totally artificial environment. Once again, there is substantial published material available for the interested hobbyist.

Here we are going to concern ourselves only with the problems of growing orchids as ordinary houseplants, a role which many miniature species fill with distinction. If you are able to grow the usual run of houseplants — such as ferns, philodendrons, begonias and so on — in your living room, sunroom or bathroom, then you have a very good chance of being able to cultivate many orchid species under basically the same conditions.

Light is not normally a problem in a modern house, and it is usually possible to find a spot for your orchid plants where they receive full morning sunlight and indirect light for the rest of the day. Even a bright windowsill with no direct sunlight will often be found adequate for species that do not require high light levels. Choose the plants according to the conditions of light that apply in your home. Unless you have double-glazed windows, it is important that plants be positioned far enough away from the glass so that they are neither burned in summer nor frosted in winter.

Temperature is seldom a problem with orchids grown in the home. In most cases, temperatures at which human beings are comfortable will be satisfactory for orchids. Avoid both 'hot spots' and draughty areas.

Watering should follow the general pattern for greenhouse-grown plants, except that plants grown in the less humid atmosphere of the home may dry out much faster. And here we come to the biggest problem when it comes to indoor cultivation. The rooms of our homes are so much drier than the air in a greenhouse that we must take special pains to rectify this deficiency, especially during the growing season.

Try to identify those areas in your home where the air is — at least intermittently — humid. The bathroom will almost certainly be the most humid room in the house, and is often the most satisfactory place to grow a few plants. The area around and over the kitchen sink is another. However, most of us want to have at least some of our plants in positions where they can more readily be admired. And if you want to do this, there are a number of things you can do to increase humidity about your plants.

A decorative tray can be filled with small stones or gravel, and the potted plants placed on top. If the pebbles or gravel is kept wet, evaporation will humidify the air about the plants. For mounted plants, try using a more moisture-retentive material for the slab or totem. A very effective totem for indoor conditions can be made by wrapping a twig or stick with sphagnum moss and binding it in place with monofilament fishing line. Trim the moss, mount the plant, and stand the totem in a pot, wedging it in place with more moss. Saturate the mossy totem from time to time and it will deliver constant humidity to the plant it hosts.

Always keep a spray bottle or syringe handy, and lightly spray the foliage of the plants regularly. Regular humidification is much more effective for house-grown plants than occasional heavy watering. It is also an effective means of introducing a little fertiliser to the plants, which will absorb it through the leaves.

Sponge the leaves of all plants regularly. As well as providing some moisture, this will remove accumulated dust and keep plants looking fresh and attractive.

As long as the weather is mild, plants may be stood outside in gentle rain. And in summer, by all means give your plants a spell out of doors in a sheltered position. Stand them under trees where they will get broken sunlight, under arbours or trellises. In summer they may be left outside for days or weeks. The lower night temperatures they experience will do them no harm, and may assist in promoting flower buds for the next season.

If you have a small greenhouse try to rotate your plants so that they do not live their entire life in the drier atmosphere of the home.

Because the light in our houses usually comes laterally from windows, and plants tend to grow in the direction of the light source, flowers will often open facing the nearest window. To keep plants from developing a permanent lean in one direction, the plant may be rotated from time to time. However, once a plant comes into spike it should not be moved until all flowers are open and set. If the plant's position in relation to the light source is changed while flowers are developing, the spike will most likely be twisted and distorted as individual flowers attempt to re-orient themselves to the light.

Successful cultivation of orchids in the home is largely a matter of ingenuity and persistence, and a clear appreciation of the conditions that particular species require.

ACCLIMATISING PLANTS

One of the saddest and most disappointing things that can happen to an orchid grower is to spend time and effort tracking down a wanted plant only to have it gradually fade away and die. It happens to all of us from time to time, and no doubt always will. But there are ways to minimise such disappointments.

The risk is lessened if you are able to visit a nursery, inspect the stock, and buy a healthy well-established specimen. Many of us, unfortunately, can't do this. Most of us, particularly if we are specialist collectors, are often confronted with the problem of re-establishing a plant that has been substantially disturbed by the process of packing and transport.

Once again, it would be nice if you could buy always from the same source, and come to learn in time how plants from that source should be treated. Unfortunately, in the process of building a collection, you are usually compelled to buy plants from a wide range of sources, some grown in the tropics, some in cold climates, some in other countries even. And you often have very sketchy knowledge of the growing conditions in the nurseries concerned.

Let us start from the beginning. Plants grown in temperate climates usually adapt quickly to warmer conditions, but the reverse is not always true. And cooler-growing plants that have been established in tropical nurseries often sulk and decline when re-introduced to cooler conditions. So, if possible, buy plants from nurseries with geographical situation and climatic conditions similar to your own. Buy the largest, best established plants you can afford; small divisions are much harder to re-establish than larger ones. The only exception here is with seedlings — you may find that small seedlings adapt better than larger ones. And seedlings raised in flasks in your own growing conditions usually do best of all.

If you buy plants in the warmer

months, when plants are in active growth, they will be a little quicker to re-establish than plants obtained in colder months. Quicker, but not necessarily easier. Dormant plants travel quite well, and provided they are treated correctly, will eventually do as well as plants received in active growth.

Some nurseries pack better than others. If you are a mail order customer, favour the nursery that packs its plants well, completely dry, and tightly enough so that plants do not move about unduly in transit.

Over the years we have imported many thousands of orchids from all over the world and acclimatised them in our private quarantine greenhouse. Many of the plants arrive in desiccated condition, are without roots, and have been badly bruised through poor packing. The best packers in the world are probably the Thais, the worst the Peruvians. But even badly desiccated plants are a better prospect than plants that are packed damp. Dampness in a closed package is a killer of orchid plants, and must be avoided at all costs. Paphiopedilums are especially vulnerable: we have had consignments in which more than half the entire shipment was lost because the plants were packed slightly damp. Once rot sets in, it is almost always fatal to the plants. On the other hand, we have received shipments of paphiopedilums from India in which the plants had the consistency of dry brown paper, yet they recovered quite swiftly.

Whether your parcel of plants comes from across the world or from across the city, the same rules apply. First, remove the plants from their wrapping, taking care not to damage any live roots or new shoots. Examine the plant carefully for any trace of fungal infection. If you find any, cut the damaged section away carefully with a sharp knife or scissors, and dust the cut edges with sulphur or charcoal to seal the cut. If the plant is established in a pot or on a mount, place it in a position where you will be able to inspect it daily until you are sure that it has settled down satisfactorily in its new home. If the plant is loose rooted, you may be able to pot or mount it immediately. In such a situation we recommend light watering only until new root growth is observed.

When we receive a shipment of plants, we inspect them carefully as described, and lay them out in nursery trays on wire-mesh benches, which permit good air circulation. We usually give them only a light misting for the first week or so, depending on the time of year. The plants may stay there for weeks or even months until they are potted or mounted. At this stage the most important thing is to **avoid stress to the plants**. By this we mean that they must not be subjected to extremes of light, heat or water. Err on the side of shade, moderate warmth and light misting. And, most importantly, ensure that the plants are given adequate air movement; if necessary, position a small fan to give a constant air flow over them. When the plants have been potted or mounted they may be moved to the place you expect to be their final home. But watch them carefully for a few weeks, and don't be afraid to move them again if they don't appear to be thriving. Until you are certain that a plant has re-established itself, always err on the side of moderation: moderate light, heat and water. Stress kills plants as well as humans.

We budget for a 10 per cent loss in imported shipments, regardless of the time of year they are received, and our losses seldom exceed this. With plants purchased domestically from reputable nurseries, you should very rarely lose a plant if you follow our suggestions.

Sometimes you may receive plants that are in a badly dehydrated condition (like our paphiopedilums from India). If this happens, we find it helps to soak plants in a bucket of water in which a couple of tablespoons of sugar has been dissolved. You may also add a few drops of root-growth hormone. Leave the plants in the solution for an hour or so, then take them out, dry off, and place them in a shaded area to recover.

3 · Plant Names and Botanical Latin

Taxonomy

Taxonomy is the science of classification and naming, of establishing an orderly framework for comprehension of the natural world and identifying the place of each natural identity within it. While attempts at the classification of plants were made at least two thousand years ago, it was not until the 18th century that taxonomy took its place as a modern science. It has been said that God created the world, but Linnaeus gave it order. Karl von Linne (whose name is latinised as Carolus Linnaeus) was a Swedish botanist who was born in 1707 and died in 1778. He was the first to enunciate principles for defining genera and species and to develop the consistent use of specific names. In the area of botany (the system is used in zoology as well) Linnaeus based his system of classification on the floral parts of plants, specifically the number of stamens and pistils and the method of their joining. New scientific methods — such as use of the electron microscope for examination of pollen — have over the last two centuries refined the system

that Linnaeus devised; but the basic principles have remained the same.

The primary division in plant classification generally used in the orchid world is the order. (There are actually two higher groupings — the phylum and the class — but these are rarely referred to.) The order is broken down into families, subfamilies, tribes, subtribes, genera and species.

Orchids (the Orchidaceae) constitute a family within the order Liliales. The only other two categories that need concern us as practical orchid growers are the divisions of genus and species, which are the basis for the binomial system of Linnaeus.

The binomial system

The *species* (the noun is both singular and plural) is the basic unit of biological classification; it denotes a plant population with common appearance and genetic characteristics, and which is separated from other species by genetic barriers. The *genus* (plural: genera) is the next highest classification group, and constitutes a grouping of species with common or allied characteristics.

Each individual species in the plant world is given a two-part name that distinguishes it from every other species. The first part of the name is the generic (the genus), the second the specific (the species).

Within a large genus such as *Dendrobium*, taxonomists may divide the genus into *sections*, each containing a number of related species. This division is of interest to the specialist, but need not bother the average orchid grower. Similarly, taxonomists may subdivide a single species into several subgroups; these are generally recognised as the subspecies, the variety, and the form. Of these, the variety is the subdivision most often encountered, and in the area of cultivated orchids as opposed to purely botanical uses, the term *variety* is often used to cover all three terms.

It can be useful to know the conventions for writing the names of plants and their various categories, so here is a brief description. All scientific names above the rank of genus are printed in ordinary (roman) type with an initial capital. The names of genera, sections and subsections, species, subspecies and varieties are italicised when printed, and underlined when handwritten or typed. Generic names and those for sections and subsections have an initial capital, while names for species and varieties do not. The abbreviations for variety (var. or v.), species (sp., plural spp.) and subspecies (ssp.), and the names of authors are always in roman. When the name of a genus is being used in a general sense, an English derivative is used and is printed in roman type without a capital, for example: dendrobiums, cattleyas.

New names and taxonomic revisions

All this would be relatively simple but for one factor; and that is the propensity for botanists and taxonomists to keep changing the names of orchid species. Some species have had as many as twenty different names in the past hundred years or so. This causes great confusion in the orchid world, especially when it comes to maintaining an accurate register of hybrids. It also causes problems for commercial nurserypeople, let alone the amateur grower. In view of the trouble this habit causes, we should perhaps examine it in a little more detail.

A current plant name is only an indication of contemporary knowledge; it is never an absolute. It is said that there are rules for naming and renaming plants, but in truth they are fewer rules than conventions. And there is virtually no restriction on who may change a plant name. Anyone can do it who is able to produce a suitable written proposal and have it published in a relatively respectable journal. This does not mean that the name — whether of a new species or one previously named — will stand; another botanist or taxonomist may publish a revision or correction the following week.

What we must remember is that the change of a plant's name reflects no more than informed opinion; the validity and acceptance of a new name depends upon the degree to which the opinion is truly informed, and upon the reputation and intelligence of the author of the change. If the change is sensible and rational and conforms to the international conventions, then the new name will be accepted and will go into permanent usage. If it is not, then it will simply be disregarded.

And some names are just so entrenched in the orchid world that they continue to be used in practice even when a valid change has been published. The revised name *Dendrobium lindleyi* is still largely ignored in favour of the better known name of *Dendrobium aggregatum*, despite the validity of the revision.

Many reliable botanists are at present working in very important areas of orchidology, studying and revising such genera as *Epidendrum*, *Odontoglossum*, and *Bulbophyllum*. It would be very wrong of us not to take careful note of the revisions of botanists like Seidenfaden and Hagsater. But, as amateurs, we should never be in a great hurry to change our plant labels; rather we should wait and be sure that proposed changes are accepted.

It is a fact, which most practical orchid growers appreciate, that there are in practice two systems of orchid nomenclature: that of the specialist botanist and that of the horticultural amateur. The latter will often — probably quite rightly — retain old superseded names which are generally recognised until well after the time when academically inclined specialists have altered their records. From the point of view of the amateur grower, the important thing is communication, identification and recognition, and these interests are not always served by rushing to accept untried new names. Nor, of course, are they served by an obstinate resistance to change. We should aim at a middle path, noting changes as they occur, and being ready to accept them when they have been tested and found valid.

BOTANICAL LATIN

Many of our nursery customers telephone their orders, and it has been obvious to us for a long time that some of them are very uncomfortable with Latin plant names. And sooner or later, most of us will ask ourselves the question: why Latin?

Tradition and convention have played a role in the retention of Latin for botanical and zoological names; but there is a strong element of commonsense, too. Let us consider what would have happened had Linnaeus written his treatises in his native language. Is Swedish a more widely understood language than Latin? How about Chinese, or Arabic? Linnaeus wrote in Latin because in his time it was accepted as the international language of science, as well as of legal and ecclesiastical matters. In addition, no proper education of the day was complete without a study of Latin, a situation which extended well into the 20th century. Thus Linnaeus — and most of his successors — was able to use a language comprehended by much of the educated world.

There are other benefits which derive from the use of Latin. It is a very precise language — a quality that endeared it to legal writers — as well as a concise one. The Latin version of a plant diagnosis or description is always shorter than an English translation, although no less exact and complete. It is also a language of some subtlety. There are for instance at least nine adjectives in Latin for various shades of the colour white: *niveus*, *candidus*, *lacteus*, *cretaceus* and *albidus* are the five most commonly used.

In any case, whether we like it or not, we are stuck with Latin for botanical descriptions. So we may as well make the most of it.

Pronunciation
It is all very well to read words on a page, and perhaps, if we have a Latin dictionary, to learn something from them. The problem for many of us is that there are occasions when we have to actually pronounce the words and — we fear — make unholy fools of ourselves. These fears are re-inforced by the

attitudes of a few know-alls who inform us that there is but a single correct way to pronounce Latin. (It is always **their** way, of course . . . .)

Botanical Latin has developed into a very specialised language; there have been a myriad of additions and amendments to accommodate the exigencies of scientific usage. The result is that it is now largely unintelligible to the classic Latinist. Botanical Latin was derived in fact from Renaissance Latin and has developed its own distinct patterns and conventions. It is thus quite artificial, and any conventions of pronunciation are equally artificial. Even in classical Latin there are two distinct systems of Latin pronunciation: the traditional English pronunciation and the reformed academic pronunciation. Either of these two systems is quite acceptable as a basis for pronouncing botanical Latin.

To give an example, the Latin noun *Caesar* is pronounced 'See-zar' under the traditional system, and 'Ky-zar' under the reformed academic. In a botanical example, the name of the genus *Laelia* would be pronounced 'Lee-lee-ah' and 'Ly-lee-ah' respectively. We generally use the traditional form, but many of our friends pronounce it 'Lay-lee-ah', and who is to say that they are any less correct? The sole criterion must be intelligibility. If it sounds euphonious, so

much the better. And if you don't like either of the two recognised systems, well, the pronunciation of ecclesiastical Latin is based on modern Italian . . . .

It is a little easier when it comes to placing the stress on the right syllable. The same conventions apply to both major systems of pronunciation. In a word of several syllables the stress falls on the penultimate one when this syllable ends in a long vowel or a diphthong; for example, 'for-**mo**-sus', or when two consonants separate the last two vowels, as in 'cru-**en**-tus'. When the last syllable but one is short, then the accent falls on the third-last syllable, as in '**flo**-ri-dus'. Diphthongs are treated as long vowels. There are other rules for vowels that do not form diphthongs, and for words of Greek origin; but they need not concern the average orchidist. If you wish to delve deeper into the subject, we recommend William T. Stearn's excellent book, *Botanical Latin*.

For most of us, whose needs are usually restricted to ordering plants from a catalogue, commonsense will be a sufficient guide. With long names, or names that we are uncertain about, we proceed syllable by syllable. If someone criticises our pronunciation we refer them to Ben Jonson, who wrote, more than three hundred years ago, 'Custome is the most certaine mistresse of language . . .'.

ALPHABETICAL LISTING OF SPECIES

In the following pages we have included, for each species, suggestions concerning growing conditions: temperature, water, light, substrates and so on. These suggestions are based largely on our own experience, on results achieved by other growers, and on climatic habitat conditions. They **are** suggestions only, and their value will be mainly as a guide for you to adapt and experiment with to suit your own conditions.

While we are very conscious of the deficiencies of the conventional classification of growing conditions into cool, intermediate and warm, we have retained them for the simple reason that we have been unable to propose a better system. It is, however, necessary for us to define precisely what we mean by each term in relation to our own geographical situation, which we have indicated in the introductory text.

Cool: Minimum winter night temperatures of 5°C, rising to about 15°C in the daytime. Summer maximum temperatures seldom exceeding 25°C, falling to 10°C or below at night.

Intermediate: Minimum winter night temperatures in the region of 8–10°C, rising to about 20°C in the day. Summer maximum temperatures usually no higher than 30°C, dropping at night possibly to 10°C or cooler.

Warm: Minimum winter night temperatures seldom falling below 12–15°C, and rising to 25°C in the day. Summer temperatures rising as high as 35°C; summer night temperatures may fall to 10°C or lower.

We should point out that we do not have separate areas dedicated solely to these three climates. Instead, we rely a great deal on utilising temperature differentials within our greenhouses. Thus, in a greenhouse where general temperatures might be classified as intermediate, we might have heat- and light-loving species such as some cattleyas hung high up near the roof, with dendrobiums or oncidiums hung at middle levels, and cool-growing masdevallias on low benches where temperatures are lower and the shade is heavier. At floor level we might find terrestrial species from cool temperate bushland. The sensible orchid grower will find a huge variation between one greenhouse microclimate and another, and will use such variations to accommodate a wide range of species within the restrictions imposed by space, finance and geography.

On taxonomic matters, being orchid growers rather than professional botanists, we have taken a fairly conservative stance. For instance, pending a complete revision of the genus *Bulbophyllum*, we have followed Seidenfaden in including in that genus species often referred to as *Cirrhopetalum*. Seidenfaden says that he has been unable to find a method of establishing a reliable set of criteria for delimiting a separate genus, and it seems sensible in a book such as this one to accept this practical, if conservative, view.

Similarly, Jones and Clements have recently published a large number of revisions relating to the classification of Australian orchid species. There has been some resistance, especially in horticultural circles, to a number of these amendments, and indeed, we have some reservations about them ourselves. But this book is not the place to attempt an assessment, and we have decided to retain for the moment the long-accepted and better known names for the species we have included here. The proposed new names have been included as synonyms where appropriate.

A final note: an asterisk after a species' name in the text indicates that a separate entry for it may be found in the alphabetical listing.

Acianthus caudatus R. Brown

An Australian terrestrial species, which was described by Brown in 1810, *A. caudatus* is common throughout southeastern Australia and Tasmania, and as far north as the extreme southeast of Queensland. It grows among leaf litter, favouring sheltered areas in coastal heathland or open forest, where good drainage is assured.

The fleshy globular tubers are small, but multiply rapidly to form large colonies. A single heart-shaped leaf is held just above the ground. Dark green above, with a raised network of veins, the leaf is reddish-purple underneath and has undulating edges. It clasps the reddish flower stem, which is 5–25 cm tall with up to nine (usually two or three) dark maroon to almost black flowers. Appearing from late autumn to early spring, these otherwise charming flowers have a slightly unpleasant odour. The dorsal sepal is 2.5–5 cm long including its thread-like tail, which may be up to 4.5 cm long. The free lateral sepals taper to long tails reaching 1–2 cm in length. The flat recurved petals are about 0.5 cm long, while the angled lip is about 0.7 cm by 0.4 cm. Recurved at the tip, the lip has two triangular calli at the base and tiny glands on its upper surface.

Unlike many other colony-forming Australian terrestrials, *A. caudatus* can be a little difficult to maintain in cultivation. It requires a freely draining potting mix of sandy loam and leafmould, a shady position and moisture from early autumn to late spring. During the hot summer months, after the deciduous leaves have disappeared, watering should be reduced. *Actual flower size: approximately 5 cm long.*

Acriopsis indica Wight

Closely related to the genus *Thecostele*, this wide-ranging *Acriopsis* species was described by Wight in 1851. It occurs throughout South East Asia from Burma, through Thailand, Cambodia, Laos and Vietnam to Malaysia, Indonesia and the Philippines. It is found growing as an epiphyte on trees up to at least 1,000 m above sea level.

The egg-shaped pseudobulbs are tightly clustered and produce an extensive network of white branching roots that attach the plant firmly to its host tree. The pseudobulbs are 1–5 cm tall, and are covered with papery silver-white bracts. They bear two or three narrow dark green leaves from their apex, each 10–20 cm long. The inflorescence rises directly from the rhizome. Up to 30 cm long, usually with several branches, it produces a number of well-spaced flowers. These unusual pale yellowish blooms are more or less spotted with purple. The sepals and petals are approximately 0.5 cm long, with the lateral sepals joined for their entire length. The lip is slightly shorter than the sepals. It has a single lobe, the edges of which are slightly wavy, and is completely devoid of keels.

A. indica should be mounted on cork or paperbark and placed in a moderately bright position. Intermediate to warm conditions suit it best, with plenty of water during active growth. It appreciates generally high humidity. *Actual flower size: approximately 1 cm across.*

Aerides crassifolium Parish & Reichenbach (f.)

This monopodial epiphyte, which belongs to the genus commonly known as the 'foxtail' orchids, was introduced into England by Parish in 1864. However, it did not flower until 1872, and was described in the following year. It is found in peninsular Burma and northeastern Thailand at 200–1,300 m above sea level, where it grows largely in deciduous forests.

The stem grows to about 10 cm and bears several very thick leathery leaves, which may reach 20 cm but are usually 12–15 cm long by 3–5 cm wide. They are unequally bilobed at the apex and may be suffused with purple. The pendulous spikes rise from the leaf axils in summer. From 12.5 cm to 30 cm long, the spike bears twenty or more fleshy flowers about 2 cm across. The long-lasting fragrant flowers are a sparkling amethyst-purple, with a paler creamy-pink at the base of the segments. The dorsal sepal is curved slightly forward, while the broader laterals are recurved along their edges. The petals are slightly shorter than the sepals. The lip is three-lobed, the darker purple mid-lobe is shovel shaped, with two keels at the base. The spur is curved like a horn under the lip.

A. crassifolium requires bright light to grow well, good air movement and intermediate to warm conditions. Good drainage is essential, so a coarse mixture is called for. This species does well in a basket or suspended pot. Give plenty of water when the plant is in active growth, reducing to light watering or misting in winter.

Actual flower size: approximately 2 cm across.

Aerides flabellatum Rolfe

Described by Rolfe in 1925, this species is endemic to northern Thailand where it grows at around 1,000 m elevation. Because of its montane origins, it does not do well when moved to lowland tropical areas.

Related to the genus *Vanda*, this species has a monopodial habit with a stem that reaches about 10 cm in height. The closely set dark green leaves are 10–18 cm long and irregularly notched at the apex. *A. flabellatum* flowers in summer with a rather pendulous spike 10–25 cm in length carrying up to fifteen well-spaced flowers that last for about ten days. They are about 2 cm across and open more or less at the same time. The oval sepals and petals are yellowish-green with brownish-red blotches. The broad lip is reminiscent of a frilly skirt. It is white with beautiful amethyst-purple markings, and with a little yellow in the throat. The lip has two thick keels, white on the sides facing the middle and yellow on the outer sides, and is green on the reverse. The greenish spur is somewhat flattened and bent upwards at an angle.

A. flabellatum does best in an intermediate environment with good humidity and air movement. It may be grown in a basket or pot in a mixture of charcoal and treefern chunks with a little fresh sphagnum moss to provide humidity around the roots in winter. Moderate to bright light is preferred. This is a charming and rewarding species which should be in every collection.

Actual flower size: approximately 2 cm across.

Amesiella philippinensis (Ames) Garay

The sole representative of the genus, this species is found only in the Philippines, where it occurs between 850 m and 1,400 m on forested slopes in Albay, Benguet, Bontoc and Nueva Viscaya provinces of Luzon, and also in the northern parts of Mindoro Island. It grows epiphytically on mossy trees in moderate shade. Humidity is relatively high all year round. *A. philippinensis* was discovered by Merrill in 1906 on the slopes of Mt Halcon on Mindoro. The genus was named after Oakes Ames, the American botanist who first described the species in 1907 as *Angraecum philippinense*.

It is a compact plant and the short stems, which have usually four to six succulent leaves up to about 7 cm long, are attached to the host tree by fleshy grey-white roots. The short inflorescence is produced in spring with up to five fragrant white flowers, which have a satiny texture. At 3–4.5 cm in diameter, they are quite large for the size of the plant. Allied to another monotypic genus, *Neofinetia*, *A. philippinensis* also possesses flowers that have a long spur, often reaching 5 cm. The lip is slightly cupped, with dull orange colouring in the throat.

This species grows well for us when tied to cork mounts, paperbark or tea-tree sticks, and provided with a small pad of moss about the roots. Intermediate to warm temperatures seem to suit the species, together with cool nights and year-round watering. It may appreciate slightly drier conditions after the year's growth has been completed.

Actual flower size: 3–4.5 cm across.

Ascocentrum ampullaceum (Ldl.) Schlechter

Discovered by Smith in what is now Bangladesh, and later by Wallich, this species was introduced into England in 1837, becoming common in collections after about 1865. A year after its introduction Lindley described it as *Saccolabium ampullaceum*. It was transferred in 1913 to Schlechter's newly created genus, *Ascocentrum*. It is found from northern India to Thailand at 300–900 m altitude, growing as an epiphyte in indirect bright light, often on deciduous trees.

It is of monopodial habit, and has stems that may reach 20 cm but are usually between 5 cm and 15 cm, and thick leathery leaves 10–15 cm long — rarely to 20 cm — with ragged tips. A dull green, the leaves are more or less suffused and spotted with purple. They have a central groove above and a prominent keel below. In late spring or summer erect spikes 8–20 cm in length rise from the leaf axils, with up to twenty closely set flowers. These are long lasting, rosy-pink, and 1.5–2.5 cm across. The rounded sepals and petals open widely. Each flower has a spur up to 1 cm long which is slightly swollen at the tip. The lip is slightly shorter than the tepals, tongue shaped and rounded at the apex. A form with deep orange-red flowers is also known (var. *aurantiacum*).

Liking moderately bright light, this species may be grown in either pot or slat basket, and a coarse medium should be used to ensure excellent drainage. Intermediate to warm temperatures are recommended with fairly high humidity. In winter and in cooler conditions allow to dry out.

Actual flower size: 1.5–2.5 cm across.

Ascocentrum curvifolium (Ldl.) Schlechter

Wallich discovered this species in Nepal early in the 19th century. Lindley described it as *Saccolabium curvifolium* in 1832, and Schlechter transferred it to the new genus *Ascocentrum* in 1913. It grows epiphytically on mostly deciduous trees in the mountain areas of India, Nepal, Burma, Thailand and Indochina. Because of its montane origins it generally flowers poorly in lowland tropical areas.

A monopodial, its stems rarely exceed 15 cm, and are usually shorter. The narrow curved leaves are normally 10–15 cm long, but may occasionally be longer. The upright flower spike, 15–25 cm, bears many densely packed flowers in late spring or summer. The almost round flowers are cinnabar-red, 2–2.5 cm across, and last for two to three weeks. The three-lobed lip is about 0.6 cm long, and the spur about the same length. The erect side-lobes on the lip are triangular and bright yellow while the oblong mid-lobe has yellow calli and two keels at the base, which almost close the entrance to the spur. A yellow form (var. *citrinum*) is known.

Intermediate conditions are ideal for this lovely species, with bright indirect light. It may be grown in basket or pot (preferably suspended from the roof) in an open medium such as charcoal or pinebark. In cooler areas, a little fresh sphagnum moss may be added to create humidity about the base of the plant and prevent the loss of lower leaves when atmospheric humidity is low.

Actual flower size: 2–2.5 cm across.

Ascocentrum miniatum (Ldl.) Schlechter

Introduced into England by Veitch in 1846, this most attractive monopodial was described by Lindley a year later as *Saccolabium miniatum*. Schlechter transferred it to *Ascocentrum* in 1913. Kuntze's *Gastrochilus miniatus* is conspecific with this species. It occurs naturally from India to the Philippines, often found growing in exposed positions on trees in deciduous forests between 180 m and 1,000 m above sea level.

The plant is very compact, with very stiff fleshy leaves set close together on stems which are usually 5–12 cm tall, but which may occasionally reach 20 cm. The 5–10 cm leaves are channelled above and keeled beneath. The 10–24 cm flower spikes appear from leaf axils in late spring or summer and bear many densely packed orange to deep yellow flowers up to 1.5 cm across. The sepals and petals are rounded, while the three-lobed lip, about 0.4 cm, is tongue shaped. The lateral lobes are orange-yellow, while the mid-lobe is lighter in colour, bent downwards, and has its upper surface grooved. The cylindrical spur is 0.8 cm long, and slightly curved forward. The purple or black anther cap provides a strong contrast to the colour of the rest of the flower.

A. miniatum is quite adaptable, and perhaps the easiest of the genus *Ascocentrum* to manage. It will flower quite well in warm climates as well as in intermediate environments. It likes a pot or basket with any well-drained medium, in an airy, lightly shaded position with good air movement, and should never be allowed to dry out completely.

Actual flower size: 1–1.5 cm across.

Barbosella miersii (Ldl.) Schlechter

This tiny epiphyte belongs to a genus named in honour of J. Barbosa Rodrigues, one-time director of the Botanical Gardens in Manaus and later of the Botanical Gardens in Rio de Janeiro. It was originally described by Lindley in 1842 as *Pleurothallis miersii*, but Schlechter transferred it to his new genus in 1918. In 1981 Luer removed it from the genus *Barbosella* and created a new monotypic genus for it, renaming it *Barbrodria miersii*: it has a simply hinged lip, whereas other barbosellas have a ball and socket arrangement between the lip and the column foot. However, despite Luer's transfer, it is still most commonly regarded as a barbosella. It grows in the cool moist mountains of the southern Brazilian states of Rio de Janeiro, Sao Paulo, Parana and Santa Catarina.

This tiny creeping plant can form dense mats and is attached to its host by very short roots. The 0.3 cm paddle-shaped leaves, which are very fleshy, rise almost directly from the branching rhizome. The species may flower more than once a year with single straw-yellow to pale greenish-yellow flowers borne on 1.0 cm spikes. The flowers are only about 0.3 cm long with pointed segments. The narrow petals are minutely serrated along their outer half. The tiny lip sits on the lateral sepals that are joined for about one-third of their length.

A cool to intermediate shady environment is recommended for this species. It does well on a fibrous mount such as treefern and should be kept moist all year round.

Actual flower size: approximately 0.3 cm long.

Barkeria dorotheae Halbinger

A recent addition to the genus, this species was described by Federico Halbinger in 1976, naming it for Dorothy O'Flaherty who, with her husband, had discovered it in 1974. It is a species with a very limited range near the border between the states of Jalisco and Colima in Mexico, where it grows on scrubby trees and rocks from sea level to about 100 m altitude.

The slender spindle-shaped pseudobulbs vary from 3 cm to 20 cm in height, with two to seven thin deciduous apical leaves. Spikes up to 80 cm long appear in winter and bear as many as twelve well-spaced flowers. The lilac and white-to-pink flowers, which are darker on the outside, are 2.5–3.5 cm in diameter. The sepals and petals spread umbrella-like over the lip and column. The dorsal sepal is shorter than the lateral sepals and petals, and may have a white median stripe. The lip is almost white, narrow at the base and broad at the tip with the sides turned downward from the three central keels. The centre of the lip and the fleshy winged column are yellow, spotted with purple.

B. dorotheae does best mounted — ours are on paperbark branches — and hung in a bright spot in the greenhouse. Intermediate to warm conditions suit the species, with lots of water when in growth. Once growth is finished for the season and leaves have fallen, watering should be sharply reduced until new growth appears.

Actual flower size: 2.5–3.5 cm across.

Barkeria halbingeri Thien

Thien described this species in 1974, naming it in honour of Halbinger, the Mexican botanist who has done much work on the genus *Barkeria* and has described several new species. It grows on rocks in the mountainous state of Oaxaca in southern Mexico, obtaining much of its nutriment from decaying vegetation in crevices in the rocks. The area has plentiful summer rain with mist at other seasons.

The pseudobulbs of *B. halbingeri* are 10–20 cm tall with new growths springing from any of the internodes. Unlike most other barkerias, the leaves of this species may persist for two or more years. Up to 10 cm long, they are thin and spreading with dark red markings. This species flowers in spring, bearing erect or arching spikes each carrying several 4.5 cm flowers which last well, as do the flowers of most *Barkeria* species. The broad oval petals and narrow sepals are spread winglike above the broad lip. The base of the lip curls around the bottom of the column, which lies flat along the lip. The lip has three stiff paler keels and the ruffled side-lobes are reflexed. The broad column is spotted with red.

Despite its lithophytic origins, this species, we find, prefers to be mounted; cork, *Casuarina* branches, treefern or paperbark will do. It is sometimes grown in pots, but the mix must be very coarse with excellent drainage. Intermediate to warm conditions suit this species, and bright light is necessary to get the best from it. Plenty of water should be given in summer, but substantially reduced when the plant is dormant.

Actual flower size: approximately 4.5 cm across.

Barkeria naevosa (Ldl.) Schlechter

First described as *Epidendrum naevosum* by Lindley in 1853, this species was later transferred to the genus *Barkeria* by Schlechter. Some have considered it to be a subspecies of *B. chinensis*. Related to both epidendrums and cattleyas, the genus *Barkeria* falls somewhere in between. *B. naevosa* is a tropical species, found mostly on the Pacific slopes of the states of Guerrero, Michoacan and Oaxaca in Mexico, where summer rainfall is abundant.

The pseudobulbs, 4–8 cm tall, are spindle shaped, with purple-red bands around the internodes of the older pseudobulbs. The two or three mid-green leaves — up to 6 cm long — fall when the plant is in flower, or earlier. Flower spikes appear at the apex of the pseudobulb between autumn and spring and bear several rose-lavender flowers 2 cm wide. The pointed sepals and petals, often with darker veins, form a fan extending over the lip. The inside of the deflexed lip has central keels and raised darker veins. The nodding flowers may be translucent. There is also a bright yellow form with pinkish-red on the back of the sepals and petals.

This species, which produces its new growth from the base of the preceding pseudobulbs, grows best on branches of rough-barked trees, paperbark or cork. It prefers intermediate to warm conditions with bright light. Watering should be reduced after flowering until new growth appears in the spring.

Actual flower size: approximately 2 cm across.

Barkeria palmeri (Rolfe) Schlechter

Native to the Mexican states of Jalisco, Nayarit and Colima, this species was originally described by Rolfe in 1893 as *Epidendrum palmeri*. In 1918 Schlechter transferred it to the genus *Barkeria*, and it is considered by some botanists to be a subspecies of *Barkeria chinensis*. The species is found in a range of habitats, from trees in high forests up to 1,300 m altitude, to lower deciduous forests, to dry hot savannah and the moister lowlands down to 75 m above sea level. It is found usually on thorny twigs and branches.

The spindle-shaped pseudobulbs are 2–15 cm tall with two to four channelled leaves 3–8 cm long. This species flowers in winter and early spring from the apex of the pseudobulb on a simple or branched inflorescence up to 30 cm long. Each inflorescence bears up to thirty densely packed flowers 2–3 cm across; however, on occasion, spikes may bear up to a hundred flowers on a fully branched spike. Flower colour is variable from almost white through pale or bright pink to mauve or purple, with a white or pink lip that is sometimes yellow at the base. It may also be flecked with red. The 1.0–1.7 cm sepals and petals are swept forward, while the heart-shaped lip has three prominent yellow keels with lateral veins radiating from them.

B. palmeri should be mounted, given intermediate to warm conditions, bright light and frequent waterings during its period of active growth. Even when leafless it should be given an occasional misting.

Actual flower size: 2–3 cm across.

Barkeria shoemakeri Halbinger

Discovered in 1973 and described by Halbinger in 1975, this species has a very restricted range in the Mexican state of Michoacan. The climate there is tropical to subtropical with most of the annual rainfall occurring in summer.

The pseudobulbs of this species are 2–8 cm or more in height, with reddish-purple mottling when young. The two or three erect leaves occur near the apex of the pseudobulbs, and are deciduous, falling when the plant has finished flowering. The leaves are about 6 cm long with purplish-red markings. This species will flower as a very small plant, from pseudobulbs no more than 2 cm tall. The erect to arching spikes appear in winter and carry many long-lasting flowers about 1.6 cm in diameter. They are generally pale pink, sometimes almost white, with darker veins on the upswept petals and sepals. The lip is quite narrow at the base, with vivid purple streaks on its ruffled outer section. As in most *Barkeria* species, the flowers are nodding, with the sepals and petals turning their backs to the viewer. The species produces its new growth from the base of the preceding pseudobulbs.

The roots of *B. shoemakeri* should be exposed to the air, not covered with substrate, a preference the species shares with other barkerias. It should be mounted on cork, casuarina or paperbark. Even on the latter mount, roots do not penetrate the thin layers of bark very far. It needs intermediate to warm conditions, with bright light and frequent watering when in active growth. Mist occasionally at other times.

Actual flower size: approximately 1.6 cm across.

Barkeria spectabilis Bateman ex Lindley

One of the first barkerias to be cultivated, this species was discovered in Guatemala by Skinner. He sent plants to Bateman in England, who described the species in 1842. It was once considered to be conspecific with *B. lindleyana*, to which it is closely related. The major difference between the two species is that *B. spectabilis* has a larger column. Reichenbach's later name — *Epidendrum spectabilis* — is a synonym. *B. spectabilis* has a wide range through central America from Mexico to Costa Rica, where it grows as an epiphyte at elevations up to 2,500 m.

The 4–15 cm tall pseudobulbs are spindle shaped, about 0.6 cm in diameter at the thickest point. Plants of the species grow in dense tufts and bear a few quite fleshy leaves which are, however, shed by midwinter. They are 4–15 cm long, spreading, and slightly recurved. This is a summer-flowering species with either a simple or a branching inflorescence, 8–25 cm long, bearing a few to many showy flowers. Flower size ranges from 4 cm to 8 cm, with most in the middle of the range. Colour is also variable, from near white to lavender, but most in the pale lilac shades. Flowers have a large broad lip, and both lip and column are spotted and streaked with reddish-purple. The petals and sepals are 1.8–3.7 cm long, while the lip is 1.8–3.5 cm long with three to five keels.

Intermediate conditions are preferred by this species, with plenty of bright light and abundant watering during its very short growing period of about two months. It is dormant for the major part of the year.

Actual flower size: approximately 5 cm across.

Broughtonia sanguinea (Sw.) R. Brown

First introduced into England in 1793, this species was first described as *Epidendrum sanguineum* by Swartz, based on material collected by Brown. In 1813 Brown transferred the species to his newly created genus, *Broughtonia*, which he had named in honour of an English botanist who collected in Jamaica and Cuba. This species is found only in those two countries, where it grows both epiphytically and lithophytically in bright light. Among other hosts, it is found occasionally growing on giant cacti. It is essentially a lowland species, but is sometimes found up to 800 m above sea level, often growing in association with *Brassavola nodosa*.

The greyish-green pseudobulbs are 2.5–5 cm long, often somewhat flattened and furrowed with age. They are very closely set, sometimes overlapping. Each bears two leathery leaves 8–20 cm long. The arching spike carries five to fifteen flowers near its apex. Usually 20–40 cm in length, the spike may be longer, and occasionally produces branches. The showy rose-scarlet or crimson flowers are 2–3 cm across. The 1.5–2.5 cm oblong sepals are pointed, while the roundish petals are much wider, having undulating edges and slightly paler mid-veins. The large lip is up to 2.2 cm long, with irregular wavy edges, an orange-yellow blotch at the base and dark veins.

Not easy to cultivate, this species resents disturbance. It prefers a treefern or cork mount, almost full sun, good humidity, and warm to intermediate temperatures. Provide plenty of water when in growth, then a drier rest.

Actual flower size: 2–3 cm across.

Bulbophyllum aurantiacum Mueller

Although Jones has recently contended that Reichenbach's *B. schillerianum* (1860) is the correct name for this Australian species, both Rupp and Dockrill consider *B. schillerianum* to be a synonym for *B. crassulifolium*; we have chosen to retain the traditional identity. The species was first described by von Mueller in 1862. Occurring from central eastern New South Wales to northeastern Queensland, this species is found at low elevations in its southern range, while in the north it ranges from mangrove swamps to elevations of at least 1,200 m. Predominantly epiphytic, it is also found on mossy rocks and protected cliffs at the higher elevations.

B. aurantiacum grows as a small bunch of short-to-medium length pendent rhizomes with internodes of 0.5–1.5 cm. The small pseudobulbs are globular, flattened on top, and only 0.3–0.8 cm tall. The single leaf is heavy and succulent, deeply channelled, varying from 1.5 cm to 10 cm in length by 0.8 cm to 2.5 cm in width. Flowering occurs mainly from late autumn to spring. Flowers rise directly from the rhizome on very short stems, and are often profuse. The 0.3–0.7 cm long flowers do not open widely and, while they may occasionally be completely cream or pale green, typically all but the bases of the sepals are orange to red. The translucent white petals are hidden, while the tiny deep orange lip is also hidden.

The species grows well mounted on treefern and placed in a moist and cool to intermediate position. It may also be potted, with the plant encouraged to trail over the pot rim.

Actual flower size: 0.3–0.7 cm long.

Bulbophyllum bowkettae Bailey

A tropical Australian species, this bulbophyllum was first described by Bailey in 1884, and is conspecific with Rupp's *B. waughense* (1950). It occurs in Queensland along the eastern half of Cape York Peninsula from Tully to the Iron Range. In the north it grows in cloudforest above 600 m altitude, but extends to the lowlands in the south. It is usually found growing as an epiphyte, but also occurs on mossy rocks, and sometimes forms dense mats.

The pseudobulbs are 1.5 cm to 4 cm apart on a branching rhizome. The squat pseudobulbs, which slant in the direction of the developing rhizome, are ribbed, vary from 0.7 cm to 1.1 cm in length by 0.3 cm to 0.5 cm in width, and hug the rhizome closely. The single dark green leaf is up to 2.5 cm long, broad and leathery with a notched apex. This species may flower at any time of the year, but does so mainly in spring and summer. A single nodding flower 0.6–0.8 cm across is borne on a 0.5–1.0 cm inflorescence rising from an internode. While they appear to be red, the flowers are actually a greenish-cream striped with red or pink; the sepals have three broad stripes while the minute petals have a single central stripe. The tiny fleshy lip has a central groove, and is purple with a yellow tip.

B. bowkettae is a common species and grows easily in moist humid conditions with indirect light. It prefers intermediate temperatures and is happy on tea-tree, paperbark or treefern.

Actual flower size: 0.6–0.8 cm across.

Bulbophyllum crassulifolium (Cunn.) Rupp

ound in temperate mainland Australia, this species was first described as *Dendrobium crassulifolium* by Cunningham in 1839. Von Mueller described it as *Dendrobium shepherdii* in 1859 and subsequently transferred it to the genus *Bulbophyllum* in 1862. Rupp resurrected the specific epithet in 1937, when it became *B. crassulifolium.* Jones has lately proposed that it should be called *B. shepherdii* after its earliest placement in the genus. However, Dockrill and Rupp consider that *B. schillerianum* (Reich f.) 1860 is also synonymous with this species, thus predating von Mueller's name. We have stayed with the generally accepted current usage. The species occurs from southeastern New South Wales to southeastern Queensland from the coast to 900 m elevation. It grows on mossy rocks or trees, from the rainforest to fairly exposed situations.

Closely related to *B. aurantiacum*, but not pendent, this species grows in spreading clumps. Pseudobulbs are about 2.5 cm long and about 0.5–1.0 cm apart. The single leaf is pale to dark green, 1.5–4.0 cm long, succulent and deeply furrowed on the upper surface. The flowers are borne singly, mostly in spring and often in large numbers, rising on very short stems from the rhizome. They are translucent creamy-white with yellow- or orange-tipped sepals. The tiny fleshy lip is orange or reddish-brown.

This is an easy species to cultivate on slabs of treefern or *Casuarina* in semi-shade or indirect bright light. It will tolerate cool conditions, and prefers some year-round moisture.
Actual flower size: 0.4–0.5 cm long.

Bulbophyllum dayanum Reichenbach (f.)

his eerily fascinating species, first described by Reichenbach in 1865, has a number of synonyms: *B. dyphoniae*, *Phyllorchis dayana*, *Trias dayana*. It inhabits the shaded, cooler areas in the tropical jungles of Burma, Cambodia and Thailand between 500 m and 1,300 m above sea level.

The ovoid reddish-purple pseudobulbs are set 2–7 cm apart on a stout rhizome but tend to be closer in cultivated plants. The pseudobulbs, 1.5–3 cm tall, become wrinkled with age. The single leathery leaf is 6–10 cm long and up to 4 cm wide. Broadly oval, it is a dark dull green on the upper surface, which is often minutely dimpled, and reddish-purple underneath. Two to five amazing flowers are borne in spring and summer on a very short spike from the base of the pseudobulb; 2–3 cm across, they are somewhat nodding and have a faintly unpleasant odour. The broad pointed sepals are pale green, very heavily marked with lines of purple blotches. Numerous 0.5 cm long green-to-yellow hairs line the edges of both the sepals and the 0.7 cm petals. The petals are dark maroon edged with yellow. The 0.8 cm lip is green with purple ridges on the disc and covered with many tiny glands. The upturned edges are irregularly indented.

B. dayanum likes intermediate conditions, with fairly high humidity and more water than many other *Bulbophyllum* species. It does best mounted — we use paperbark sections, as the layers of bark retain moisture while allowing good air circulation about the roots. A semi-shaded position is preferred.
Actual flower size: 2–3 cm across.

Bulbophyllum elisae (Muell.) Bentham

Von Mueller first described this temperate Australian species as *Cirrhopetalum elisae* in 1868, and it was transferred to the genus *Bulbophyllum* by Bentham in 1873. It occurs from the Blue Mountains of New South Wales to southeast Queensland, usually above 600 m elevation. It inhabits rainforest trees for preference, but is occasionally found on rocks in exposed conditions. It likes moist mountain gullies, where it grows with epiphytic ferns and lichens. The third-largest of the Australian bulbophyllums, it can form quite large mats, and is sometimes found in association with *Dendrobium teretifolium*.

The crowded pseudobulbs are 1.5–3.0 cm tall, deeply grooved and wrinkled so that they resemble miniature pineapples, thus giving rise to its common name, 'pineapple orchid'. Pseudobulbs are pale yellowish-green and topped with a single stiff leaf 3.0–11.0 cm long. Flowering is erratic but occurs mainly from autumn to spring. The erect to arching spike, 8–12 cm long, rises from the base of the pseudobulb and bears five to twelve flowers each about 1.5 cm across. Usually a vivid apple-green, the drooping flowers are occasionally pale green with a pink tinge, or rarely completely reddish-brown. The dominant features are the spreading lateral sepals up to 2.2 cm long. The small petals are concealed. The fleshy 0.4 cm lip is dark red or purple-black.

This species can be difficult in cultivation. Give cool to temperate conditions with moderate light, cork or treefern mounts or suspended pots of sphagnum moss.

Actual flower size: approximately 1.5 cm across.

Bulbophyllum evasum Hunt & Rupp

Although first collected in 1889, this species was not accurately described until 1949 by Hunt and Rupp. A high-altitude tropical species from Australia, it is found in the mountains and tablelands between Ayr and Cooktown in northeastern Queensland. Found above 700 m elevation, it becomes increasingly common above 1,000 m, where it grows on mossy trees and rocks in cloudforest. This environment provides year-round humidity, and plants seldom dry out for more than a day or so.

The extensive flattened rhizome is very thin and brittle, so care is needed in handling plants. The 0.4–0.7 cm pseudobulbs are prostrate and appear fused to the rhizome at 2 cm intervals. Leaf shape varies from circular to oval. This fleshy leaf is 1.5–3.5 cm long and is bilobed. This species may flower at any time, and is distinct among Australian bulbophyllums in having a tight head of fifteen to twenty flowers borne on a dark red spike up to 10 cm tall, which rises from near or between the pseudobulbs. Each 0.3 cm flower is pink with three broad red stripes on the sepals and on the petals. The dorsal sepal and petals are tipped with yellow. The tiny deep red lip is densely covered with minute glands.

B. evasum resents disturbance. It should be grown on a fairly large treefern or tea-tree mount in semi-shade. Growing environment should be cool to intermediate with fairly high humidity and only moderate light.

Actual flower size: 0.3 cm long.

Bulbophyllum gadgarrense Rupp

A tropical Australian species first described by Rupp in 1949, *B. gadgarrense* is found mostly on the mossy trunks and branches of rainforest or cloudforest trees above the 700 m level from Townsville to Cooktown in the eastern Cape York area of Queensland. A quite common orchid in the region, it is occasionally found growing as a lithophyte.

The plant grows as a bunch of pendent stems to 20 cm in length, which branch freely and often become tangled. The rhizome is covered with purple-brown bracts, which also partly cover the 0.4–0.6 cm pseudobulbs that occur at intervals of 0.5 cm to 1.0 cm. The pseudobulbs are almost prostrate, and bear a single narrow succulent leaf 1.5–3.0 cm long. The leaf is slightly curved, with a deep furrow down the centre; it may occasionally be almost terete with only a faint furrow. When grown in temperate areas this species tends to flower mainly in spring or summer, with single flowers on 0.5 cm stems rising from the rhizome. The 0.5 cm flowers are white with the sepals and minute petals tipped with orange or yellow. The 0.1 cm lip is orange, thick and channelled.

A relatively easy species to cultivate, *B. gadgarrense* should be mounted on a slab of treefern or similar material with some moss at the base of the plant to retain moisture, and hung in a semi-shaded position. It prefers intermediate to cool temperatures with constant humidity and good ventilation.

Actual flower size: approximately 0.5 cm long.

Bulbophyllum gracillimum (Rolfe) Rolfe

This species was first described by Rolfe in 1895 as *Cirrhopetalum gracillimum*. He renamed it *Bulbophyllum gracillimum* in 1907. *Cirrhopetalum* or *Bulbophyllum psittacoides* is synonymous with this species, but not Hayata's *B. gracillimum*. Ranging from peninsular Thailand through lowland Malaysia, Indonesia, New Guinea, far northeastern Australia and into the Pacific islands, this species grows as an epiphyte, mostly on the lower part of tree trunks in the rainforest.

Not surprisingly for a species having such a wide distribution, *B. gracillimum* is quite variable, especially in flower size and colour. The egg-shaped pseudobulbs may be clustered or up to 2 cm apart on a slender rhizome, and often form medium-sized clumps. They are 1.5–2 cm tall with a single leathery leaf usually 6–8 cm long, but which may sometimes reach 12 cm. Flowering time is variable, but the wiry spikes, which reach 15–30 cm, are mostly borne in spring and summer. Six to ten fragrant flowers are clustered at the apex of the spike. These are predominantly dark purple-red and mostly 2.5–3 cm long, with specimens up to 5 cm being reported. Both the hooded dorsal with its short thread-like tail and the tapering petals are edged with hairs. The lateral sepals are joined for about 0.5 cm before tapering to narrow tails. The mobile lip is purple-violet, fleshy and only about 0.2 cm long. The anther cap is white.

A comparatively easy grower in intermediate conditions, this species needs moderate shade and water, good air movement and high humidity.

Actual flower size: approximately 2.5–3 cm long.

Bulbophyllum japonicum (Makino) Makino

We have never been able to find a great deal of information about this lovely little miniature species. It was first described by Makino of Japan in 1891 as *Cirrhopetalum japonicum*. He renamed it *Bulbophyllum japonicum* in 1910. It occurs in Japan on Honshu, Shikoku and Kyushu, but its range extends to Kwangtung province in mainland China and to Taiwan. In Taiwan it was described by Hayata as *Bulbophyllum* or *Cirrhopetalum inabai*, but this identification was found to duplicate Makino's and was reduced to synonymy with *B. japonicum*.

It is a true miniature with small conical pseudobulbs to 1 cm tall closely set on a creeping rhizome. The single leaf is 2–3 cm long. The short spikes bear umbels of tiny pink flowers up to 0.5 cm long with a darker pink lip. A yellow-flowered form is believed to exist.

When we imported our plants of this species we established them on old mossy slabs of treefern, which seem to suit them. We grow them in well-shaded intermediate to cool conditions and give them moderate water all year round, never letting them dry out completely. *Actual flower size: approximately 0.5 cm long.*

Bulbophyllum johnsonii Hunt & Rupp

This is such a variable species that in 1949 Hunt and Rupp examined three different specimens and described them as different species. *B. kirkwoodii* and *B. whitei* have since been reduced to synonymy with *B. johnsonii*. A native of Australia, it occurs in tropical northeastern Queensland. In some areas it grows down to sea level, but is generally confined to mountain areas between 600 m and 1,200 m elevation, both in the rainforest and in more exposed areas.

The thin, rambling rhizome bears pseudobulbs 1–8 cm apart; they may be green, red or purple depending on light intensity, and are up to 1.8 cm long, conical and depressed, hugging the rhizome. The single leaf is oval to circular, leathery and 1.5–7.0 cm long. This species may flower at any time, and often does so several times a year. The 1–3 cm spike rises from an internode carrying a single short-lived flower 1–2 cm wide, which is dominated by the spreading lateral sepals. They are usually a glossy yellow, but may be greenish-yellow, red or orange, with three or four red stripes and sometimes red spotting. The tiny petals are yellowish with a large red blotch near the apex, and may also have a red stripe or spots. The 0.4–0.8 cm lip is usually red with a yellow tip.

Preferring cool to intermediate conditions and a fairly humid atmosphere, this species may be grown in bright light or in shade. It is not particular about mounts and will do well on any well-drained material. *Actual flower size: 1–2 cm across.*

Bulbophyllum macphersonii Rupp

This delightful Australian species was first described by Bailey in 1884 as *B. purpurascens*. However, as that name had already been used for an Asian species, Rupp renamed it *B. macphersonii* in 1934. It occurs in eastern Australia from the Tropic of Capricorn to Cooktown and Cape York Peninsula, and is largely confined to areas above the 450 m level. It grows predominantly on trees, only occasionally on rocks, mostly in rainforest but sometimes in more exposed places.

The plant develops into dense matted clumps, often growing over itself. The inconspicuous pseudobulbs are 0.1–0.15 cm long and very crowded on the creeping rhizome. The narrow dark green or sometimes reddish leaves are 1.0–2.5 cm long, usually lying flat against the host, but occasionally erect. They are fleshy, with a central furrow above. This species flowers mostly from autumn to winter, but may do so at other times. The 2–5 cm spike bears a single inverted flower 1.0–1.5 cm across. The deep maroon flower opens widely. Its petals taper to thread-like ends and are edged with tiny hairs. The very mobile lip is 0.4–0.6 cm long with longish hairs on its margins. A white-flowered form has been reported.

A hardy species, *B. macphersonii* is easy to grow mounted on treefern, paperbark or tea-tree placed in a cool humid position with moderate light levels. In bright light the plant develops a reddish cast. It should be kept moderately moist all year round.
Actual flower size: 1–1.5 cm across.

Bulbophyllum minutissimum (Muell.) Mueller

One of the world's smallest orchids, this tiny species was discovered as early as 1849 in the Sydney area in New South Wales. It was described by von Mueller as *Dendrobium minutissimum* in 1865, and transferred to the genus *Bulbophyllum* in 1878. Endemic to Australia, it occurs from southern New South Wales to southeastern Queensland in a variety of habitats from coastal lowlands to low mountain ranges. It grows epiphytically in rainforest and on rock faces in gullies. Its two most favoured hosts are *Ficus macrophylla* and sandstone rocks, where it grows among mosses and lichens and is hard to distinguish from them. After *B. globuliforme* (another Australian species), it is the smallest of the genus *Bulbophyllum*.

The green to reddish pseudobulbs are only 0.2–0.3 cm across and much flattened. They are closely set on a creeping rhizome, and over a long period may form dense mats. Each pseudobulb has a single tiny pointed green leaf less than 0.1 cm long. Single flowers 0.4–0.5 cm across appear in late spring on extremely short stems. The cream flowers with broad red stripes last up to a week.

B. minutissimum can be grown on tree branches, hardwood planks or shingles, on cork or paperbark, or on a flat piece of sandstone. It prefers intermediate to cool conditions in an airy place with good light. While not needing as much water as other Australian bulbophyllums, it should not be subjected to prolonged dry periods. It grows best for us on small paperbark branches, which retain some water in the bark layers but drain well.
Actual flower size: 0.4–0.5 cm across.

Bulbophyllum negrosianum Ames

This unusual bulbophyllum was first described in 1912 by Professor Oakes Ames who established the Orchid Herbarium at Harvard University and who did much work on Philippine orchid species. The range of *B. negrosianum* is very limited, being reported only from Negros Oriental, where it is found in the south of the island at Dumaguete and in the Cuernos Mountains at 1,100 m above sea level. It grows epiphytically in the mossy woods. The temperature in the area is warm throughout the year, with rain from May to October and a relatively dry period from November to April.

The apple-green pseudobulbs are conical, up to 2.5 cm long with a single leathery leaf up to 20 cm long and 4 cm wide. The flower spike is produced from the base of the pseudobulbs in the spring. It grows to about 40 cm, with the apical 15 cm bearing many velvety purplish-brown flowers that open a few at a time. Although small, the flowers are attractive on account of their colour and velvety texture. The lateral sepals are 0.6 cm long with smooth edges, while the dorsal sepal (0.6 cm) and the petals (0.3 cm) have minutely hairy margins. The hinged lip is 0.4 cm long.

B. negrosianum grows well mounted on treefern slabs in a warm spot. It will tolerate fairly bright light as well as moderate shade. It should be given plentiful water from spring to autumn and a relatively dry rest during winter months.

Actual flower size: 0.5 cm long.

Bulbophyllum picturatum (Lodd.) Reichenbach (f.)

Belonging to the section *Cirrhopetalum* in this genus, *B. picturatum* was introduced into England in about 1840 by Loddiges, who named it *C. picturatum*. Reichenbach transferred it to the genus *Bulbophyllum* in 1861. Its range extends from Assam through Burma and northern Thailand to Vietnam. It grows often on deciduous trees in fairly bright light, and occurs between 900 m and 1,550 m above sea level.

The closely set pseudobulbs, 2.5–5 cm tall, are pale green to yellow-green and become angled and furrowed with age. Each pseudobulb bears a single fleshy leaf 7–15 cm long by 2 cm wide with rounded lobes at the apex. The slightly fragrant flowers are produced in spring on a more or less erect purple-spotted spike 12–25 cm long. Five to ten flowers, each 2.5–5 cm long, are arranged in an umbel at the apex of the spike. These flowers are greenish-yellow or yellow with heavy red-purple spotting on the dorsal sepal and the petals. The 0.7 cm dorsal is concave, projected over the column, and has a reddish-purple thread-like tail about 1 cm long. The lateral sepals are joined along both edges to form a sleeve-like tube. The 0.4 cm petals are irregularly fringed, while the dark red tongue-like lip is strongly recurved and highly mobile.

This species does well on treefern or cork mounts in moderately bright light. Intermediate conditions are ideal. Plants should be given plenty of water when in growth, followed by a slightly drier resting period.

Actual flower size: 2.5–5 cm long.

Bulbophyllum planibulbe (Ridley) Ridley

Ridley originally described this species in 1893 as *Cirrhopetalum planibulbe*, but in 1907 transferred it to the genus *Bulbophyllum*, where it remains. It was originally placed in the section *Cirrhopetalum*, but Seidenfaden has since transferred it to the section *Desmothanthes*, members of which have free and more or less similar sepals instead of the joined lateral sepals that are a feature of the former section. This lowland epiphyte is confined to peninsular Thailand, including nearby islands, and Malaysia.

It has an unusual habit, with reddish pseudobulbs lying flat along a slender branching rhizome to which they are almost fused. The 1.5 cm pseudobulbs are usually 3–5 cm apart, and bear a single leaf. This stalkless leaf is about 2.5 cm long and bilobed at the apex. The purplish spike is up to 9 cm long with two to five flowers about 2.5 cm across the tips of the spreading lateral sepals. The sepals, which are a glossy maroon on the reverse, are reddish-purple with yellow edges and tips. The 1 cm dorsal sepal is concave and tapers to a sharp point, while the 1.5 cm lateral sepals have swollen gland-like ends. The diamond-shaped petals are yellow, with three veins, and present an attractive colour contrast. The short orange-red lip is curved, and has a paler tip. J. J. Smith's var. *sumatranum* has lateral sepals to 2.5 cm.

B. planibulbe should be mounted on cork, paperbark or treefern and hung in semi-shade in a warm environment with high humidity. It requires year-round watering.

Actual flower size: approximately 2.5 cm across.

Bulbophyllum propinquum Kraenzlin

Belonging to the large section *Racemosae*, the members of which have many smallish flowers in dense racemes, this species was described by Kraenzlin in 1908. Schlechter's *B. chlorostachys* is a later synonym. *B. propinquum* is confined to the immediate vicinity of Chiang Mai in northern Thailand, where it has been found on Doi Suthep and Doi Saket at about 1,400 m above sea level.

The conical pseudobulbs are set at 2 cm intervals on a thick rhizome, which has 0.8 cm internodes. Covered with a cobweb-like netting when young, the pseudobulbs are 1.5–2.0 cm tall, sometimes reaching 3.5 cm. The single leathery leaf is quite stiff and up to 11 cm long by 2 cm wide. The arching spike is about 8 cm long with several closely set flowers on the upper half. The sepals, which have five veins, are a dull yellow but almost completely covered with heavy reddish-purple markings so that the flowers appear to be dark red-purple. The 0.6 cm dorsal sepal is oval, while the 0.8 cm laterals are oblong with rolled-up edges near the apex. The tiny more or less triangular petals are whitish, with a few purple blotches and a thin median line of the same colour. The hinged 0.5 cm lip is yellow underneath but red-purple on top with a shallow furrow down the middle. At the base are two erect lobes, which are toothed at the front.

B. propinquum does well mounted on treefern or similar material and given a position with moderately bright light and intermediate conditions. Moderate watering and a drier rest in winter are recommended.

Actual flower size: approximately 1 cm long.

Bulbophyllum serratotruncatum Seidenfaden

Ridley described this species as *Cirrhopetalum ochraceum*, transferring it to *Bulbophyllum* in 1907. Although Cogniaux had earlier used the name *B. ochraceum* for a Brazilian bulbophyllum, it was not until the early 1970s that Seidenfaden renamed this species *B. serratotruncatum*. The specific epithet refers to the sharply cut-off and serrated apices of the column wings. This feature distinguishes the species from *B. lepidum* and *B. cummingii*, whose column wings are entire. This species has always been considered to be of Malaysian origin, but our plants were imported some years ago from the Philippines as unnamed bulbophyllums. It is very close in appearance to the Philippine species *B. cummingii*, and may in the past have been mistaken for it. The ridged glossy green pseudobulbs are about 3 cm tall and set 1.5–3.0 cm apart. Each bears a single leathery leaf 7–11 cm long and up to 3.5 cm wide. In spring a brittle pinkish spike 10–20 cm long carries an almost circular umbel of flowers. The sepals and petals are pale yellow suffused with pinkish-red. The lateral sepals are joined for almost their entire length. The tiny petals and dorsal sepal are edged with hairs and taper to long filiform tails. The tiny lip is highly mobile.

Plants of this species do very well for us mounted on treefern slabs and grown in moderately bright light with plenty of water when in growth. An intermediate to warm environment seems best, with high year-round humidity. *Actual flower size: 2.5–3.5 cm long.*

Bulbophyllum wadsworthii Dockrill

Closely related to *B. gadgarrense** this Australian bulbophyllum was not described until 1964 when Dockrill named it. Found in the tropics of northeastern Australia, it shares the same geographical area as *B. gadgarrense*: from Townsville to Cooktown above the 700 m level. It is quite common there on the trunks and branches of trees in the rainforest and cloudforest where there is constant moisture and high humidity all the year round.

The plant comprises a small bunch of pendent stems with roots only at the base. The rhizomes, which may reach 25 cm in length, do not branch freely. They are covered with green bracts. The small prostrate pseudobulbs, about 0.5 cm long, are carried on the rhizome at intervals of 1–3 cm and are partly obscured by the bracts. The stemless fleshy leaves are 2–6 cm long, dark green, with a V-shaped channel on the upper surfaces. The 0.5 cm spike appears from between the bracts with one to three small white, cream or pale green flowers 0.5–0.7 cm long. All segments are fleshy, and the tiny lip is pale orange in colour. This species is very floriferous, and a plant covered in tiny flowers can be quite showy.

An easy species to grow, *B. wadsworthii* should be attached to a slab of treefern or paperbark with a pad of moss at the base, kept moist and put in a humid, cool to intermediate spot with good light and air movement. *Actual flower size: 0.5–0.7 cm long.*

Bulbophyllum wendlandianum (Krzl.) Dammer

This species, with its court-jester-like flowers, was originally described by Kraenzlin in 1891 as *Cirrhopetalum wendlandianum*. Dammer reclassified it as a bulbophyllum in 1907. *Cirrhopetalum collettii* is a synonym. It grows as an epiphyte in northern Burma and northern Thailand between 200 m and 1,500 m above sea level.

The pseudobulbs, green when young, become yellowish and rather shrivelled with age. They are 2.0–2.5 cm tall and set 1–4 cm apart on a stout rhizome. Each one bears a single very stiff leaf 4–8 cm long. The flower spike rises from the centre of the developing new growth in spring or summer. Up to 15 cm long,

it bears a head of three to six pale yellow-and-red striped flowers, which may reach a length of 15 cm including the long tails. Both the erect dorsal sepal and the petals have hairs along the edges and several broad flat red appendages — the petals at the tip and the dorsal along the tail. Irregularly shaped, these flutter in the slightest breeze. The lateral sepals are joined at the base to form a 'sleeve' before tapering to long freely hanging tails. The highly mobile fleshy lip is glossy red.

One of the most interesting and attractive of the Asian bulbophyllums, this species should be mounted and hung in a moderately bright position. Intermediate to warm conditions are preferred. The plant is in general an easy one to manage in cultivation. Give plenty of water when in growth and keep fairly dry in the cooler months.

Actual flower size: approximately 9–15 cm long.

Cadetia taylori (Muell.) Schlechter

First described by von Mueller in 1874 as *Bulbophyllum taylori* and named for its collector, this charming species was subsequently known as *Dendrobium taylori* and *D. uniflos*. In 1912 Schlechter created the new genus of *Cadetia* for a group of plants found mostly in New Guinea, and transferred this species to it. *Cadetia taylori* is found in New Guinea, where it occurs in rainforest up to 600 m elevation, and in eastern tropical Australia, where it is found on rainforest trees and rocks up to 1,200 m in protected positions in open forest, and in mangrove swamps.

The thin pencil-like pseudobulbs have vertical grooves, are 2.5–10 cm long, and usually

form dense clumps. Each pseudobulb has a single leathery leaf 1.5–5 cm long, which is dark green and bilobed at the apex. The main flowering period is from November to May, but flowers may appear at any time. The flowers are produced singly, or occasionally in pairs, from the top of the new pseudobulbs, on a spike about 1.5 cm long. They are elegantly shaped and up to 1.2 cm across. The narrow petals curve sharply inwards. Colour is a beautiful glistening white with a thick densely hairy lip 0.6–0.8 cm long, which may be yellow or pink.

C. taylori is a relatively easy species to cultivate in cool to intermediate conditions with semi-shade. It may be mounted on a treefern slab but grows well potted in a well-drained fibrous mixture with a little moss added. It should be kept moist all year round.

Actual flower size: approximately 1 cm across.

Capanemia superflua (Rchb. (f.)) Garay

The clustered cylindrical pseudobulbs are 1.5–3 cm long, but very narrow. Covered with papery bracts, they bear a single terete leaf 5–10 cm long with a single furrow on the upper surface and tapering to a narrow point. Arching spikes appear from the base of the pseudobulbs in spring or summer with about twelve delicate flowers that last quite well. Each flower is up to 1 cm long with sparkling white petals and sepals, which may have a pinkish stripe on the back. The dorsal is somewhat concave, the petals point forward, and the oblong lateral sepals are spreading. The fiddle-shaped lip is about 0.6 cm long and has two clear yellow calli at the base: in all a very attractive flower.

Reichenbach described this species in 1864 as *Oncidium superfluum* based on material from Widgren. In 1967 Garay transferred it to *Capanemia*, a genus created by Barbosa Rodrigues in 1877. *Capanemia uliginosa*, *C. juergensiana* and *Rodriguezia anomala* are conspecific with this species. It occurs in the cooler mountains in the southern part of Brazil and into Argentina, growing on slender twigs together with mosses and lichens at altitudes above 500 m.

C. superflua will grow in cool to intermediate conditions in a semi-shaded position. It does well mounted on a small treefern slab or on small branches. It likes year-round moisture, but should be allowed to dry out between waterings, especially in winter.

Actual flower size: approximately 1 cm long.

Cattleya aclandiae Lindley

This charming miniature was introduced into England by its discoverer, Lieutenant James, in 1839. In 1840 it flowered in Sir Thomas Acland's collection, whereupon Lindley described it, naming if for Lady Acland, who illustrated it for him. Confined to the northeastern state of Bahia in Brazil, this species grows at altitudes between 100 m and 400 m, and occurs up to 100 km inland from the coast. Now quite rare in its native habitat, it grows in broken shade on rough-barked trees scattered across the very hot, dry caatinga. However, it usually receives sea breezes and night-time dew.

The slender pseudobulbs are 5–12 cm long with two or occasionally three oval horizontally spreading leaves 2–9 cm long. The leaves are fleshy and more or less suffused or spotted with dark reddish-brown, depending on the level of light. This species flowers from spring to summer and sometimes again six months later. The spike has no sheath, but is enclosed within the leaves of the developing pseudobulb. It bears one or two long-lasting waxy flowers 6–8 cm across, which have a faint spicy fragrance. The colour of the flowers varies, with green or yellowish tepals covered with dark red-brown, or sometimes almost black, blotches. The contrasting lip ranges in colour from creamy-white to magenta, streaked and suffused with darker veins.

Smallish slabs of cork seem to suit this species in cultivation. It may be watered all year round but prefers to dry out quickly. Intermediate conditions suit it, with as much light as possible short of burning.

Actual flower size: 6–8 cm across.

51

Cattleya forbesii Lindley

The Brazilian botanist Vellozo first described this somewhat neglected species as *Epidendrum pauper* as early as 1790. However, later botanists remained ignorant of Vellozo's description until Stellfeld unearthed it in 1945. Although Lindley's description did not appear until 1823, when he named it in honour of Forbes, an orchid collector who had sent plants to London from Rio, his *Cattleya forbesii* remains the generally accepted name. This species inhabits swampy areas and forested river banks, mostly on trees but occasionally on rocks, up to 200 m above sea level. It occurs in Brazil in a narrow band almost parallel to the coast from the state of Rio de Janeiro south to Santa Catarina.

The slender pseudobulbs are typically 10–15 cm tall, but may be slightly longer. Indeed, we have had plants flower on 4 cm pseudobulbs. The two leathery leaves are 6–15 cm long with a rounded apex. The two to five long-lasting flowers are borne on a 9–15 cm spike in late spring or summer. The flowers are apple-green to greenish-yellow or tan, about 6–11 cm wide. The long tubular lip curls around the fleshy column, concealing it. The exterior of the lip is pinkish-white, while the interior has a central yellow-gold stripe and is streaked with reddish-brown. The lip on some plants may be golden-yellow.

This species is very adaptable, growing and flowering in unheated greenhouses with temperatures down to −2°C in winter. Intermediate conditions are preferred though, with a warm humid summer. Plants may be potted in well-drained material or mounted on treefern, cork etc.

Actual flower size: 6–11 cm across.

Cattleya luteola Lindley

A somewhat variable species, *Cattleya luteola* was described in 1853 by Lindley, based on plants from Amazonian Brazil. Among its many synonyms are *C. meyeri*, *C. flavida*, *C. sulphurea* and *Epidendrum luteolum*. It is widely distributed throughout the Amazonian basin, with major populations in Brazil and Peru, and reports of it from Ecuador, Colombia, Venezuela and Bolivia. In Brazil it is found up to 600 m above sea level in the states of Amazonas and Para. In Peru it inhabits the Andes and the Amazon basin, mostly between 100 m and 1,200 m elevation, but occasionally up to 2,000 m. Both areas are subject to long hot dry periods followed by heavy rains.

The furrowed flattened pseudobulbs are closely set on a stout rhizome. They are sometimes tinged with reddish-brown and are commonly 5–15 cm tall, although Peruvian specimens are sometimes larger. Brazilian plants tend to average about 15 cm in height. The single stiff leaf is 6–17 cm long. The four to six flowers are borne on a terminal spike from summer to autumn. The flowers are among the smallest of the genus, being only about 5 cm across. They are typically pale yellow, but may be apple-green or greenish-yellow. The tubular 2.8 cm lip is generally bright yellow inside, spotted or streaked with crimson and white along the frilled edges.

C. luteola does best when mounted, placed in a bright humid environment with warm to intermediate conditions, and given plenty of water in the growing season with a decided dry rest in winter.

Actual flower size: approximately 5 cm across.

Cattleya walkeriana Gardner

Gardner discovered this species in 1839 and described it in 1843, naming it for his assistant who looked after the plant collections during Gardner's excursions in Brazil. Synonyms are *C. princeps*, *C. bulbosa*, and *C. gardneriana*. Confined to Brazil, this species has a variety of habitats up to 2,000 m altitude in the states of Minas Gerais, Goias, Sao Paulo and Mato Grosso. It grows on old giant trees on rocky limestone plateaux, on small rough-barked trees and granite cliffs. It is often exposed to full sun and high temperatures, with only cloud and mist providing some relief.

The club-shaped pseudobulbs are 3–12 cm tall, well spaced on a stout rhizome. They may be green or reddish-purple. Each bears a single leathery leaf (rarely two) 4–12 cm long, which is often tinged with red. The flowers, which last about six weeks, are borne one to three per spike in autumn or spring. The spikes usually rise from the base of the pseudobulb, but sometimes from the apex in the variety *walkeriana* (however, Braem contends that this is probably a natural hybrid between *C. walkeriana* and *C. loddigesii*). The pale to dark rosy-pink flowers are 8–10 cm across. The narrow pointed sepals contrast nicely with the almost diamond-shaped petals. The three-lobed lip is up to 4.5 cm long with a deeper colouring and veins on the mid-lobe, and a pale yellow or white disc streaked with purple.

C. walkeriana is very adaptable, and grows well on treefern or cork mounts in bright light and intermediate to cool conditions. It needs plenty of water when in growth.

Actual flower size: 8–10 cm across.

Caularthron bicornutum (Hook.) Rafinesque-Schmaltz

More commonly known by Bentham's 1881 name of *Diacrium bicornutum*, this species was described by Hooker in 1834 as *Epidendrum bicornutum*. In 1836 Rafinesque-Schmaltz transferred it to *Caularthron*. *Diacrium amazonicum* is also synonymous. It is common in Trinidad and Tobago, growing epiphytically on rocks and overhanging the sea on cliffs where it is sometimes subjected to salt spray. There it is rarer inland, but in Venezuela, Colombia, Guyana and Brazil it inhabits inland forests.

The clustered, spindle-shaped pseudobulbs are usually 9–20 cm tall, although on most of the plants we have seen they are quite short. They produce two or three stiff leathery leaves 7–20 cm long. An erect spike carries three to twenty white flowers in spring. This spike, 15–30 cm tall, rises from between the leaves. The closely set fragrant flowers are up to 6 cm across and last for two to three weeks. The sepals and broader petals are pointed at the apex. The more or less concave sepals are sometimes marked with lavender on the backs and at the tips. The three-lobed lip and column are spotted and streaked with purple. The pointed mid-lobe is about 2.5 cm long and yellow down the centre. Near the base there is a fleshy crest with two prominent yellow ridges.

C. bicornutum, which rather resents division, enjoys warm to intermediate conditions with bright light and good ventilation. It grows well when potted in a fairly coarse mixture of treefern chunks, broken brick and coarse bark. Keep on the dry side during winter dormancy.

Actual flower size: approximately 5 cm across.

Chytroglossa marileoniae Reichenbach (f.)

Described by Reichenbach in the latter half of the 19th century, this species is rarely seen in collections although its striking flowers make it a worthy addition. Related to *Ornithocephalus*, this genus comprises only three species, all confined to southern Brazil. *C. marileoniae* grows in mountainous areas in the states of Rio de Janeiro and Sao Paulo, where rain is common throughout the year and cooling mists form late in the day as hot air rises from the land.

The olive-green leaves form fan-like growths. The narrow pointed leaves are 3–4 cm long with a slightly reflexed apex. From four to six flowers 2 cm long are borne in spring on a pendent wiry spike about 5 cm long. The petals and sepals are apple-green to yellow, while the lip is white at the base with dark red-brown blotches providing a focus. The almost erect dorsal and rounded petals are curved inward at the tip. The short lateral sepals are virtually hidden by the lip, which is minutely serrated, as are the petals near the tips. The lip has two calli at the base and an upturned mid-lobe.

C. marileoniae prefers a fibrous mount such as treefern and cool to intermediate conditions with year-round humidity. It needs semi-shade to full shade, regular watering, and — most importantly — good air movement.

Actual flower size: approximately 2 cm long.

Cleisostoma arietinum (Rchb. (f.)) Garay

First described by Reichenbach in the 19th century, probably as *Sarcanthus* or *Saccolabium arietinum*, this unusual monopodial was described again in 1925 as *Sarcanthus recurvus* (Rolfe ex Downie), a name by which the species is better known. Garay transferred it to the genus *Cleisostoma* about 1972. This species is synonymous with *Sarcanthus kunstleri*. Endemic to Thailand, it occurs in the north and northeast of the country at altitudes of 400–1,100 m above sea level.

The plant comprises a 'ladder' of tough terete leaves arranged alternately. The fleshy downward-curving leaves are about 6 cm long and rounded at the apex. This species is very slow growing, taking years to exceed a height of 10 cm. New stems often form on the lower part of the existing stem or, more rarely, on the upper section. The flower spike, 6–8 cm long, appears in summer and bears up to fifty blooms. These well-spaced flowers are about 0.5 cm across. The spreading sepals and petals are a creamy-white tinged with pale pink, and rounded at the apex. The lip, with its bright magenta mid-lobe, is the focus of the flower. The small rounded side-lobes are erect, and the bilobed white spur at the base is almost closed by a fleshy callus on the inside back wall at its entrance.

C. arietinum should be placed on a mount of treefern or similar material. An intermediate semi-shaded environment is preferred, with year-round moisture except for a dry resting period in winter.

Actual flower size: approximately 0.5 cm across.

Cochlioda noezliana (Rchb. (f.)) Rolfe

This much admired species was discovered in 1888 by Noezli (or Noetzli), for whom Reichenbach named the plant *Odontoglossum noezlianum* in 1890. Rolfe transferred it to *Cochlioda* in 1891, the same year it was introduced into Europe by Linden of Brussels. It is a native of the Peruvian Andes, where it grows as an epiphyte at altitudes of up to 3,000 m.

The 3–5 cm pseudobulbs (rarely to 7.5 cm) are tightly clustered on a short rhizome, and are often much wrinkled. The dark green leaves are usually 7.5–15 cm long, occasionally longer. Flowering time is rather variable, with the arching spike rising from the base of the pseudobulb with up to fifteen widely spaced flowers. Vivid scarlet, they are 2.5–3.5 cm across, with slightly reflexed petals and sepals, which are pointed. The petals are broader than the sepals and have undulating margins. The lip is fused to the column for the latter's entire length. The lip, bright orange-scarlet and 1.7–2 cm long, has three lobes and a yellow disc furnished with four hairy keels. The lateral lobes are almost round.

C. noezliana, which because of its colour has been much used for hybridising with odontoglossums, may be mounted or potted in coarse treefern fibre or similar material. It prefers an intermediate environment, requiring a cool shady spot in summer so that temperatures do not exceed 25°C. Good air movement is essential. Keep moist when in growth, and allow to dry out when growth is complete for the year. *Actual flower size: 2.5–3.5 cm across.*

Coelogyne confusa Ames

This species was described by Ames in 1915, and is reportedly rare, coming only from Camiguin Island to the north of Luzon. Our plants turned up years ago in a batch of unnamed coelogynes from the Philippines. *Coelogyne confusa* grows as either an epiphyte or a lithophyte in an area that has year-round rainfall — at most the dry season lasts about a month and a half — and is subject to typhoons. Both temperature and humidity are high throughout the year.

The pear-shaped pseudobulbs are about 5 cm tall with two pleated leaves up to 20 cm in length. The flower spike is up to 25 cm long with loosely arranged flowers about 3.5 cm in diameter. The lip with its pretty orange markings has slightly wavy margins and three ridges from the base to the middle of the mid-lobe. The disc is covered with minute hairs.

C. confusa grows well in well-drained pots of treefern chunks or some similar substrate, or mounted. It requires intermediate conditions with year-round moisture and plenty of indirect light.
Actual flower size: approximately 3.5 cm across.

Coelogyne cristata var. *lemoniana* Lindley

The type species was first discovered in northern India by Wallich, and first described by Lindley in 1821. Early synonyms include *Cymbidium speciosissimum* and *Pleione speciosissima*. This species ranges through Nepal, Bhutan and northern India at altitudes of 1,500–2,600 m, making it a true cool-climate grower. Its habitat sees year-round fog and mist, but also very bright winter light. Plants grow either on mossy trees or in pockets of humus on exposed rock outcrops. These are all valuable hints for cultivation, and need little comment.

The pseudobulbs of the variety *lemoniana* are almost spherical, and less crowded than those of the type species. This variety makes a wonderful basket plant (though it may be grown equally well in a pot) with its pendulous spikes of large fragrant flowers in late winter and spring. It is a shallow-rooted plant, so make sure that drainage is adequate. A thin layer of fairly fine compost over lots of crocks seems ideal. The blooms make wonderful cut flowers, lasting four to five weeks if kept away from moisture, which spots the segments. This variety differs from the type mainly in the colour of the throat, a wonderful citron-yellow rather than orange. Both have heavy decorative keels on the lip. The varietal name, curiously, is derived not from the colour of the throat, but from the fact that it was first flowered in about 1880 by Sir Charles Lemon.
Actual flower size: 6–9 cm across.

Coelogyne merrillii Ames

Ames described this Philippine species in 1911, naming it in honour of Merrill, at whose instigation he had begun describing orchid collections at the Philippine Bureau of Science where Merrill was the director. This species is found growing on mossy boulders among leaf litter in the provinces of Benguet and Rizal on the island of Luzon and also on Negros. It occurs between 300 m and 2,300 m above sea level.

The erect, somewhat clustered, pseudobulbs are 5–7 cm tall and about 2.5 cm in diameter. Dull green, they are pear shaped and become furrowed and wrinkled with age. The pointed leathery leaves are 9.5–15 cm long, with between two and five prominent veins. The very fragrant flowers, which last for between two and three weeks, are held on a 5–15 cm spike that rises from between the new leaves at the apex of the pseudobulb. Erect or, more usually, slightly pendulous, the spike carries two to four whitish, pale salmon or straw-coloured flowers each 3.5–5 cm long. The 3.7 cm dorsal sepal arches over the column and, like the oblong lateral sepals, has an acute apex. The extremely narrow petals are 3.5 cm long and swept up and backwards. The 3 cm long lip is three-lobed, with yellow-orange markings on the erect lateral lobes and five hairy keels on the mid-lobe.

Once established, *C. merrillii* grows well in cultivation, and should be potted in coarse treefern or mounted and placed in semi-shade in an intermediate environment. We hang the pots to ensure good air movement.
Actual flower size: 3.5–5 cm long.

Coelogyne nitida Lindley

Described in 1822 by Lindley from material collected in Nepal by Wallich, this species is often known by its synonym *Coelogyne ochracea*. An early synonym was *Cymbidium nitidum*, as described by Wallich; the *Cymbidium nitidum* of Roxburgh is considered to be a separate species. This very fragrant species has a wide range: from Kumaon, Nepal, Sikkim, Darjeeling, Bhutan and the Khasia hills into Yunnan, north Burma, Thailand and Laos. It occurs in temperate and subtemperate zones at 1,500–2,300 m altitude with fog and mist nearly all year round. In winter it receives plenty of bright light with low temperatures. It is found growing as a lithophyte or an epiphyte on moss-covered trees.

The clustered apple-green pseudobulbs are oblong, often four-angled, and 4–10 cm tall. There are two arching leaves 7–20 cm long. The inflorescence, 11–24 cm long, rises from the developing new growth and bears six to eight crystalline white flowers about 4 cm across. The lip is attractively marked.

One of the easiest of the coelogynes to grow, this species is happy in cool to intermediate conditions. It grows well in a pot or basket in a medium that retains some moisture without becoming waterlogged; alternatively it may be mounted on a treefern slab. Give semi-shade in summer and bright light during winter months to encourage flowering.

Actual flower size: approximately 4 cm across.

Comparettia coccinea Lindley

A Brazilian species first imported into England by Loddiges in 1837, *C. coccinea* was described by Lindley in 1838. However, it was then lost to cultivation until re-introduced in 1865. It grows on either trees or rocks in generally broken sunlight in the cooler areas of the states of Espirito Santo, Sao Paulo, Rio de Janeiro, Parana and Minas Gerais in Brazil.

The clustered pseudobulbs are rather compressed and tinged with red. They are usually 1.5–3 cm long and bear a single fleshy leaf at the apex. The narrow leaf, 5–15 cm long, is pointed, dark green above and purplish beneath. The arching, often branched, spike may appear at any time between summer and winter. From 15 cm to 22 cm long, it carries between three and ten flowers, each about 2 cm in diameter, towards its end. The sepals and petals are usually yellow-orange, shaded with red. The 0.8 cm dorsal sepal and petals protect the column, while the joined laterals are obscured by the lip except for the curved 1.0–1.5 cm spur formed at their base. The wide lip is bright scarlet with two yellow keels and two thread-like projections from the base. These projections are hidden within the spur. The lip has wavy edges and is bent slightly outwards.

C. coccinea does best mounted, but may be potted in a coarse well-drained mixture. It likes intermediate to cool temperatures in semi-shade to moderately bright light. Give plenty of water when in active growth, followed by a drier rest in mid-winter.

Actual flower size: approximately 2 cm across.

Comparettia falcata Poeppig & Endlicher

This species, on which the genus *Comparettia* was based, was discovered in Peru by Poeppig who, along with Endlicher, described it in 1836. Lindley's *C. rosea* is conspecific. The most widespread of the comparettias, *C. falcata* occurs from Mexico through Central America and the West Indies, and extends as far south as Bolivia and Brazil. It is usually found growing on trees and shrubs in humid forests up to 1,800 m elevation.

Plants are quite variable, with clustered pseudobulbs 1–4 cm tall. They are compressed and bear a single leaf 3–18 cm long. This oblong very fleshy leaf is folded inward at the base and is often suffused with red-purple.

Flower spikes, from 6 cm to 90 cm in length, may appear at any time of the year. Sometimes branched, they carry anything from two to thirty flowers about 2 cm long. These are a deep rosy-pink, paler towards the centre and with darker veining. The concave dorsal sepal and slightly broader spreading petals are arranged round the column, while the joined lateral sepals, which form a slender slightly compressed spur, are hidden behind the large three-lobed lip. Two slender appendages at the base of the lip are contained within the spur. The lateral lobes of the lip are small, while the kidney-shaped mid-lobe is large with undulating edges and may have a white central keel at the base.

Preferring to be mounted, this species likes semi-shaded intermediate to cool conditions with moderate light. Fairly high humidity and good air movement are needed, with year-round moisture.

Actual flower size: approximately 2 cm long.

Corybas aconitiflorus Salisbury

Commonly known as the 'spurred helmet orchid', this Australian terrestrial species was described by Salisbury in 1807. It is a widespread species, ranging from Queensland to Tasmania and also occurring in New Zealand. It favours damp shady positions among the undergrowth of dry sclerophyll forests and occurs mostly in coastal areas or nearby hills. It grows mainly in poor acid soil where there is a light covering of leafmould.

It commonly establishes large colonies, as the small globular tubers reproduce freely. The tubers remain dormant during the hot summer months, then produce a single heart-shaped leaf 1–3 cm long in the autumn. The dark green leaf, which has a reddish-purple underside, sits flat on or just above the ground. The single flower is produced in late autumn to winter on a very short stem so that overall height is no more than 3 cm. The dominant feature of the flower is its dorsal sepal, which forms the 'helmet' and is up to 2.5 cm long. The lateral sepals and petals are inconspicuous. The broad lip is whitish, marked with red or purple and forms a curved tube with two narrow spurs at the base.

Relatively easy to cultivate, the tubers of this species should be planted about 2 cm deep in a mixture of sandy soil and leafmould, and set in a cool shady spot. We grow ours on the floor of a greenhouse, under the benches. A thin layer of leafmould should be sprinkled on the surface of the pot. Plenty of water should be given during the growing season, but reduced during dormancy.

Actual flower size: approximately 2 cm long.

Cryptochilus sanguinea Wallich

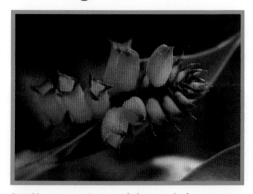

The genus *Cryptochilus*, with few species, is closely related to *Eria*, from which it is distinguished by its cup-shaped flowers. *C. sanguinea* was described by Wallich in 1824. It is a native of Nepal, Sikkim and the Khasia and Naga hills, where it is found growing as an epiphyte in mixed forest from 1,300 m to 1,700 m above sea level. This is an area with plentiful summer rain accompanied by high temperatures. The winters are cool, dry and sunny.

This unusual species has 4–6 cm pseudobulbs with one or two acutely pointed leaves which are 10–20 cm long. The flower spike appears in summer from the centre of the developing pseudobulb. It is 15–25 cm long and bears two rows of red to scarlet flowers all facing in the same direction. The sepals join to form a tube about 2 cm long in which the bright yellow lip is hidden, as implied by the generic name. The outside of the tube is pubescent.

C. sanguinea should be grown mounted or in well-drained pots or shallow pans of sphagnum moss and treefern chunks or similar substrate. A warm summer, followed by a cooler winter with a short dry resting period, and plenty of bright light suit this species. Give moderate shade in summer.

Actual flower size: approximately 2 cm long.

Cryptostylis subulata (Labill.) Reichenbach (f.)

An Australian terrestrial, this species was described as *Malaxis subulata* by Labillardiere in 1806. Reichenbach later transferred it to *Cryptostylis*. Brown's *C. longifolia* is conspecific. This mostly evergreen species is widespread from southeast Queensland to Tasmania and South Australia, growing usually in swampy areas among tall grass.

Unlike most terrestrials it has no tubers, but a long brittle rhizome and extensive thick fleshy roots. The one to three leathery leaves are 12–15 cm long including the stalks, and are tapered at both ends with a prominent mid-vein and occasional dark brown markings on the underside. The flower spikes, 25–80 cm tall, rise in spring and summer with two to twenty well-spaced flowers opening successively. From 2.0 cm to 3.5 cm in length, each flower is dominated by the orange-red to reddish-brown fleshy lip, the lateral edges of which are reflexed to form a tube. The lip is concave near the base so that it cups the column, and has two dark purple warty ridges and two finer ones that end in a large callus near the apex. The 1–2 cm petals and the 2–3 cm sepals are dark green-brown to yellow-green, narrow with inrolled edges, and taper to a fine point.

This species, which does not like to be disturbed, needs a large container (at least 15 cm across) to accommodate the long rhizome and roots. A mix of coarse sand, heavy loam, leafmould and coarse sawdust is a suitable medium. *C. subulata* prefers to be wet all year round. A cool semi-shaded spot with indirect bright light is ideal.

Actual flower size: 2–3.5 cm long.

Dendrobium aemulum R. Brown

escribed by Brown in 1810, this charming species was introduced into England in 1823 when Cunningham sent a few specimens from Australia. Although there are several vegetative forms of this species all but one have pseudobulbs less than 20 cm long. The 'ironbark' form grows in exposed conditions on eucalypts and has reddish stems; the 'brushbox' form grows in heavier shade on *Tristania* species, and stems tend to be pendent. Flowers are the same in both forms. There is a distinctive form from the north Queensland mountains with shorter thicker pseudobulbs and larger flowers. This species ranges from southeastern New South Wales to north Queensland at elevations up to 1,200 m. Usually an epiphyte, it also occasionally grows on rocks.

The pencil-shaped pseudobulbs are mostly 5–15 cm tall, usually dark reddish-brown and found in small- to medium-sized clumps. There are two to four leathery dark green leaves to 5 cm at the apex of the pseudobulbs. This species begins flowering late in July (it is usually the first to flower of the Australian dendrobiums) but in some areas it may flower as late as September. The 5–10 cm spikes are produced from the upper part of the pseudobulb. A single pseudobulb may produce up to four spikes, with up to twenty or more flowers on each. The flowers are pure crystalline white. The lip has three parallel ridges forming a yellow crest. Flowers are fragrant.

A cool-growing species, *D. aemulum* prefers semi-shade to moderate light. It must be mounted — cork, treefern or hardwood slab — as it declines when potted.

Actual flower size: approximately 2.5 cm across.

Dendrobium bairdianum Bailey

lthough first described by von Mueller as *D. fellowsii* in 1854, this species continues to be generally known as *D. bairdianum* as described by Bailey in 1886. Other synonyms are *Callista bairdiana* (Kuntze) and *D. giddinsii* (Hunt). This epiphyte occurs only in tropical Australia between 500 m and 1,000 m elevation in northeastern Queensland. It grows in small clumps or as single plants on trees in open forests, sometimes in association with *D. agrostophyllum*. In its habitat it receives plenty of bright light, with warm days and cool nights.

The pencil-shaped pseudobulbs are variable in length from 3 cm to 18 cm, with the odd plant exceeding 20 cm. The pseudobulbs are dark purple-brown and become furrowed with age. There are two to five dark green apical leaves which are deciduous, keeled, and 5–10 cm long. Flower spikes up to 8 cm long are produced on both new and old pseudobulbs in late spring and summer. The two to seven flowers are up to 2.5 cm in diameter, with the deep purple-brown markings on the lip providing a striking contrast to the green sepals and petals. There are two callus-like ridges on the lip, which is covered with fine hairs.

D. bairdianum is well worth cultivating, but has a reputation for being difficult to keep alive for more than a few years, and we lost a number of plants before we found the answer. Now we place plants on small mounts — cork or treefern — and hang them up high with the cattleyas and hard-cane dendrobiums, where they thrive. They get plenty of light and water, except in winter, when watering is reduced.

Actual flower size: 2–2.5 cm across.

Dendrobium bellatulum Rolfe

This miniature epiphyte, which when not in flower is almost indistinguishable from *D. margaritaceum,** was discovered by Henry in the Yunnan province of China in 1898. Veitch sent specimens to Kew in 1900, and in 1903 Rolfe described the species. As well as in southwestern China, it occurs at elevations of 900–1,600 m through Burma and Thailand, where it is found growing with *D. draconis* and *D. cariniferum*, to Laos and Vietnam.

The clustered, sometimes almost globular, pseudobulbs are 2–8 cm long. Mostly spindle shaped, they are covered with short black hairs, as are the two to four dull grey-green leaves. These leaves, 3–5 cm long, are bilobed at the apex. In late winter and spring very short spikes appear from the upper nodes of the pseudobulb, with from one to three long-lasting flowers 2.5–4.5 cm across. The spreading sepals and petals are creamy-white, while the mid-lobe of the lip is deep red on the basal half and yellow-orange on the rest. These colours intensify as the flower ages. The erect lateral lobes of the lip are somewhat rounded. A glossy median band runs from the base of the 2.5–3.0 cm lip, dividing into five warty keels on the strongly recurved apical half. These keels become minutely hairy towards the apex.

This is a very easy species to grow, requiring a bright sunny spot and cool to intermediate temperatures. It does best when mounted on a small piece of treefern or similar material and hung up high in the greenhouse. It should be kept moderately dry in winter.

Actual flower size: 2.5–4.5 cm across.

Dendrobium canaliculatum R. Brown

Discovered by Banks and Solander in the early 1800s and described by Brown in 1810, this Australian epiphyte was not introduced into England until 1865. Commonly known as the 'onion' or 'tea-tree' orchid, *D. canaliculatum* is synonymous with *D. tattonianum* (Bateman). The typical species (var. *canaliculatum*) occurs in northern Queensland and the Western and Central provinces of New Guinea. It inhabits both the swampy areas near the coast and the hot dry inland savannahs up to 750 m above sea level. It appears to grow exclusively on *Melaleuca* spp. (paperbarks) especially *M. viridiflora*. The pseudobulbs vary in shape and size from almost globular to elongated, swollen in the middle. They are typically 3–10 cm tall, but may reach 15 cm. The two to six terminal leaves are semi-terete, dark green with reddish edges, and 5–10 cm (occasionally 15 cm) long. The 10–40 cm erect or arching flower spike rises from the apical nodes of the pseudobulb and carries from five to fifteen or more very pretty fragrant flowers to 2.5 cm across. Flowering occurs from late winter through spring. Petals are twisted, sepals and petals are white tipped with yellow. *D. canaliculatum* is closely related to the rarer *D. carronii*, whose pink and brown petals are not twisted.

D. canaliculatum is a popular species and one we have found easy to cultivate in intermediate or warm conditions. It should be mounted on cork or paperbark, and given lots of bright light. It should be given plenty of water when in growth, and kept very dry in winter.

Actual flower size: 2–2.5 cm across.

Dendrobium canaliculatum var. *nigrescens* Nicholls

This is a well-known and popular variety of the species. It occurs in far north Queensland, ranging from just north of the Atherton Tableland to the tip of Cape York Peninsula and extending to many of the islands of Torres Strait. We have found it on Prince of Wales, Thursday, Possession and Hawkesbury Islands. All these areas are subjected to very hot dry conditions for a large part of the year, followed by monsoonal rains between December and March. These xeric conditions often cause plants to become extremely desiccated and they may even become deciduous in extremely dry seasons. Like the type species, this variety inhabits *Melaleuca* trees in open savannah country and is rarely found in large clumps.

The flowers differ from those of the type in that the ends of the petals and sepals are coloured brown instead of yellow. In the southern part of its range many intergrades with the type are found. The tips of the petals and sepals of these plants tend to be coloured a dirty brownish-yellow rather than the clear deep brown of the true variety, such as is found particularly in the forms from the Torres Strait islands. With a third variety (*D. canaliculatum* var. *foelschei* Rupp), the species extends its range into the Northern Territory and the northern part of Western Australia. In this third variety the pseudobulbs are only slightly swollen and the flowers are usually pale yellow to light tan.

Culture for the varieties is as for the type — bright light, intermediate to warm conditions and a dry winter.

Actual flower size: 2–2.5 cm across.

Dendrobium capillipes Reichenbach (f.)

Discovered by Parish in Burma and introduced into England by Low in 1866, this species was described by Reichenbach in 1867. Later synonyms are *D. acrobaticum* and *D. braiaense*. Apart from Burma, it also occurs in India, Thailand, Vietnam and southwest China, growing predominantly on deciduous trees between 800 m and 1,300 m above sea level.

The clustered knobbly pseudobulbs are usually 5–10 cm long, but may reach 15 cm. Green at first, they become yellowish with age. Four or five deciduous leaves, each 8–12 cm long, are borne near the apex. They are quite thin, strap shaped, and taper to an acute point. In spring erect spikes grow from the upper nodes of the leafless pseudobulbs. From 6 cm to 15 cm long, they carry between one and four yellow flowers 2.5–4.0 cm across. The narrow sepals are acute, with the laterals, which are hidden behind the petals and lip, having a sharp claw-like point on the reverse side near the tip. The broad rounded petals are about 1.5 cm long, while the large lip is 2 cm long and 2.5 cm across. It has slightly undulating edges. The lip has a large golden-yellow disc with normally a few light brown or red streaks near the base. The specimen pictured, with fairly dense reddish streaks, is probably not typical.

Like many other growers, we have found this species a difficult one in cultivation. It likes bright light, intermediate temperatures, and should be kept dry in winter. It should be mounted and hung fairly high in the greenhouse.

Actual flower size: 2.5–4 cm across.

Dendrobium compactum Rolfe ex Hackett

This epiphyte was briefly described by Hackett in 1904 based on a specimen from Yunnan, which was then in flower at Kew and which had been received from a Belgian nursery. Hackett used the name suggested by Rolfe, who gave a fuller description in 1906. This species is extremely closely related to *D. wilmsianum*, from which it is separated only by the slightly different configuration of the callus on the lip. It occurs in Burma and northern Thailand, where it grows at 800–1,800 m elevation, as well as in southwest China.

The clustered pseudobulbs vary from 2.5 cm to 8.0 cm in length. Somewhat conical, they bear about six deciduous leaves 4–8 cm long and arranged alternately. In late spring or summer spikes appear from the internodes opposite the leaves. Approximately 4 cm long, they are densely packed with up to ten rather nodding flowers up to 1 cm across. The 0.6 cm pointed sepals and petals are white, with the broadly triangular lateral sepals forming a chin beneath the 0.7 cm long crisped lip. The arching lip is greenish, shading to white near the base. The sides are erect, and there is one broad central callus which is fattest at the apex.

This species should be grown mounted on treefern or similar material, or potted in small pots of fibrous medium and placed in a bright spot. Intermediate to cool temperatures are called for, and the plant should be kept dry during its dormant period.

Actual flower size: approximately 1 cm across.

Dendrobium cucumerinum Macleay ex Lindley

This curious and delightful little Australian species was first described in 1842 and became immediately popular with growers in England. It is probably little grown today outside Australia, due more likely to scarcity overseas than to any lack of attraction. It is a most unusual and attractive plant, even when not in flower, with its rambling prostrate habit and curious sage-green gherkin-shaped leaves, which rise directly from the rhizome.

D. cucumerinum has the reputation of being a somewhat difficult plant in cultivation. This is probably due mostly to the fact that the stems are brittle, and when disturbed a plant tends to break up into small pieces that do not readily re-establish. It is best then, if possible, to buy an established plant of reasonable size. Small plants tend to sulk, refusing to produce new roots, and gradually withering away. Once established, however, this species is not really difficult to cultivate. The clues to good culture lie in the plant's origins in northern New South Wales and southern Queensland where it grows in profusion on the rough bark of *Casuarina cunninghamiana* at about 600 m above sea level, where nights are cool and rain seasonal.

Lacking the original host, we have found natural cork slabs best. Give plenty of air and light, keep dry in winter. Night temperatures down to zero don't seem to trouble the plant. And once established it rewards the grower each summer to autumn with spikes of from two to ten perfumed flowers, creamy-white striped with dark red.

Actual flower size: approximately 2 cm long.

Dendrobium delacourii Guillaumin

Originally described by Reichenbach (f.) in 1883 as *D. ciliatum* var. *breve*, this species is still regarded by some as a variety of *D. ciliatum* (the correct name of which is actually *D. venustum*). However, Seidenfaden, the recognised authority on Thai orchids, considers it a distinct species and hence characterises it with Guillaumin's 1924 epithet. It is common throughout Thailand at 1,000 m or more, where it mostly inhabits deciduous forests in full sunlight. It also occurs in Burma and Indochina.

The very closely clustered pseudobulbs are 1–5 cm long, very occasionally reaching 9 cm in cultivation. Between two and four deciduous mid-green leaves grow near the apex of the pseudobulb and are 2–3 cm long. In late spring and summer a short erect spike emerges from near the apex of the newly leafed pseudobulb and bears six to ten flowers 1.5–2.0 cm across. Colour is variable, from cream to greenish-white or clear yellow. The oblong pointed sepals are 1.3 cm long. The lateral sepals are somewhat falcate. The narrow petals are irregularly wavy at the ends. The three-lobed lip may be cream or golden-brown. There are three yellow-brown keels down the centre; the upturned lateral lobes are usually covered with dense purple stripes. The midlobe has several club-shaped fringes at its apex — these too may be golden-yellow or white.

This is an interesting species which does best mounted and hung up fairly high in an intermediate to warm environment. It requires copious water in summer with a short dry rest in winter.

Actual flower size: 1.5–2 cm across.

Dendrobium kingianum Bidwill

Among the most popular and most easily grown of the Australian dendrobiums, this species, known commonly as the 'pink rock lily', was described in 1844 by Bidwill, who was also responsible for introducing the species into England in the same year. A temperate species found from eastern New South Wales to central Queensland, *D. kingianum* favours mountain areas up to 1,200 m altitude but is sometimes found at much lower elevations. It is almost exclusively lithophytic on boulders and cliff faces in pockets of leafmould. It grows in both shady and open sunny positions and is frequently found near streams.

The habit of this species is very variable, pseudobulbs ranging from 2–5 cm tall up to 20 cm or 30 cm. Typically the pseudobulbs are slightly bulbous at the base, tapering to a narrow apex. Northern populations tend to be taller than southern ones. The pseudobulbs may be green, yellowish or reddish-purple, are furrowed when older, and grow in dense clumps. Adventitious plantlets are often produced from the upper part of the pseudobulbs. The two to nine apical leaves are 3–12 cm long. In late winter and spring, flowers are borne on erect or arching spikes up to 20 cm long, produced near the apex of the pseudobulb. The colour ranges from pure white through various shades of pink to deep mauve with darker mauve-purple markings on the broad lip. The flowers open well, and are usually 2–3 cm across.

D. kingianum does best in well-drained pots of any fibrous material. Provide moderate light, cool to intermediate conditions, and a dry winter.

Actual flower size: 2–3 cm across.

Dendrobium kingianum var. *album* (hort.)

*D*endrobium kingianum* is an enormously variable species in both habit and flowers, and has produced a number of fine pure white forms which — like all albino orchids — are much sought by growers. There are numerous named clones of the pure white form of *D. kingianum*, and all are worth growing. In habit they are as variable as the type, but all respond well to similar cultural conditions. Greenhouse subjects in cooler climates, all varieties may be treated as outdoor subjects in frost-free areas where they can provide an attractive addition to rockeries or ferneries. *Actual flower size: 2–3 cm across.*

Dendrobium lamellatum (Blume) Lindley

This most unusual species was first described as *Onychium lamellatum* by Blume in 1825. In 1830 Lindley renamed it *D. lamellatum*. Its other synonyms are *D. compressum* (Lindley) and *D. platycaulon* (Rolfe), and it is still sold under the latter name by many nurseries. This species is widely distributed throughout tropical Asia, occurring in Burma, Thailand, the Malaysian Peninsula, Sumatra, Java, Borneo and the Philippines. It grows on tree trunks in warm sheltered positions at 500–550 m above sea level. In the areas of its habitat, rainfall is evenly distributed throughout the year, creating an environment that is constantly humid.

D. lamellatum is a most unusual plant: its pseudobulbs are almost completely flattened as if run over by a steamroller. They are up to 12 cm tall and 2.5–3 cm wide with a very narrow base. They carry two to three apical leaves up to 7.5 cm long. This species is said to flower at various times of the year, but our plants always flower in winter. The flowers appear at the apex of the pseudobulb in clusters of up to four pendulous blooms 2.2 cm long. They do not open fully. Flowers are a greenish-yellow with three yellowish keels on the lip. With age the flowers turn yellow.

A warm humid environment is required for this species, and a semi-shaded position. It grows well either mounted on treefern slabs or in pots packed with treefern chunks or similar material.

Actual flower size: approximately 2.2 cm long.

Dendrobium leonis (Ldl.) Reichenbach (f.)

Lindley first described this species as *Aporum leonis* in 1840, having received a plant from Wallich at the Botanical Gardens in Calcutta. It was introduced into general cultivation by Loddiges, and was transferred to the genus *Dendrobium* by Reichenbach in 1861. Commonly found growing as a lowland epiphyte in Thailand, Malaysia, Indonesia and southern Indochina, it has been reported at up to 1,450 m above sea level.

This species has a most unusual and attractive habit. Each flat growth comprises a number of alternately arranged somewhat triangular leaves that clasp the stem. Each stem is usually considerably shorter than 20 cm: 8–15 cm is usual, but they may occasionally reach 25 cm. The clustered stems may form fan-shaped or almost circular plants. The overlapping succulent leaves are 1.5–2.0 cm long. The one or two vanilla-scented flowers are borne in winter near the apex of the stem. About 1.5 cm long, the fleshy flowers range in colour from cream to golden-yellow and are often flushed or streaked with reddish-purple or red-brown. The sepals are up to 1.2 cm long, with the laterals forming a chin beneath the tongue-shaped lip. The narrow rounded petals point forward.

D. leonis can prove difficult to maintain; it is best grown mounted or in suspended pots of freely draining material. It requires high humidity with relatively bright light in an intermediate to warm environment. Most plants lost in cultivation owe their demise to overwatering.
Actual flower size: approximately 1.5 cm long.

Dendrobium lichenastrum var. *prenticei* (Muell.) Dockrill

Von Mueller, who named this species in 1881, mistook it for a bulbophyllum, calling it *B. prenticei*. Nicholls later named it *Dendrobium prenticei* and *D. variabile*. In 1956 Dockrill recognised it as a variety of *D. lichenastrum*. Endemic to northeastern Queensland from Ayr to Cooktown, it occurs at sea level in the wet lowland forests of the coast, and also in highland rainforests and open tablelands to 1,200 m above sea level. It is more common than the type species, and grows on both trees and rocks.

The leaves rise almost directly from the rhizome, which branches freely, forming a dense mat with time. The succulent leaves are extremely variable in form, 1–4 cm long, almost terete, straight or slightly curved, mostly erect, and may be slightly channelled. The surface of the dark green leaves is minutely dimpled. Flowers may appear at any time, with plants flowering several times a year, or even continuously. The single flowers are similar to the type and are produced on a stalk up to 1.5 cm long from the rhizome near the base of the leaf. The flowers, 0.4–0.7 cm across, open fully and range from dull white to pink, with a varying number of red stripes on the petals and sepals. The thick lip may be yellow or orange.

A very hardy species, *D. lichenastrum* will grow well in cool to intermediate conditions. If protected and kept dry it will tolerate temperatures down to −2°C for short periods. It does best on cork or a treefern slab in low to bright light, and should be kept moist except when temperatures are very low.
Actual flower size: 0.4–0.7 cm across.

Dendrobium linguiforme Swartz

This species was not only the first Australian orchid to be described (in 1800), but was the species used by Swartz to establish the genus *Dendrobium*. William Bligh (of the *Bounty*) is said to have introduced it into England in 1810.

Its common names of 'tongue', 'thumbnail' or 'button' orchid reflect the shape of the thick flat leaves, which have lengthwise furrows and are about 4 cm by 1.5 cm. Arranged alternately on a creeping rhizome, the dark green leaves turn purplish in bright light. Depending on habitat, leaves can be closely set or (in dry areas) wide apart. Between six and twenty flowers appear in late winter or spring on a thin spike 6–15 cm long produced from the base of the leaf. The spidery flowers are usually white with purple markings on the recurved lip. Sepals and petals are up to 2 cm long. Although rare, a creamy-yellow form does exist (we have found it near Gympie in southeastern Queensland).

D. linguiforme is found from southeast New South Wales to northeast Queensland, from sea level to 1,000 m in a variety of habitats. It grows on both rocks and trees in open forest where it finds bright light or semi-shade. It forms very large mats when conditions suit it. This species will grow in cool to intermediate or warm conditions, and in bright light to heavy shade. It should be mounted: cork or the bark of any rough-barked tree is ideal. A dry cool winter suits the plant very well.

Actual flower size: approximately 2 cm across.

Dendrobium linguiforme var. *nugentii* Bailey

Recognised as a distinct variety by Bailey in 1902, this is the tropical form of *D. linguiforme*.* It occurs only in northeastern Queensland, from south of Townsville to the southern end of Cape York Peninsula. It is rarely found in coastal areas, but is fairly common in the rainforest or open bush of the mountains and tablelands. It is equally at home on rocks or trees. The region is subject to monsoonal rains and an extended dry season, with some areas receiving no rain for six months or more. During the dry season, the leaves of the plant may shrivel a great deal, but plump up again with the next rainy season.

The leaves of this variety are characterised by their rough, sandpapery texture. They also tend to be more deeply furrowed than those of the type, are broader and often more rounded at the apex. The creamy-white flowers have shorter petals and sepals than the type species, reaching about 1.5 cm. The flowers are more densely set on the spikes and less spidery. Like the type, this variety branches freely, often growing through and over itself.

Because of the brittle nature of the rhizomes and the lack of pseudobulbs it is better, if possible, to secure an established plant of this variety, or else the largest piece available, as small pieces can be difficult to establish. This variety should be treated in the same manner as the type species. Despite originating in the tropics, this variety grows mainly at high altitudes, and in cultivation tolerates cool to cold temperatures in winter.

Actual flower size: approximately 1.5 cm across.

Dendrobium margaritaceum Finet

A wonderful miniature with very large flowers relative to the modest size of the plant, this species is synonymous with *D. chrysti-anum*, according to Seidenfaden. As it comes from the elevated areas of northern Thailand and Vietnam, where even brief frosts are sometimes encountered, this species is one of the easier members of the nigro-hirsute section to grow in cooler climates.

Plants of this species are almost indistinguishable from those of its close relative, *D. bella-tulum,** although the pseudobulbs tend to be a bit slimmer. The pseudobulbs of both species are covered with minute black hairs, and are seldom longer than 5–10 cm.

Plants of *D. margaritaceum* do very nicely tied to a piece of treefern or something similar and hung up high where they get plenty of light. They will tolerate quite cool night temperatures (5–8°C in winter) as long as they are kept fairly dry. The flowering period is generally from summer through autumn, but it is not unusual to find the odd flower at other times through the year. The flowers, like those of most nigro-hirsute species, last quite well on the plant.

Actual flower size: approximately 4 cm across.

Dendrobium monophyllum Mueller

Commonly known as the 'lily of the valley' orchid, this Australian species was first described by von Mueller in 1859. It occurs from Cooktown on Cape York Peninsula south to northeastern New South Wales. In the tropics it is found only above 600 m elevation, but in the subtropics it is widespread from sea level to 1,000 m. It grows both epiphytically and lithophytically. In the rainforest it favours high exposed branches, but in more exposed habitats it is found on boulders and cliff faces. In southern areas it also likes to grow on *Casuarina glauca*.

The creeping rhizome bears several hard conical pseudobulbs 3–10 cm tall. These are strongly furrowed, and bear a single leaf (rarely two) at the apex. The bright green thin leaf is 5–10 cm long. This species is an irregular flowerer, with the main flush coming in the late winter through spring. It may, however, flower at any time of the year. The single spike, emerging near the apex of the pseudobulb, is 5–20 cm long with between five and twenty small bell-shaped fragrant flowers to 1 cm. The lip has two ridges on the mid-lobe. The tropical high-altitude form has plumper less ridged pseudobulbs and slightly smaller flowers than the southern form.

This species will grow in cool conditions and is best mounted on cork or paperbark or some similar material. It should be hung up where it will receive bright light and be allowed to dry out between waterings. Give plenty of water when in growth and a dry winter rest in cooler areas.

Actual flower size: approximately 1 cm across.

Dendrobium pachyphyllum (Kze.) Bakhuizen

Although this species was known as early as 1814, when Roxburgh called it *Dendrobium pumilum*, its first valid name was *Callista pachyphylla*, put forward by Kuntze in 1891. In 1963 Bakhuizen transferred it to *Dendrobium*. Unfortunately, Roxburgh's epithet, along with Blume's *Desmostrichum pumilum* and *Dendrobium carnosum* (Teijsmann & Binnendijk) proved to be homonyms (that is, they had already been used for other species). *D. pisibulbum* is a later synonym. Rarely found in collections today, this species occurs in northeast India, Burma, Thailand, Malaysia, Singapore, Indonesia and Vietnam, growing as an epiphyte from the lowlands to about 1,400 m above sea level.

The fat pseudobulbs are 1–5 cm tall (rarely 7 cm), often not exceeding 2.5 cm. They have a very narrow stalk-like base, are circular in cross-section, and frequently ribbed. The two stiff leathery leaves are spreading, 1.5–2.5 cm long, and at times resemble an elongated heart with a rounded apex. Single flowers — occasionally two or three — appear on a 1 cm stem from between the leaves. From 1.0 cm to 1.5 cm long, the short-lived flowers are white with purple lines on the sepals and petals and a greenish-yellow spot on the lip. The broadly triangular lateral sepals form a chin at the base of the 1 cm long reflexed lip.

D. pachyphyllum does well when mounted on cork or paperbark and hung in a bright position in an intermediate to warm environment. If potted, it needs perfect drainage.

Actual flower size: 1–1.5 cm long.

Dendrobium rigidum R. Brown

Discovered by Banks and Solander on the Endeavour River in northern Queensland, this species was described in 1810 by Brown. It is found from Cape York Peninsula, through the Torres Strait islands, to Papua New Guinea and Irian Jaya. It ·grows on trees and rocks from sea level to 700 m altitude in habitats ranging from mangrove swamps to savannah and low hilly inland ranges.

Usually found in small clumps of stems up to 15 cm long, this species may occasionally produce stems up to about 35 cm in length. Rising from a short creeping rhizome, the wiry stems, which branch near the base, are erect at first but soon become pendent. The thick tough leaves, developed to cope with the highly xeric environment, grow straight from the stem and range in colour from green to reddish-purple. Shaped rather like a knife blade, they are 2–6 cm long and have a rough surface. Flowering is sporadic through the year, with two to seven flowers on a spike which may reach 5 cm. The spike rises from the base of the leaf or on the first node below the leaf. The creamy 1.5 cm flowers are typically marked with reddish-brown on the three-lobed reflexed lip and column. A yellow-lipped variety exists, as do plants with almost completely red flowers.

A very slow grower, *D. rigidum* is best mounted on cork, paperbark, or a branch from some coarse-barked tree. It needs bright light throughout the year and copious water during the growing season. Intermediate to warm temperatures with high humidity are ideal.

Actual flower size: approximately 1.5 cm across.

Dendrobium schneiderae Bailey

Closely related to *Dendrobium monophyllum,** this species was named by Bailey in 1886 after Mrs Schneider who originally collected it. This is a much smaller plant than *D. monophyllum*, has two leaves, is much rarer, and is said to be hardier; under cool conditions it is certainly an easy plant in cultivation. There is reputed to be a variety *majus* of this species, but Dockrill considers that it falls within normal size range for the species.

The closely set oval pseudobulbs are 1–2.5 cm tall on a creeping rhizome. They are dark green to yellowish and conspicuously ribbed, with two dark green leaves, 3–7 cm long and often twisted. The flower spikes rise from the apex of the new pseudobulbs in late summer to early winter. The spikes are up to 17 cm, but usually shorter, carrying between five and twenty-five waxy bell-shaped yellow flowers about 0.7 cm across. The sepals and petals are often curved inwards and are outlined in pink, red or mauve. This species occurs from 500 m to 1,500 m elevation in the ranges from northeastern New South Wales to central eastern Queensland. It grows in cloudforest where trees are stunted and mosses plentiful, and in tableland rainforest trees where it is common on exposed branches, particularly on hoop pines. It also occurs in small dense clumps as a lithophyte. Mount this species on cork or hardwood and grow it in a cool to intermediate situation with plenty of bright light. It can be difficult to maintain in tropical or lowland subtropical conditions.

Actual flower size: approximately 0.7 cm across.

Dendrobium senile Parish & Reichenbach (f.)

This intriguing species was discovered in Burma by Parish who, with Reichenbach, described it in 1865. It occurs also in northern Thailand and adjacent areas in Laos as well as being reported from peninsular Thailand. It grows epiphytically between 500 m and 1,200 m above sea level.

The pseudobulbs, which rise from a short rhizome, are 5–12.5 cm long and may be quite stout. They are covered with a dense growth of fine long silvery hairs, which serves to protect them from the effects of excessive light and heat. These hairs, which after several years fall off, also cover the soft deciduous leaves arranged alternately along the pseudobulb. These are 5–10 cm long, and may persist for several years. One or two waxy flowers are borne on short spikes from nodes near the apex of the pseudobulbs in late winter and spring. The flowers are 3–5 cm across, have a pleasant lemon fragrance, and last for three or four weeks. The pointed sepals and petals are yellow, while the broad lip is yellow near the pointed apex with a large yellow-green disc and some reddish-brown streaks at the base.

D. senile can be difficult to grow. It is reported to do better potted than mounted, but our plants are mounted on small treefern blocks and hung up high in the greenhouse during winter. In summer they are lowered 30–60 cm to reduce light and heat. Intermediate temperatures are recommended, with fairly bright light, good air movement and high humidity. In winter, mist or water only very lightly.

Actual flower size: 3–5 cm across.

Dendrobium striolatum Reichenbach (f.)

First described by Reichenbach in 1857, this pretty Australian species has several synonyms: *D. schoeninum* (Ldl.), *D. milliganii* (Mueller) and *Callista striolata* (Kuntze). It is almost exclusively lithophytic, growing on granite boulders near the coast in northeastern Tasmania, on Flinders Island, and northward through eastern Victoria to central eastern New South Wales, where it grows on rock faces up to 1,000 m altitude. It usually occurs in exposed positions, but occasionally in shade, and is the only native Tasmanian dendrobium.

The numerous terete leaves spring almost directly from creeping rhizomes. The plant often forms large congested clumps. The 6–12 cm leaves are faintly ridged, slightly curved, and dark green. Those exposed to bright light often turn reddish. In spring, one or two cream, yellow or greenish-yellow flowers about 2 cm across appear from the base of the leaf. They are delicately fragrant and are striped on the outside with reddish-brown basal markings. The pure white lip is recurved with three ridges and crisped edges. The Tasmanian form is a stronger grower than the northern form, and has slightly larger and more brightly coloured flowers with fewer markings.

D. striolatum can be mounted on treefern, hardwood or cork, or potted in a mixture of broken sandstone or brick and leafmould or treefern fibre. It makes a good basket specimen as it does not object to hanging over the basket edge with its aerial roots free. It should be grown cool and given plenty of bright light and a dry cool winter.

Actual flower size: approximately 2 cm across.

Dendrobium toressae (Bailey) Dockrill

Originally described as *Bulbophyllum toressae* by Bailey in 1890, this species was transferred to the genus *Dendrobium* by Dockrill in 1964. It is endemic to the northeastern Queensland region between Tully and Cooktown, growing on rock faces in coastal gorges, on rainforest trees and on exposed rocks in open tableland forest up to 1,200 m above sea level. The smallest of the dendrobiums, it is sometimes known as the 'wheat ear' orchid, with its tiny succulent leaves resembling grains of wheat.

The 0.4–0.8 cm leaves are channelled on the upper surface, which is finely pitted or dimpled. The underside is keeled. The leaves have a sparkling appearance and are arranged alternately on a freely branching creeping rhizome. The plant, which lies flat against its host, is extremely slow growing and is seldom found in patches exceeding 10 cm in diameter. The single flowers have no stem and nestle in the hollow of the leaf. About 0.6 cm long, they appear at any time of the year. They are translucent, yellowish-white with a few red spots on the relatively large lip.

Closely related to *D. lichenastrum,** this species is very hardy. It grows well in either low or bright light, relishes cool conditions and should be kept reasonably moist all year round. As it is a slow grower it should be disturbed as little as possible. It will do well on most mounts. Our best plants, however, are growing on small sections of *Melaleuca* (paperbark) trunk. Even when not in flower this is a most attractive species.

Actual flower size: approximately 0.6 cm long.

Dendrobium trigonopus Reichenbach (f.)

First introduced into cultivation in England by Low and Co., this species was described by Reichenbach in 1887. Rolfe's *D. velutinum* is synonymous with this species. In Thailand it is commonly known as 'kam pak gai' or 'golden chicken's beak'. It is a native of Burma, northern Thailand, Laos and south-western China, where it grows on trees at altitudes between 300 m and 1,500 m above sea level.

The somewhat spindle-shaped pseudobulbs are 10–17 cm tall and up to 2 cm in diameter. Covered in short black hairs when young, they become yellow to purplish-black with age. Near the apex they bear up to four spreading leaves 6–11 cm long which are covered with short hairs. In late spring or summer short spikes near the apex of the pseudobulbs carry one to three, occasionally four, very waxy fragrant flowers up to 5 cm across. The golden-yellow sepals and petals taper to sharp points. The 2.5–2.8 cm sepals have a prominent keel on the back. The beak-like lip is greenish, edged with yellow, and has reddish-brown streaks at the base. It is three-lobed with small rounded lateral lobes that are toothed along the front edge, and a broadly triangular mid-lobe. Almost the entire upper surface of the 3.5 cm lip is covered with tiny glands.

Not a difficult subject in cultivation, *D. trigonopus* may be mounted on a treefern or cork slab, or potted in a coarse well-drained mixture. Intermediate temperatures suit the species well, with bright light and a dry rest in midwinter.

Actual flower size: 4–5 cm across.

Dendrobium unicum Seidenfaden

There is a certain amount of confusion regarding the true identity of this species, which is often sold under the name of *D. arachnites*. Thouars' *D. arachnites* later became *Aerides arachnites*, while Reichenbach's *D. arachnites* refers to a different species. Seidenfaden finally described *D. unicum* in 1970. Quite common in northern Thailand and neighbouring Laos, it grows mostly on bushes amid low scrub-like vegetation, or on rocks, at elevations between 800 m and 1,550 m. It is quite an amazing little plant, looking for much of the year like a small bundle of dead twigs, but producing a brilliant display of unusual flowers from late spring to winter.

The purplish-brown pseudobulbs are somewhat wizened, and normally 7–12 cm tall. In sheltered positions they may occasionally reach 19 cm. There are a few narrow leaves 5–7 cm long near the apex of the pseudobulbs. Sometimes suffused with red, they fall in their second year. The 3.5–4.0 cm flowers are carried on short spikes from any of the nodes, mostly but not always on the leafed pseudobulbs. There are usually several spikes to a pseudobulb, each carrying about three brilliant orange-red flowers. They are quite fleshy, and smell of orange. The narrow petals and sepals curl back and are often twisted. The lip, curled almost into a tube, is cream with orange-brown veining.

D. unicum grows well mounted on paperbark or treefern and given intermediate temperatures. It does best in bright light with a dry rest in winter.

Actual flower size: 3.5–4 cm long.

Dendrochilum pulcherrimum (Ames) L. O. Williams

This truly delightful miniature dendrochilum was originally described as *Acoridium pulcherrimum* by Ames and later transferred to the genus *Dendrochilum* by Williams in 1951. It is endemic to the Philippines, where it has been found on both Mt Natoo in Benguet Province and Mt Poho near Bontoc in Mountain Province, north Luzon. It grows in the mossy forest at about 1,900 m above sea level, where the trees, rocks and ground are covered with mosses, ferns, liverworts and lichens. It grows both epiphytically and lithophytically along with other dendrochilums and pitcher plants. Here the humidity is very high, keeping surfaces of trees and rocks damp at all times. Temperatures are

much lower than in the lowlands, with quite cool nights and pleasantly warm days. Frequent fogs and mists reduce the light intensity as well as providing moisture.

The small clustered pseudobulbs are egg shaped and up to 4 cm long. The leaves are up to 11 cm in length with three prominent veins. The flower spikes are synanthous, appearing from the centre of the new growths in winter and early spring. Spikes are generally shorter than the leaves, and bear many tiny golden flowers in two rows. The sepals are only 0.4 cm long. Although often regarded as being purely of botanical interest, a small plant bearing several neat spikes is a charming sight.

This species grows very happily on a small treefern slab with moss about the base. Intermediate to cool conditions are ideal, with constant moisture.

Actual flower size: approximately 0.4 cm across.

Diaphananthe rutila Summerhayes

This species has a very extensive range throughout equatorial Africa, being found in Zambia, Zaire, Tanzania, Malawi, Zimbabwe, Angola, Gabon, Cameroon and Uganda. In this area of heavy summer rainfall, plants are found growing as epiphytes in misty tropical

rainforests at elevations of 600–1,700 m.

D. rutila is a naturally pendent species with a thick straggling root system attaching it firmly to its host. The alternate pairs of leaves are flat and sometimes tinged with red. The leaves are deciduous with age and it is from the scars of these fallen leaves that between two and four flower stems arise in summer and autumn bearing up to ten delicate yellow or pinkish translucent flowers. These flowers, strongly perfumed, are up to 1.5 cm long, including the 1 cm spur. The fan-shaped lip is finely fringed.

Best grown on small logs or treefern slabs in a shady position, *D. rutila* requires high humidity during summer and a short dry period when growth is completed. Temperatures may range from intermediate to warm.

Actual flower size: approximately 1.5 cm long.

Dipteranthus duchii Pabst

Belonging to a genus containing a number of little-known species, this delightful miniature was described by Pabst, the well-known Brazilian taxonomist. The genus, established by Barbosa Rodrigues, is closely related to *Ornithocephalus, Zygostates* and *Capanemia.* A rather delicate species, *D. duchii* comes from the hot humid lowlands of Pernambuco in northeastern Brazil. It grows predominantly on the outer twigs of trees that overhang rivers or streams, or in clearings. These positions provide good air movement, which is essential in an environment where temperatures are high for most of the year, with only the humidity fluctuating.

The tiny clustered pseudobulbs are almost obscured by the bases of the 2–5 cm long leaves, which are acute and have a prominent keel below. Spikes are produced from the base of the pseudobulbs, are up to 5 cm long, and bear several flowers. The 0.7 cm sepals are bright apple-green, and swept backward. The edges are sparsely toothed and the apex is rounded. The 0.3 cm petals are white and project forward on either side of the column. The almost circular lip is 0.5 cm across and has a horseshoe-shaped callus at the base. It is a translucent white with orange-yellow markings in the centre.

We have found that plants of this species prefer small mounts — for example, pieces of cork, or twigs or small branches of paperbark — with their roots exposed to the freely moving air. A humid semi-shaded spot in an intermediate to warm environment suits it best.
Actual flower size: approximately 1 cm long.

Dipteranthus pustulatus (Krzl.) Pabst

Sometimes sold as *Zygostates pustulatus,* this charming miniature was originally described by Kraenzlin late in the 19th century as *Ornithocephalus pustulatus.* Pabst later transferred it to *Dipteranthus.* Found only in Brazil, it inhabits the cool moist mountains in the southern states of Parana and Santa Catarina, which experience year-round rain. The forests of these areas are bathed each evening with mist, which forms as the hot air at the base of the mountains rises. The plants grow on small lichen-encrusted twigs in shaded positions.

The tightly clustered pseudobulbs are almost egg shaped, 0.5–0.8 cm tall, and are at first glossy pale green, later turning duller and darker. A single 2–6 cm leaf rises from the top of the pseudobulb, while several pairs of leaves clasp the base. The more or less erect spikes, from 5 cm to 10 cm long, rise from the base of the pseudobulbs in spring. They each carry about fifteen delicate white flowers and present a wonderful sight. The spreading 0.2 cm sepals and 0.4 cm petals are rounded at the apex. The lateral sepals are hidden by the 0.5 cm lip. The lip is somewhat concave and has a patch of yellow-green in the throat.

D. pustulatus is particularly easy to grow — perhaps the easiest of the genus — and is very rewarding in its regularity of flowering. Give it cool to intermediate temperatures and a shady position with year-round moisture. It grows especially well, we find, on small treefern mounts.
Actual flower size: approximately 0.8 cm across.

Disa uniflora Bergius

Disa uniflora was described by Bergius in 1767 and Linnaeus (f.) in 1781 as *Disa grandiflora*. Occurring from sea level to 2,000 m in the southwest of Cape Province, this terrestrial species is known in its native South Africa as 'the pride of Table Mountain'. Found growing in black peaty soil, white sand or moss, its roots are firmly established in fast-flowing streams. Dense colonies inhabit stream banks above the midsummer water level. During heavy winter rains, the entire plants are often completely submerged.

This species has no true dormancy, the new shoots appearing soon after flowering finishes, either at the base of the old growth or on long stolons. These shoots produce the next year's tubers. Each growth has five to eight leaves up to 15 cm long forming a basal rosette for the flower spike, which may grow up to 70 cm but is usually 20–30 cm long. Up to eight flowers appear from December to March, each 8–12 cm across, and range in colour from crimson, scarlet or red through pink and orange. Both pure white and rare yellow forms have been recorded.

The essentials for good cultivation are a cool root environment with good drainage to allow the free passage of water, and excellent air movement. Humidity of 50–70 per cent is recommended, together with semi-shade. Coarse river sand or live sphagnum moss appear to be the best potting materials.

Actual flower size: 8–12 cm across.

Dryadella lilliputana (Cogniaux) Luer

This tiny relative of the much-admired masdevallias was discovered by Edwall in the state of Sao Paulo in Brazil. Cogniaux, curator of the Brussels herbarium, described it in 1906 as *Masdevallia lilliputana* and named it for Swift's fictional land of Lilliput in *Gulliver's Travels*. Luer created the new genus of *Dryadella* in 1978 and transferred this species to it. *D. lilliputana* grows as an epiphyte in the moist and humid rainforests in the Brazilian states of Sao Paulo, Rio de Janeiro, Parana, Santa Catarina and Rio Grande do Sul.

The leaves are quite succulent and grow in tightly clustered clumps 1.2–1.6 cm tall. Minutely dimpled, the leaves are dark green with a very pale base. They have a deep channel on the upper surface and a rounded underside. The flowers of this species, which appear in winter, stand just above the leaves and so are more easily seen than those of most other species in this genus. The sepals form a very short tube before opening widely. The concave dorsal and the joined lateral sepals are pale cream lightly spotted with crimson both inside and out. The free parts of the sepals, which narrow to slender tails about 0.4 cm long, are about 0.3 cm wide. The yellow spotted lip and the erect petals are very small.

D. lilliputana seems to be the most difficult of the genus to maintain in cultivation. It needs cool to intermediate conditions with good humidity and really excellent ventilation or air movement. It should be kept moist but not wet. Use a small pot and ensure adequate drainage.

Actual flower size: approximately 1 cm long.

Dryadella zebrina (Porsch) Luer

Belonging to the genus named for the mythical dryads, or wood nymphs, this delightful species was collected by von Wettstein at the beginning of the 20th century and sent to the Botanical Gardens of Vienna where it was studied by Porsch. He described it soon afterwards as *Masdevallia zebrina*. However, Luer transferred it to the genus *Dryadella* in 1978. It comes from areas with temperate climates in the Brazilian states of Sao Paulo, Santa Catarina and Rio Grande do Sul, where it receives abundant rainfall. Mist and fog often descend on the forests late in the day, providing additional moisture.

The plant has stiff pointed leaves 5–6 cm long and 0.5–1 cm wide with a central keel. The leaves are sometimes reddish-purple towards the apex. The plant often forms small dense clumps. Very short spikes are produced in winter, each bearing a single flower which may be hidden by the thick foliage. The greenish-yellow flowers have variable crimson spots, blotches and stripes, with only the 'tails' being unmarked. The flowers, produced in some profusion, are about 1.5 cm in diameter across the tips of the tails. The dorsal sepal is hooded so that its tail points forward. The laterals are free except for the very short tube and often have a central yellow vein. The tiny tongue-like lip may be orange or yellow with deep red blotches.

Grow this species in a cool humid situation in semi-shade and keep moist. It may be mounted or potted in a fibrous well-drained medium.

Actual flower size: approximately 1.5 cm across.

Encyclia amicta (Ldl. & Rchb. (f.)) Schlechter

First described more than one hundred years ago by Lindley and Reichenbach as *Epidendrum amictum*, this species was later transferred to the genus *Encyclia* by Schlechter. *Encyclia linearifolioides* and *E. bicornuta* are synonyms. This species inhabits the warm lowlands in the central Brazilian states of Para, Algoas, Minas Gerais, Goias and Mato Grosso, where the vast expanses of tropical forest create a very humid atmosphere. Short violent storms are followed by relatively dry days. The epiphytic orchids of this region seek, as their hosts, trees on open slopes, along stream banks or in clearings where air movement is good.

The clustered egg-shaped pseudobulbs of *E. amicta* are 1.0–2.5 cm tall and bear one or two very narrow arching leaves from 10 cm to 23 cm long. Arching spikes up to about 16 cm rise from the apex of the pseudobulbs from late spring to winter with a few flowers on each. The pointed sepals and petals are 1.4–2.0 cm long, and are yellow-green to green, more or less suffused or blotched with purple-brown, sometimes only on the reverse. The 1.0–1.5 cm long lip is three-lobed; the white lateral lobes are triangular, while the amethyst mid-lobe is rounded. The central callus has two keels.

E. amicta is a relatively easy grower in intermediate to warm conditions and moderately bright light. It is a compact species, and will grow happily for many years on a mount no bigger than 10 cm by 8 cm. It may be potted, but we prefer treefern mounts.

Actual flower size: 2.5–3 cm across.

Encyclia cyanocolumna (Ames, Hubb. & Schwf.) Dressler

Closely related to *Encyclia tenuissima*, this species was originally described as *Epidendrum cyanocolumnum* by Ames, Hubbard and Schweinfurth in 1935. Dressler transferred it to *Encyclia* in 1961. This species is endemic to Mexico, inhabiting the Sierra Madre Oriental and the Sierra Madre de Oaxaca, where it grows on trees in the oak forests at 1,500–2,000 m above sea level.

The tightly clustered pseudobulbs are conical, 1–2 cm tall and only 0.5–0.8 cm in diameter. At the apex of each are two or three very narrow strap-like leaves 4–10 cm long. The slightly zigzag spike, which is often branched, appears from between the leaves in spring and early summer. It may vary between 4 cm and 30 cm in length, and bears at least five (often more) flowers. These appear bell shaped, and seldom open fully. The yellow-green to olive-green sepals and petals are 0.8–1.0 cm long, with the petals considerably narrower than the sepals. The lip is joined to the dark-purple or bluish-violet column for about one-third of the latter's length. The 1.0–1.5 cm long lip is white, and may be spotted with purple. More or less oval, its edges are waved. It has a callus at the base. There are also five to seven shallow keels which become warty near the apex.

This dainty little species requires intermediate to cool temperatures and semi-shade to moderate indirect light. It does well for us either mounted on treefern, paperbark or a branch or any rough-barked tree, or potted in chopped treefern chunks.

Actual flower size: approximately 1.5 cm long.

Encyclia fausta (Rchb. (f.) ex Cogn.) Pabst

This species is still often sold under its original name, *Epidendrum faustum*, as described by Cogniaux in the latter part of the 19th century. It was transferred to the genus *Encyclia* in the second half of the 20th century by Guido Pabst, the eminent Brazilian amateur taxonomist and founder of the Herbarium Bradeanum in Rio de Janeiro. This species is endemic to Brazil, being found in the southern states of Rio de Janeiro, Parana, Santa Catarina and Rio Grande do Sul. The areas of its habitat are characterised by chains of hills where the humid air collecting at the base of the ranges condenses into cooler rain and mist as it rises late in the day. Humidity is high, although less so in winter when temperatures are relatively low.

The spindle-shaped pale green pseudobulbs, set at intervals of 1.0–1.5 cm on a sturdy creeping rhizome, are 5–11 cm tall and bear a pair of narrow strap-like leaves at the apex. Leaves are 8–12 cm long. The erect inflorescence rises from the apex of the pseudobulb in summer or autumn. About 12 cm long, it typically bears between four and ten starry white flowers with a pleasant astringent fragrance. The acute sepals and petals are reflexed, the former about 3 cm by 0.7 cm, the latter 2.8 cm by 1.0 cm. The pointed lip, which is held uppermost, is 2.2 cm long with turned-down sides and purple streaking.

E. fausta grows quite happily mounted or in baskets of coarsely chopped treefern and sphagnum moss. It likes a cool to intermediate environment with moderately bright light.

Actual flower size: approximately 5 cm across.

Encyclia ghiesbreghtiana (Rich. & Gal.) Dressler

Closely related to *Encyclia hastata*, this species was described in 1845 by Richard and Galeotti as *Epidendrum ghiesbreghtianum*. Dressler transferred it to the genus *Encyclia* in 1961 in the course of his study of Mexican encyclias. It inhabits the Sierra Madre del Sur in the Pacific coastal states of Guerrero and Oaxaca, growing in the sometimes quite wet pine-oak forests at between 2,000 m and 2,700 m above sea level.

The 2.0–6.5 cm pale green pseudobulbs are clustered on a creeping rhizome. The two to three strap-shaped leaves are 6–20 cm long and 0.7–1.3 cm across. The 4–12 cm long spike rises from between the leaves in spring with one to three flowers about 3–4 cm across. The oblong sepals and petals taper to a sharp point. Between 1.4 cm and 2.4 cm long, they are pale green, but so densely spotted and streaked with reddish-brown that they appear to be the latter colour. The frilly rounded lip is joined to the column only at the base. From 1.5 cm to 2.7 cm long, it is white with red streaks near the base. The oblong callus at the base of the lip separates into three fleshy veins which extend to near the apex. The 0.5–0.7 cm fleshy column has large red spots.

This is not a difficult subject in cultivation. It is happy in cool to intermediate temperatures and moderately bright light. It may be potted, but does best for us on a treefern mount.

Actual flower size: 3–4 cm across.

Encyclia mariae (Ames) Hoehne

One of the most popular of the genus *Encyclia* because of its compact habit and large flowers, this species was only discovered in the late 1930s by Oestlund in northern Mexico near the border with Texas — a dry region, which had been largely overlooked by orchid botanists. Ames described it as *Epidendrum mariae* in 1937, and in 1953 Hoehne transferred it to the genus *Encyclia*. It inhabits the eastern Mexican states of Vera Cruz, Tamaulipas, Hidalgo and San Luis Potosi between 1,000 m and 1,200 m above sea level. An epiphyte, it favours the rather dry oak forests which do, however, experience nightly dews.

The clustered pseudobulbs are shaped like elongated onions. They are 2–4 cm tall with two distinctive grey-green leaves 9 cm to 18 cm long. The erect or arching spike is 5–27 cm long and bears between one and five flowers in late spring or summer. The flowers, which last well, may be 5–8 cm across and up to 9.5 cm long. The greenish-yellow to olive-green sepals and petals are similar with their acute tips being recurved. The large frilly lip is the dominant feature of the flower. It varies in size from 4.7 cm to 7.5 cm in length and from 3.0 cm to 4.8 cm in width, and has several prominent green veins in the throat. There is also a callus comprising two narrow ridges up to 3 cm long.

A lovely species, *E. mariae* presents few difficulties in cultivation if given moderate light in cool to intermediate conditions. It may be potted or mounted. When watering, err on the dry side and give the plant a definite dry winter rest.

Actual flower size: 5–8 cm across.

Encyclia ochracea (Ldl.) Dressler

Skinner discovered this species in Guatemala, and sent plants to Sir Charles Lemon in England in 1835. Lindley described it as *Epidendrum ochraceum* in 1838. Richard and Galeotti's *E. triste* is a later synonym. In 1961, Dressler transferred it to *Encyclia*. This species occurs throughout Central America, from Mexico to Costa Rica, growing in most habitats between 800 m and 3,500 m above sea level. In fact, it has become something of a pest in some areas, particularly in coffee-growing regions, as it colonises rapidly, often self-pollinating and producing vast quantities of seed.

The oval to spindle-shaped pseudobulbs are clustered or 1–2 cm apart on a stout rhizome. Between 3.5 cm and 8.0 cm tall, they are mid-green and much tapered in the upper part. The two or three narrow leaves are 6–23 cm long with a prominent keel below. Plants are typically less than 20 cm high. Unbranched spikes 4–15 cm long appear at any time with six to twelve rather unremarkable flowers. Some clones are cleistogamous, pollinating themselves before the flowers open. The bluntly pointed sepals and more rounded petals are 0.4–0.6 cm long, the petals being narrower than the sepals. The segments are quite fleshy, yellow-brown to greenish-brown. The small lip is white, with an oblong callus near the apex. The tiny lateral lobes are rounded, and clasp the column.

A tolerant species, *E. ochracea* grows well in cool to intermediate conditions with moderate to bright light. We grow our plants mounted, but no doubt they would also grow well potted. *Actual flower size: approximately 1 cm across.*

Encyclia polybulbon (Ldl.) Dressler & Pollard

More commonly known as *Dinema polybulbon*, this species was first described by Swartz in 1788 as *Epidendrum polybulbon*; Lindley transferred it to the monotypic genus *Dinema*, and Dressler and Pollard later removed it to *Encyclia*. Since its introduction to cultivation in Britain in 1841 its ease of culture has ensured its continuing popularity. Its distribution ranges widely through Central America — Mexico, Guatemala, Honduras — to Cuba and Jamaica. It has been found growing both on rocks and on scattered oaks from 600 m to 3,200 m above sea level. *E. polybulbon* resembles *E. pygmaea* when not in flower, but is easily distinguished from the latter species by its leaves, which are notched at the apex.

This species tends to ramble and will easily form dense mats of 2–3 cm tall pseudobulbs with three leaves to 3 cm long. The single flower rises from the top of the pseudobulb on a short stalk and is sweetly perfumed. The yellow-white lip contrasts nicely with the brownish petals and sepals. Flowering can be almost continuous when conditions suit this species, but the main flowering is usually from late autumn to early spring.

The rambling nature of this species makes it eminently suitable for cultivation on cork or treefern slabs or even weathered palings. It prefers full sun and intermediate to cool conditions, but it will grow and flower with winter temperatures down to 0°C, although this usually delays flowering and flowers are smaller. *Actual flower size: approximately 2.5 cm across.*

Encyclia pringlei (Rolfe) Schlechter

One of the many Mexican encyclias, this species was described by Rolfe in 1904 as *Epidendrum pringlei*, and transferred to the genus *Encyclia* by Schlechter in 1918. It is closely related to *E. hastata*, but has smaller flowers and a relatively wider lip. It occurs in the southern states of Guerrero, Michoacan, Morelos and Oaxaca, where it inhabits the rather damp pine-oak forests between 1,800 m and 2,500 m elevation.

The clustered pseudobulbs are oval to pear shaped, 1.5–3.5 cm tall and only 0.4–1.2 cm in diameter. The one or two strap-shaped leaves are 4.5–10 cm long with acute or subacute ends. The 7–16 cm spike rises from the apex of the pseudobulb in spring and bears up to four pretty flowers. The narrow pale green or pale brown sepals and petals are 0.8–1.5 cm long, tapering to an acute point. The sepals are strongly reflexed, swept back away from the lip. The petals may also be reflexed or held at the sides of the scoop-shaped lip. White with a few faint purple spots, the lip is significantly broader than it is long, a feature distinguishing it from the other encyclias. It is 0.7–1.0 cm long and 0.9–1.8 cm wide with turned-up sides and a sharp point at the apex. The oblong callus becomes three fleshy veins which extend to near the apex. The dark purple anther cap is a focal point of the flower.

Plants of this rather delicate species do best mounted on treefern or some similar material and hung in semi-shade. They prefer cool to intermediate conditions.

Actual flower size: approximately 1–1.5 cm across.

Encyclia tripunctata (Ldl.) Dressler

In 1961 Dressler removed this species from the genus *Epidendrum*, where it had been originally placed by Lindley in 1841 (as *Epidendrum tripunctatum*). Other synonyms include Reichenbach (f.)'s *Epidendrum micropus* and Ames' *Epidendrum diguetti*. *E. tripunctata*, an epiphyte, is restricted to the Mexican states of Nayarit, Jalisco, Michoacan, Guerrero, Morelos and Oaxaca, where it occurs from 1,200 m to 2,000 m above sea level growing on oaks in forests of oak or mixed oak and pine.

The clustered pseudobulbs are slightly flattened; 2–4 cm tall, they bear two or three strap-like leaves 8–17 cm long which fall at flowering time — an unusual feature among encyclias. Flowering occurs in spring or early summer on leafless pseudobulbs, with a 3–10 cm spike bearing up to five flowers about 2.5 cm across. The acute sepals and petals are somewhat reflexed at the tips when the flower is fully open. They are 1.3–2 cm long with the petals slightly shorter than the sepals. The broad white lip is 1.4–1.8 cm long and bears three to five fleshy ridges forming a triangular callus. It is sometimes streaked with purple at the base, and along with the column is a natural focus for the eye. The 0.8 cm column is dark purple-maroon with three yellow- or orange-tipped 'teeth' at the apex, to which the specific name refers.

E. tripunctata may be mounted or potted in fine fir-bark and sphagnum moss, and should be kept damp. It likes an intermediate to cool position with moderately bright light.

Actual flower size: approximately 2.5 cm across.

Encyclia vitellina (Ldl.) Dressler

Lindley described this very popular species in 1831 as *Epidendrum vitellinum*, using a preserved herbarium specimen. Live plants were first introduced to cultivation in England in 1839. Dressler transferred the species to the genus *Encyclia* in 1961. It occurs in Guatemala and in southern Mexico between 1,500 m and 2,600 m altitude in mixed pine and oak forests, in cloudforest, or in the scrubby vegetation of the lava fields.

The clustered slightly compressed pseudobulbs are egg shaped to cone shaped, 2.5–5 cm tall, and 1.3–3.0 cm in diameter. They are a dull dark green with up to three leaves at the apex. These strap-like leaves, 8–20 cm long, arch outward and have several paler veins. This species flowers from spring to summer on the previous year's growth. The 12–30 cm spike is erect to arching, sometimes branched, with between four and fifteen fiery orange-red flowers which last for about two months. These flat flowers are up to 4.5 cm across with pointed sepals and petals. The narrow dagger-shaped lip and the column are yellow or orange tipped with orange-red. The lip has an oblong callus which separates into three short veins down the centre. The sides of the lip are sharply curled downward.

E. vitellina is a spectacular species, and undemanding in cultivation. It grows well either potted in coarse fibrous material or mounted. Intermediate to cool temperatures suit the species well. For best flowering results give it plenty of light, a dry rest in winter, and plenty of water in the growing season.

Actual flower size: approximately 4 cm across.

Encyclia widgrenii Lindley

This very pretty epiphyte from Brazil, which is restricted to the state of Minas Gerais, was described by Lindley in honour of Widgren, who collected plants between 1841 and 1847. The topography of Minas Gerais is characterised largely by savannah country with a succession of flat-topped hills. Between 500 m and 1,000 m above sea level, it is an area of temperature extremes with hot dry days and very cool nights when temperatures can fall as low as 0°C in winter. Humidity ranges from 20 per cent to 60 per cent. Here, epiphytes are restricted to the narrow stretches of woodland — usually small trees and stunted scrub — along rivers and around lakes.

The pale green to yellowish pseudobulbs are spindle shaped and somewhat flattened. Covered with light brown bracts when young, they are 5–9 cm tall and 0.7–1.2 cm across, set at intervals of 1.5–2.5 cm on a creeping rhizome. Each pseudobulb bears two narrow leaves 8–9.5 cm long near the apex. In winter and early spring the erect inflorescence rises from the top of the pseudobulb with two or more very fragrant flowers about 5 cm long. The glistening white to cream flowers are non-resupinate, holding the 2 cm long lip uppermost. Streaked with purple near the base, the lip has two calli on the section obscured by the column. The sepals and petals are slightly reflexed with a prominent mid-vein.

Plants of this species do well in pots of chopped treefern chunks in a moderately bright position with intermediate to cool conditions. Keep on the dry side through winter.

Actual flower size: approximately 5 cm long.

Epidendrum longipetalum Richard & Galeotti

Closely related to *Epidendrum tortipetalum* and *E. rowleyi*, this species was described by Richard and Galeotti in 1845. *E. antenniferum* is a later synonym. From Mexico, it is limited to the Sierra Madre del Sur and the Sierra Madre Oriental in the states of Oaxaca, Puebla, Hidalgo and Vera Cruz. It grows as an epiphyte or lithophyte in cool mixed forest between 1,750 m and 2,150 m above sea level. Night temperatures are cool with high humidity.

The 2–10 cm pseudobulbs are slender at the base with the upper part wider and flattened. There are two or three broadly oval leaves 2.5–8.0 cm long near the apex. They are dark green, often marked with purple, especially on the underside. This species flowers throughout the year, with the erect to arching inflorescence rising from the apex of the pseudobulb. Bearing up to twenty flowers one at a time, the wiry spike continues to lengthen and may reach 75 cm. The translucent greenish flowers are suffused with red, pink or bronze and are 3.0–4.5 cm long. The narrow petals, 2.5–3.5 cm long, hang straight down, becoming twisted and longer as the flower matures. Rounded at the apex, the petals have prominent mid-veins and two other fainter veins. The broad rounded lip is 0.6–0.8 cm long with three keels united at the base.

E. longipetalum grows well on mounts of cork, paperbark or treefern, less well in a pot. Cool to intermediate conditions are ideal for this species, which should be given a bright position with high humidity. It is generally rather a slow grower for us.

Actual flower size: 3–4.5 cm long.

Epidendrum pugioniforme Regel

Described by Regel in 1890, this Mexican species remains virtually unknown in collections. Found only between 1,800 m and 2,500 m on the Sierra Madre del Sur in the states of Guerrero and Oaxaca, it grows mostly as an epiphyte on oaks in mixed pine and oak forests, but also occasionally on rocks.

The habit is pendent, usually producing roots only near the base of the plant, and growing in clumps with each spindle-shaped pseudobulb rising from the base of the previous one. Each may be 6–15 cm long, but is usually less than 10 cm. There are between three and five pointed leaves clustered near the apex of the pseudobulb. They are 8–15 cm long, and fall after the first or second year. This species flowers from winter to late spring on arching 5–9 cm long spikes. Each spike bears three to eight starry flowers which open simultaneously. They are about 6 cm across and fragrant at night. Sepals and petals are slightly recurved, the petals being slightly shorter than the 3.3–4.8 cm sepals. Colour ranges from green to coppery-brown. The green to yellow-green lip is joined to the white column and has a red disc. From 2.3 cm to 3.4 cm long, the lip is three-lobed and strongly recurved. The lateral lobes are a rounded oblong in shape, while the mid-lobe is triangular. There are two calli at the base of the lip and three keels on the mid-lobe.

Fairly easy to grow in cultivation, this species should be mounted because of its pendent habit. It is not choosy about mounting material, and is happy in intermediate conditions with light shade.

Actual flower size: approximately 6 cm across.

Eria dasyphylla Parish & Reichenbach (f.)

This intriguing species, described by Parish and Reichenbach in 1874, is grown as much for its interesting foliage as for its diminutive flowers. Kraenzlin's *Trichostosia dasyphylla* of 1911 is conspecific. A subtropical to tropical species, *E. dasyphylla* has a very wide distribution: from Sikkim, Darjeeling and the Khasia hills of India, where it grows at 500–1,000 m altitude in mixed forest, through Burma and Thailand to Laos. It is found throughout Thailand from 1,250 m above sea level in the north to 50 m near the Malaysian border.

The thin branching rhizome bears no pseudobulbs but is covered with very hairy oval leaves 2 cm by 0.8 cm. These are dark green and quite fleshy to provide some storage facility for moisture and nutrients. The single flowers, 1–1.2 cm long, are produced in summer on very short hairy spikes. They are greenish, flushed with yellow, and have fine short hairs on the outside of the sepals. The erect dorsal sepal is 0.5 cm long while the triangular concave laterals are 0.7 cm long. The small petals are oblong and the fleshy lip has three lobes.

E. dasyphylla prefers intermediate to warm conditions with fairly high humidity and moderately bright light. It is often supplied by Thai nurseries mounted on hard coconut husk, on which it does well. Treefern or similar mount, however, is quite satisfactory. With few reserves of moisture, this species should be watered all year round. The other important requirement is good air movement. Stagnant conditions encourage fungal infections, to which the plant is prone.

Actual flower size: 1–1.2 cm long.

Eria pannea Lindley

A widely distributed eria, this species was described by Lindley in 1842. In 1891 Kuntze renamed it *Pinalia pannea*, which was later reduced to synonymy. Its range is through India, Burma, Thailand, Malaysia, Sumatra, southern China and Vietnam. In India it occurs in Sikkim and Darjeeling at 600–1,200 m above sea level, where summer temperatures reach 30°C during the day, dropping to 20°C at night. Winters are cool, dry and sunny with dew providing enough moisture to sustain the plants. This species also grows, however, in the lowlands of Malaysia where temperatures are warm to hot throughout the year.

The creeping rhizome, covered with fine hairs when young, bears erect pseudobulbs which may be closely set or up to 5 cm apart. The one to four fleshy dull green leaves are 4.5–15 cm long and almost terete, are covered with wool-like hairs when young, and fall off with age. The short woolly spike appears in summer from the top of the pseudobulb. About 2.5 cm long, it carries up to four pale yellow to golden-brown flowers 1.6–2.0 cm wide. Delightfully vanilla scented, the flowers are densely woolly on the outside of the spreading sepals. The oblong fleshy lip is dark brown, orange or purple with paler edges. It has two yellow calli which are not connected; one is narrow and elongated and occurs near the base; the other, broader, one is situated at the apex.

In cultivation this species prefers intermediate to warm conditions. It may be either mounted or grown in shallow pots of free-draining medium. It requires indirect bright light and high humidity.

Actual flower size: 1.6–2 cm across.

Eria queenslandica Hunt

One of the relatively few erias found in Australia, this species was discovered by Wilkie in 1946 and described by Hunt in 1947. As its name implies, this species occurs in northern Queensland from the Atherton Tableland to Cooktown between 750 m and 1,000 m above sea level. It is found either on trees in rainforest and cloudforest or on nearby rocks. In this habitat mists are frequent, providing moisture even in dry seasons.

The plants of this species form medium to large clumps with closely set cylindrical pseudobulbs on a branching rhizome. The apple-green pseudobulbs are quite succulent, 2.5 cm long and 0.8–1.2 cm in diameter. The two dark green leaves stand almost erect near the apex of the pseudobulb, and are fleshy, 5–12 cm long and bilobed. This species flowers erratically throughout the year, but mostly in late winter and early spring. There are usually between one and three spikes, each 1–4 cm long, bearing up to twelve tiny translucent flowers about 0.4 cm across. On many specimens the flowers do not open at all, while on others they open only slightly. The flowers may be cream, yellow, or a rather dull pink, with the 0.3 cm long sepals covered with tiny hairs. The pointed lip, which is held uppermost, has three keels. The mid-lobe curves downward.

Easy to grow, this little species prefers intermediate conditions with high humidity and semi-shade all year round. It may be mounted or potted in a fibrous well-drained mix. It also does well for us potted in fresh sphagnum moss and suspended in a shady spot.

Actual flower size: approximately 0.4 cm across.

Erycina echinata (HBK) Lindley

This charming Mexican miniature was originally described as *Oncidium echinatum* in 1815 by von Humboldt, Bonpland and Kunth after von Humboldt discovered it near Acapulco. In 1853 Lindley transferred it to his newly created genus, *Erycina*. It occurs from 30 m to 800 m altitude along the Pacific coast from Sinaloa in the north to Oaxaca in the south. It grows on deciduous trees in the hot lowlands, which are dry for about eight months of the year. Plants are often suspended by their thin wiry roots from the branches or twigs on which they grow.

Slightly flattened pseudobulbs 1.5–3.0 cm long are spaced along a creeping rhizome and almost enclosed by their two tough leaves. The 3–10 cm green leaves are streaked with reddish-brown and are usually recurved. This species flowers in late winter and early spring with zigzag branching spikes 10–25 cm long. Many 2 cm flowers are borne on the spikes. They are bright yellow, and dominated by the large three-lobed lip which has a large fleshy callus on the mid-lobe. The brown or green sepals and reflexed petals are only about 0.4 cm long. The dorsal is hooded over the column.

E. echinata should be tied to small treefern or cork mounts with the roots hanging free. While in growth it should be given plenty of water and light shade. When growth has finished plants need only an occasional misting and more light. Warm to intermediate conditions suit this species best.

Actual flower size: approximately 2 cm across.

Gastrochilus dasypogon (Ldl.) Kuntze

Lindley first described this vandaceous monopodial in 1833 as *Saccolabium dasypogon*. It was transferred to the genus *Gastrochilus* by Kuntze in 1891. It is found in the warmer areas of Nepal, Sikkim and Bhutan, as well as in southern India at about 300 m elevation, and in northern, central and southeastern Thailand from the lowlands to 1,000 m or more above sea level.

This slow-growing species has a very short stem, usually only 1–3 cm long. The three to five leaves are 10–15 cm long, occasionally reaching 20 cm, and up to 2.5 cm wide. They are stiff and unequally bilobed at the rounded apex. The spikes, which are up to 2.5 cm long, appear from the underside of the foliage in spring and carry between five and ten flowers. These flowers, 1.5–2 cm across, open simultaneously, producing a ball-like cluster. The spoon-shaped sepals and petals spread well to form an open fan above the lip, and bend slightly inward at the tip. Colour varies from cream to bright yellow, greenish-yellow or pale orange, with or without a few purple spots. The fixed lip, which forms a 0.4 cm deep sac at the base, is mainly white with yellow in the bottom of the sac and on the finely toothed semi-circular mid-lobe, which also carries some purple spots. The column may, in some plants, be dark reddish-pink.

This species grows well when mounted on a treefern slab and hung in relatively bright shade. Give intermediate to warm conditions with year-round moisture and high humidity. A delightful species, but rather a slow grower. *Actual flower size: 1.5–2 cm across.*

Gastrochilus fuscopunctatus Hayata

A lovely but slow-growing miniature, this species is believed to be synonymous with *G. matsuran*, and is endemic to Taiwan. It is a very attractive climbing or rambling plant made up of little ladders of grey-green leaves with pretty purple spots — a feature that is reflected in its specific name.

The stems, which reach 9 cm, branch freely and produce aerial roots from the leaf axils. The short flower spikes also rise from these leaf axils and bear a few tiny cream flowers with rose spots.

The plants grow well on treefern slabs. They should be permitted to follow their inclination to arch and curve away from the mount as this makes it easier to view the flowers, which occur on the reverse side of the leaves. Plants grow well — if slowly — in cool to intermediate conditions. Moderate to heavy shade suits this species well, although brighter light will emphasise the spotting on the leaves. It requires some moisture all year round, which means quite heavy watering in summer, with frequent misting on bright winter days. As it tends to grow aerially, away from its mount, drainage is generally not a problem with this species. Like most ramblers, it is unsuited to pot culture. In general, an easy and rewarding species for cooler climates.

Actual flower size: approximately 0.5 cm across.

Gastrochilus intermedius (Griff. ex Ldl.) Kuntze

Another fairly slow-growing species, this epiphyte was described by Lindley in 1859 as *Saccolabium intermedium*. In 1891, Kuntze transferred it to *Gastrochilus*. It grows on trees in mixed forest in northeastern India between 1,000 m and 1,800 m elevation, and in peninsular Thailand from the lowlands to about 1,800 m above sea level.

The pendent stems are up to about 10 cm long and covered with old leaf bracts at the base. Fleshy roots are produced from anywhere along the stem, which may branch. Several mid-green leaves are set at 1 cm intervals along the stem. These may be 7.5–20 cm long,

but do not usually exceed 10 cm. They are quite fleshy, channelled above with a prominent keel below, and are finely notched at the acute apex. The short spike rises from the stem in spring or summer, and carries a cluster of three to six flowers about 1 cm across, which all open together. The sepals and petals, with rounded ends which curve forward, are yellow, very heavily suffused and blotched with reddish-brown. The obscurely three-lobed lip has a cup-like sac on the apical lobe. Predominantly white, with a few purple spots, it has a yellow blotch on the outer lobe and in the sac.

G. intermedius grows well attached to a mount of cork or paperbark and hung in moderately bright indirect light. Intermediate conditions suit it best, with year-round watering and generally high humidity.

Actual flower size: approximately 1 cm across.

Gastrochilus japonicus (Makino) Schlechter

This species occurs in both Japan and Taiwan, a condition which caused a little confusion among taxonomists. It was probably first described by Makino as *Saccolabium japonicum*. Schlechter transferred the species to the genus *Gastrochilus* in 1913. Hayata described a Taiwanese specimen as *G. somai*. Eventually *G. japonicus* and *G. somai* were pronounced conspecific. *Saccolabium somai* is

another synonym. This species occurs in mountainous areas at 1,000–2,000 m above sea level on the branches of broad-leaved trees or pines, and is commonly known as the 'yellow pine orchid' in Taiwan.

The plants resemble *Sarcochilus falcatus* from Australia in form with their 5–8 cm falcate leaves. The two to seven flowers are produced on a short spike from the leaf axils, usually in autumn. A plant may produce several spikes at the one time, making it a very attractive sight. As in most *Gastrochilus* species, the feature of the flower is the lip; in this case of heavy texture, yellow, rimmed with white.

G. japonicus prefers semi-shade with intermediate to cool conditions and should be kept moist all year round. It will grow happily on a treefern mount or small branches of sheoak (*Casuarina*) or of any other tree with rough bark.

Actual flower size: 1–1.5 cm across.

Haraella retrocalla Kudo

Endemic to Taiwan, this species was first described by Kudo in 1930, based on material collected by Yoshi Hara, after whom the genus was named. *H. retrocalla* is considered by some — including Taiwanese authorities — to be conspecific with *H. odorata*, while others believe it to be a distinct species. The genus *Haraella* is closely related to *Gastrochilus*, but differs from that genus by having no spur on the lip. *H. retrocalla* is a charming species which inhabits the ancient forests of Taiwan at 1,000–2,200 m altitude, indicating cool to intermediate conditions in cultivation. It grows as an epiphyte in semi-shaded positions where it receives some moisture all year round.

The falcate leaves are 5–8 cm long, and fleshy. Flower spikes are produced in autumn to early winter. Each spike has up to three delightful 2 cm flowers which open successively. A large part of the charm of this species lies in the velvety red blotch — which resembles a beetle — on the lip. Although slow growing, this species branches at the base, eventually forming nice clumps.

Plants should be mounted rather than potted — they are not choosy about the material — and hung in semi-shade. Keep moist at all times. Regular misting is desirable, except in very cold weather.

Actual flower size: approximately 2 cm across.

Holcoglossum kimballianum (Rchb. (f.)) Garay

Discovered by Boxall in Burma, this species was described by Reichenbach in 1899 as *Vanda kimballiana* in honour of Mr Kimball, a New York orchid grower. Garay transferred it to the genus *Holcoglossum* in 1972. It comes from the cooler areas of Burma, Thailand and Yunnan growing at 1,200–1,800 m above sea level, mostly on rocks in fully exposed conditions, but sometimes on trees in partial shade.

The 3–10 cm pendent stems occasionally branch near the base. Although the almost terete, needle-shaped leaves occasionally exceed 20 cm, this plant takes up very little room and qualifies, we feel, as a miniature. Each stem bears up to eight leaves, which are green, suffused and spotted with purple, and have a narrow channel along the upper surface. Flowering occurs mostly from late summer to early autumn, but sometimes in spring. The spikes are up to 20 cm long and carry several long-lasting flowers 3.5–5.0 cm across. The sepals and petals are mainly white. The 2 cm dorsal sepal and petals are spoon shaped, while the 2.5 cm lateral sepals are sickle shaped. At its base, the three-lobed lip forms a 2.5 cm pale violet spur which curves forward. The lateral lobes are yellowish with red-brown spots on the inside, and have sickle-shaped points on the front edges. The mid-lobe is deep red-violet with a callus and five keels.

An attractive species, *H. kimballianum* prefers cool to intermediate conditions with bright light. It does best mounted on cork, paperbark, treefern or a similar substrate. Plenty of water when in growth and a short dry rest in winter are required.

Actual flower size: 3.5–5 cm across.

Homalopetalum pumilio (Rchb. (f.)) Schlechter

This charming species with its comparatively large flowers was originally described by Reichenbach in 1844 as *Brassavola pumilio*. Schlechter transferred it to the genus *Homalopetalum* in 1923. Due to its modest size, this species is often over-looked. It has been reported from Mexico, Guatemala, Honduras, Costa Rica and the West Indies, and it may well be still more widespread. It inhabits oak or oak and pine forests between 1,500 m and 2,000 m above sea level, where it grows on moss- and lichen-covered rocks and scrubby trees. It has also been found in sheltered gorges. In Mexico it grows in association with *Cuitlauzina pendula*, *Erycina diaphana* and *Pleurothallis tribuloides** etc.

The globular pseudobulbs are 0.4–1.2 cm tall and may be green or pale bronze, often tinged with purple. The single leaf stands erect, and is 1–3 cm long. A single flower is borne on a 2.5–7 cm spike from the apex of the pseudobulb in summer. Despite their delicate appearance, the almost translucent flowers last quite well. Colour ranges from almost white to greenish-white to beige, often suffused with purple and with red-purple veins. The 1.5–3.0 cm sepals and petals are broad at the base, tapering to slender recurved tails. The lip, attached by a short claw, has a large fleshy callus at the base.

Once established, this species should be disturbed as little as possible. A mount such as paperbark is ideal, draining well but retaining humidity about the roots. Intermediate to cool conditions and moderate light are needed.

Actual flower size: approximately 5 cm long.

Hymenorchis javieri (?)

We are somewhat uncertain regarding the correct identification of this unusual miniature monopodial from the Philippines. Because of its miniscule size it was overlooked by botanists and has only recently found its way into cultivation under the common name of the 'Red Angraecum'. It was named — we believe by Valmayor — in the late 1980s in honour of Eli and Alicia Javier, owners of the Kabukiran orchid nursery in Manila. We first saw plants there several years ago, soon after their discovery on the Javiers' property at Santa Fe. It grows as an epiphyte in the forests of central north Luzon between 1,100 m and 1,200 m above sea level.

Hymenorchis is a small genus, established by Schlechter in 1913, of plants with delicately textured flowers that are usually greenish-yellow. Flowers typically do not open widely, and have finely toothed tepals. Leaves are also distinctly serrated. Our plants, however, have very short stems and 3–4 cm leaves set very closely. They are dark green, slightly channelled above and rounded below; and while the surfaces are minutely dimpled and the edges slightly rough, serrations appear to be absent. In addition, short spikes from the leaf axils bear two or three flowers about 2 cm across of delicate crystalline texture, which, unlike the rest of the genus, open widely. Tepals are about 2 cm long and have faintly irregular margins. The narrow lip is white with an orange forward-curving spur.

Our plants grow well in intermediate conditions, mounted on paperbark, where roots wander freely through the layers which trap moisture. Light shade is required, and plants should never dry out completely.

Actual flower size: approximately 4 cm across.

Ionopsis utricularioides (Swartz) Lindley

One of the most wide-spread orchids of the Americas, this species was named *Epidendrum utricularioides* in 1788 by Swartz, based on a plant from Jamaica. Lindley transferred it to the genus *Ionopsis* in the 1820s. It occurs from Florida in the north to Brazil and Paraguay in the south, growing from sea level to 1,050 m. Common in areas with very dry winters, such as deciduous lowland forests, it also occurs in dense humid forests and in citrus orchards. It frequently grows into large clumps.

The 2–3 cm pseudobulbs are almost obscured by the two to four sheathing leaves, each 5–17 cm long, stiff and leathery, often reddish on the undersides. This late winter to summer flowering species produces spikes from the base of the pseudobulbs. Typically 40 cm long but sometimes up to 70 cm, each spike carries few or many delicate flowers. These are very variable in colour, and may be white, pale rose or red-rose with darker veins and a magenta blotch on the 0.7–1.6 cm lip, which dominates the flower. The sepals and petals are 0.3–0.6 cm long, with recurved ends. The dorsal sepal and the petals hide the tiny column, while the lateral sepals form a small sac. The bilobed lip has wavy edges and two small thin calli at the base.

Preferring a warm to intermediate, semi-shaded position, this species should be mounted on twigs, cork or paperbark. While plenty of water may be given in the growing season, the plant should be kept drier in winter, and perhaps a little cooler. Keep humidity high at all times.

Actual flower size: approximately 1–2 cm long.

Isabelia pulchella (Krzl.) Senghas & Teuscher

This pretty Brazilian miniature was originally described by Kraenzlin as *Neolauchia pulchella*, a name still frequently used for the species today. In recent times Senghas and Teuscher transferred it to *Isabelia*, a genus created by Barbosa Rodrigues to honour Princess Isabel de Alcantara who was a contemporary patron of horticulture. Porsch's *Meiracyllium wettsteinii* is conspecific. This species grows in the cool damp mountains in the southern states of Rio de Janeiro, Sao Paulo, Parana, Santa Catarina and Rio Grande do Sul at moderate elevations.

Pseudobulbs are borne 1–3 cm apart on a flexible, freely branching rhizome which often outgrows its mount and hangs freely in the air with no apparent harm. The 0.6–1.0 cm conical pseudobulbs are often flushed with reddish-purple and are covered at their bases with fibrous sheaths. The single grassy leaf is 5–11 cm long by 0.3 cm wide and acutely pointed. The thread-like spike rises from the apex of the pseudobulb in autumn to winter. It bears a single rosy-pink to bright magenta flower 1.5–2.0 cm across, which does not open widely. The oblong petals are slightly longer than the 1 cm sepals, which form a rounded spur at the base, concealing the chin formed by the lip and column foot. The outer lobe of the lip is almost circular with toothed edges and darker veins.

Because of its rambling habit, this species is best mounted on treefern or similar material. Place it in moderate shade in intermediate to cool conditions and keep fairly damp.

Actual flower size: 1.5–2 cm across.

Isabelia virginalis Barbosa Rodrigues

The original member of this Brazilian genus of only two species, *I. virginalis* was described by Barbosa Rodrigues in the late 19th century. Frequently sharing its habitat with orchids such as *Cattleya loddigesii*, *Oncidium sarcodes* and *Masdevallia infracta*, this charming and easily grown species comes from the coastal mountains of Sao Paulo, Rio de Janeiro, Parana and Minas Gerais. It grows on small twigs and branches in the cool misty forests.

The 0.7–1.0 cm pseudobulbs are egg shaped and almost obscured by a regular network of yellow to brown fibres like miniature baskets. The pseudobulbs are closely set on a creeping rhizome, and in time form dense mats. Each pseudobulb has a single needle-like leaf 2.5–7.5 cm long with a single narrow groove. The 1.0 cm flowers are borne singly on short spikes from the apex of the pseudobulbs. The tepals are white, sometimes flushed with pink or mauve. This flushing is usually restricted to the sepals, which are oblong with rounded ends. The narrow petals are curved forward. The lateral sepals form a spur with the base of the broad rounded lip, which is pure white. The white column is marked with amethyst and has an anther cap of the same colour. Flowering is mainly in late autumn to spring but can occur intermittently through the year.

I. virginalis may be grown in shallow pans, but does best for us when mounted on small rough-barked branches or treefern slabs. Provide intermediate to cool conditions, year-round moisture and good air movement.

Actual flower size: approximately 1 cm across.

Jacquiniella leucomelana (Rchb. (f.)) Schlechter

Most people, on first sight of this small epiphyte with the large name, do not believe that it is an orchid, resembling as it does a small succulent plant. This species was originally described in 1882 by Reichenbach as *Epidendrum leucomelanum*. In 1920 Schlechter transferred it to *Jacquiniella*, a genus closely related to *Isochilus*. It is largely restricted to Mexico, where it grows at elevations of 1,500–2,000 m in the states of Jalisco, Nayarit, Michoacan, Vera Cruz and Chiapas. It occurs in lightly shaded positions in dry oak or pine forests where heavy summer rains are prevalent, followed by dry winters when moisture is provided by low cloud and fog. This species is also said to occur in other Central American countries.

The erect or arching stems are usually 2–10 cm tall, occasionally to 15 cm, and form moderately large clumps. The somewhat zigzag stems are covered with green to dark purplish-red leaves about 1.3 cm long. These are slightly curved and highly succulent. This species may flower at any time of the year, but does so mainly from summer to early winter. The light-yellow to yellow-green flowers — among the smallest in the orchid world — usually appear in succession, sometimes a few at a time, from the apex of the stems; flowers are tiny, only about 0.25 cm in diameter. Flowering may be over an extended period.

J. leucomelana needs intermediate to cool conditions with moderate light. It may be potted in a fairly fine medium or mounted. Year-round moisture is required.

Actual flower size: approximately 0.25 cm across.

Kingidium deliciosum (Rchb. (f.)) Sweet

More commonly known as *Phalaenopsis decumbens*, this species was originally described as *Aerides decumbens* in 1851 by Griffith, based on collected plants of his own. Reichenbach named it *Phalaenopsis deliciosa* in 1854. In 1917 Rolfe created the new genus *Kingiella*, adding Griffith's specific epithet. However, *Kingiella* had already been used to name a genus in the mistletoe family, so Holttum renamed the species *Phalaenopsis decumbens* in 1947. Hunt found it sufficiently distinctive to justify its transfer to his new genus *Kingidium* in 1970. Sweet soon discovered a deficiency in Griffith's original drawing, making his name invalid, and so the species reverted to Reichenbach's specific epithet to produce its present name. It is a widely distributed species, ranging from India and Sri Lanka, throughout South East Asia to the Philippines, mostly at elevations below 600 m.

The stem is 0.3–2.0 cm long with between two and five broadly oval leaves 6–15 cm long. This species may flower several times a year on a 6–15 cm spike, which may be branched, and produces several waxy flowers 1.5–2.0 cm across and lasting about two weeks. The oblong sepals and petals are white with purple spots at the base of the broad lateral sepals. The three-lobed lip is white with pale or bright rosy-purple markings. The erect rounded lateral lobes are striped with purple, with the mid-lobe usually darker.

K. deliciosum may be potted or mounted, and should be given intermediate to warm conditions with year-round watering, high humidity and moderate shade.

Actual flower size: 1.5–2 cm across.

Laelia bahiensis Schlechter

Described by Schlechter in 1921, this Brazilian species occurs only in the Serra da Sincora in the state of Bahia at elevations of 1,000–1,200 m. This is a region of extremes of temperature with a long dry season. The only yellow-flowered rupicolous laelia in this area, it is often found growing alongside *L. pfisteri.** It clings to rocks amid lichens and mosses in areas of low stunted scrub and tall grasses.

The robust reddish-brown pseudobulbs are 7–10 cm long, conical, and bear a single leathery curved leaf 9–15 cm long. From late spring to autumn erect spikes 30–50 cm tall carry five to ten or more flowers which open over a relatively short period so that the majority are open together. The buttercup-yellow flowers are 3–4 cm across with pointed sepals and blunter, slightly narrower, petals about 2 cm long. They are narrow at the base and often recurved. The pale yellow lip is veined with reddish-brown and has three lobes. The lateral lobes are curled over the column to form a narrow tube. About 1.5 cm long, the lip has a very frilly burnt-orange mid-lobe.

A freely draining medium is required for this species as roots tend to rot easily, a problem common to most of the rupicolous laelias. A horizontal piece of treefern is a suitable mount. For potting, we suggest a mix of coarse gravel and bark. The medium should be allowed to dry out between waterings. Intermediate to cool conditions, bright light and good air movement are needed, and a dry rest in winter with occasional misting.

Actual flower size: 3–4 cm across.

Laelia dayana Reichenbach (f.)

Closely related to both *L. pumila** and *L. praestans*, this species is still regarded by some Brazilian orchid specialists as a variety of *L. pumila*, and many plants sold as the latter turn out to be *L. dayana*. In fact, *L. dayana* was originally imported into England by Low and Co. as *L. pumila*. It was discovered by Boxall and described by Reichenbach in 1876, using material supplied by Day, for whom the species was named. The exact location of its native habitat has been something of a mystery for many years. It appears now to be limited to the state of Rio de Janeiro at 900–1,300 m above sea level. Its range extends from the Organ mountains near Rio to the Serra do Rio Preto in the east. It prefers to grow in indirect light on lichen-encrusted trees along river banks.

The cylindrical pseudobulbs are 3–7 cm long with extensive white sheaths. They bear a single fleshy leaf up to 10 cm long. Single flowers are borne on 3 cm spikes from summer to autumn, with the occasional flower appearing in spring. The rosy-pink to dark mauve flowers are about 4.5 cm across with strongly reflexed sepals and petals. The large trumpet-shaped lip is obscurely three-lobed with the lateral lobes meeting above the column. The edges of the lip are frilled, and turn outward. The throat is white with a few obscure calli and several prominent velvety red-purple veins. The rest of the lip is dark rose-purple.

Our plants do well on treefern slabs in bright light and intermediate conditions. A dry rest in winter is required.

Actual flower size: approximately 4.5 cm across.

Laelia endsfeldzii Pabst

Another of the Brazilian rupicolous laelias, this species was not described until 1975 during Pabst's study of these fascinating rock dwellers. It is a highly endemic species, restricted to a small area near Itutinga in Minas Gerais at 900 m above sea level. This area experiences a continental climate, with large variations in temperature between day and night. The vegetation provides little shade, as it comprises mostly tall grasses, vellozia bushes and other low shrubs. Cold dry seasons may last for up to six months.

The clustered pseudobulbs are 5–12 cm long, tapering in the upper half, and tinged with purple. The more or less erect leaves are usually less than 10 cm long, but may reach 17 cm. They are reddish-purple beneath and along the upper margins. The upper surface is rough, with a central channel and a network of transverse wrinkles. Flower spikes from 40 cm to 50 cm long are produced in autumn and winter, carrying several well-spaced flowers which open in succession. The starry, pale yellow flowers are 3–4 cm across, with dagger-shaped sepals and petals about 2 cm long. The lateral lobes of the 1.3 cm lip meet above the column, while the mid-lobe is recurved and crisped.

Plants grow well when potted in a well-drained mix. Chopped treefern chunks are satisfactory, but must be allowed to dry out completely after each watering. A bright intermediate environment is ideal, with plenty of water in the growing season and a fairly long dry rest with occasional mistings in winter.

Actual flower size: 3–4 cm across.

Laelia furfuracea Lindley

Although discovered by Karwinski in 1832, this attractive Mexican laelia is still not common in collections. Introduced into England in 1838, it was described by Lindley the following year. It grows as an epiphyte amid tillandsias and lichens in the dry highlands of Oaxaca at 2,000–2,700 m above sea level. Here, there is little moderating influence from the sea, and the area experiences cold winters and a short dry season with only nightly fogs to sustain the plants.

The clustered pseudobulbs may be short and fat or elongated. From 3 cm to 9 cm tall, they taper towards the top and become furrowed with age. They usually carry a single leathery leaf 5–15 cm long. Flowering is from late autumn to winter, so that blooms are used as Christmas decorations in the species' area of origin. The 15–30 cm arching spike carries one or two (occasionally three) long-lived flowers about 8 cm across. They are fragrant and have a waxy texture. The 4–5 cm elongated sepals and the rhomboidal sharply pointed petals are a deep rose-purple. The 3–3.5 cm lip is three-lobed. The broad erect lateral lobes are paler than the sepals and do not enclose the column. The bright purple mid-lobe is almost triangular, with a sharply pointed recurved apex. It is attached to the lateral lobes by a narrow neck and has two yellow keels.

L. furfuracea grows slowly and dislikes disturbance. It grows well when mounted on treefern or cork in indirect bright light. Intermediate to cool conditions are best, with a dry winter rest.

Actual flower size: approximately 8 cm across.

Laelia itambana Pabst

Described by Pabst in 1973, this species is found only in eastern Minas Gerais in Brazil, growing on sandstone outcrops on Pico da Itambe at 2,000–2,300 m above sea level. It grows among mosses, lichens and leaf litter in the crevices of the rocks. This area is subjected to climatic extremes and the vegetation is mainly low scrub. During the long dry period, plants are sustained by evening dews.

The tightly clustered pseudobulbs are cylindrical and 2.5–6.0 cm tall. The boat-shaped leaves are very succulent and stiff; erect or arching, they are 2.5–6.0 cm long and occasionally tinged with purple. One or two flowers are borne in late spring or summer on an erect spike up to 10 cm long, which rises from the top of the pseudobulb. The very open yellow flowers are 3.5–4.0 cm across. The sepals are an elongated oval with blunt apices, with the laterals slightly shorter than the 2 cm dorsal. The petals are shaped like an elongated diamond, with a very narrow base. The three-lobed lip is 1.5 cm long with a small recurved and crisped mid-lobe. The lateral lobes scarcely meet above the column.

L. itambana grows well in intermediate to cool conditions with plenty of bright light and good air movement. A dry winter rest should be given after growth and flowering have finished. Treefern mounts seem to retain too much moisture for this species, and we recommend potting in a material such as broken sandstone and coarse leaf mould. We hang our potted plants for maximum light.

Actual flower size: 3.5–4 cm across

Laelia jongheana Reichenbach (f.)

This popular species was discovered about 1854 by Libon, who sent plants to de Jonghe of Brussels. Reichenbach described it in 1872, based on material received from Lueddemann, and named the species after de Jonghe at Libon's request. Unfortunately this beautiful species is nearing extinction in its limited habitat in central Minas Gerais in Brazil, where it grows at 1,300–1,600 m above sea level in medium-sized forests close to the summit of the few mountain ranges in the area.

The slightly compressed pseudobulbs are 3.0–5.5 cm long, and up to 1 cm apart on the stout rhizome. Becoming wrinkled with age, each one carries a single, very thick, stiff leaf, which is 7.5–12.0 cm long with a pointed apex and a shallow V-shaped cross-section. Flowers are produced, usually in pairs, from late winter to early spring on 4 cm spikes. The almost flat flowers are very large for the size of the plant, 10–16 cm across. The sepals and petals range in colour from mid- to dark pink or rose-purple. The sepals taper to a sharp point, while the petals, which are twice as wide, are almost diamond shaped with wavy edges near the apex. The 5.5 cm tubular lip points downward. It is pale mauve on the outside and golden-orange inside, and edged with cream and mauve. There are seven wavy keels which run almost to the apex of the very frilled mid-lobe.

An easy grower in intermediate conditions, *L. jongheana* likes as much light as possible short of burning the leaves. Treefern mounts are ideal. Give plenty of water when in growth. *Actual flower size: 10–16 cm across.*

Laelia lilliputana Pabst

The smallest of the laelias, this species was discovered by Ghillany and named by Pabst in 1973 for Swift's fictional land of Lilliput. Restricted to a small area on the Serra do Ouro Branco in the Brazilian state of Minas Gerais, it grows at about 1,600 m altitude on sloping ledges of granite and gneiss. It is usually found amid lichens and around the roots of vellozia bushes. The area experiences a long dry season relieved only by nightly dews. The plants are subjected to ten hours of direct sunlight each day, but good winds help to moderate temperatures.

The round pseudobulbs are 0.5–1.0 cm in diameter and 0.7–1.5 cm tall. They are tightly clustered and often tinged with purple, as are the very succulent boat-shaped leaves, which are stiff and upright and vary between 1 cm and 3 cm in length. One or two flowers are produced on spikes 3–4 cm long in late spring or summer. The widely opening flowers are 2–3 cm across, with 1.0–1.7 cm sepals and petals. These range in colour from white to pale pink and have a crystalline texture. The 1.0 cm tubular lip is three-lobed, with the lateral lobes meeting above the column and the much crisped mid-lobe recurving at the apex. The lip is yellow-orange inside, edged with white or pink.

L. lilliputana does well in cool to intermediate conditions with plenty of bright light and good ventilation. We grow ours in small suspended pots of coarse freely draining material. Give plants a dry rest in winter with only moderate misting. *Actual flower size: 2–3 cm across.*

Laelia lucasiana Rolfe

First described by Rolfe in 1893, this Brazilian species is conspecific with Hoehne's *L. ostermeyeri*, which was only reduced to synonymy with *L. lucasiana* by Garay about ten years ago. It is found in the mountain ranges from the Serra do Piedade to the Serra da Caraca in eastern Minas Gerais. Growing on rocky outcrops between 1,400 m and 1,700 m altitude, this species is subjected to a long dry cold season that may last up to six months. It grows among lichens in fully exposed positions and is often found in the company of *Pleurothallis teres*.*

The clustered pseudobulbs are 1.5–4.0 cm long, with very succulent pointed leaves 3–8 cm long. They are somewhat boat shaped with a prominent keel beneath. The entire plant is often tinged with purple, especially when grown in bright light. Plants flower from late spring to summer, with one to three pale to dark pinkish-mauve flowers on erect spikes to 6 cm long. The flowers, which are paler towards the centre, are 3–5 cm across, with rounded sepals and petals 2.0–2.5 cm long. The 1.5 cm lip is bright yellow-orange, with the broad lateral lobes folded over the column. The mid-lobe is much crisped.

L. lucasiana should be grown in smallish pots of coarse material such as broken rock with some leafmould added. Bright light in a cool to intermediate environment is best, with good air movement and a dry rest in winter.

Actual flower size: 3–5 cm across.

Laelia lundii Reichenbach (f.) & Warming

This species was discovered in the Brazilian state of Minas Gerais by Warming who, along with Reichenbach, described it in 1881. *L. regnellii* and *L. reichenbachiana* are later synonyms. In Minas Gerais, where it is not common, this species grows on small trees atop rocky hills or on the rocks themselves. It is found more commonly in the drier inland areas of Sao Paulo and Parana, growing in shady humid positions on forest trees along small rivers.

Usually less than 3 cm long, the glossy pseudobulbs are up to 2 cm apart on a stout rhizome, and are about 1.2 cm in diameter. They are unique among the Brazilian laelias in that they bear two very fleshy erect leaves 6–15 cm long. These are very narrow, with a depressed channel on the upper surface and a rounded underside. One or two flowers appear in winter on short spikes from the developing growth. The starry flowers, which last a little more than a week, are 3–4 cm across. The pointed sepals and petals are white and may be tinged with pink. About 2 cm long, they have several pale veins. The three-lobed lip is tubular at the base, where the lateral lobes meet above the column, with the broad frilly mid-lobe opened out. The lip has several keels in the throat and is veined with rich maroon-purple.

L. lundii may be potted or grown in a basket in coarse material, but does best for us when mounted on a paperbark or treefern mount and hung in a bright position. An intermediate to cool environment is ideal, with good air movement and fairly high humidity.

Actual flower size: 3–4 cm across.

Laelia mantiqueirae Pabst

Another of the Brazilian rupicolous laelias, this species was described by Pabst in 1975. It comes from Minas Gerais, where it is a common plant in the tableland area bounded by Sao Joao del Rei, Piedade and Ouro Preto. This plateau has a continental climate with a wide diurnal temperature range. The hot days are tempered by strong winds and the cooler nights are quite humid, seeing the formation of heavy dews. The dry season may be up to six months long.

The clustered conical pseudobulbs are 5–10 cm tall, and tinged with purple. Although the leathery leaves are 7–19 cm long, they are spreading, so that the average height of the species is about 12 cm. The leaves are purple beneath and on the upper edges, and have a prominent keel. Flowering from spring to summer, this species has seven or more well-spaced flowers 4–5 cm across borne on tall spikes. The starry flowers are rich rosy-pink, paler at the base, and have a crystalline texture. The sepals and petals are recurved at the pointed apices. The tubular lip is 2 cm long. The side-lobes are veined and edged with dark violet, while the recurved mid-lobe is white in the centre with its ruffled edges dark violet.

L. mantiqueirae grows well in intermediate conditions with bright light and good air movement. Our plants are hung in baskets of chopped treefern and broken brick. The mixture must be allowed to dry out between waterings, and the plant needs a dry rest in winter.
Actual flower size: 4–5 cm across.

Laelia pfisteri Pabst & Senghas

Described by Pabst and Senghas in 1975, this species is found only around the Serra da Sincora in central Bahia, a northeastern state of Brazil. It grows on the rocky hills amid stunted vegetation at between 1,100 m and 1,400 m above sea level, a habitat shared with *L. bahiensis.** During the cool dry season, which may last for half the year, the plants are sustained by heavy dews.

Plants are usually 15 cm or less tall, although much larger specimens have been found. The clustered pseudobulbs are usually 6–7 cm tall, with an enlarged base and tapered apex. They are reddish-purple and bear a single leathery leaf 5–12 cm long. It is almost flat, recurved and edged with purple. Flower spikes rise from the apex of the pseudobulbs in spring or summer. Up to 1 m tall, they may carry thirty or more well-spaced flowers which open successively so that no more than half the number are open together. The lilac-pink flowers are 3–4 cm across. Sepals and petals are frequently reflexed. The lip is three-lobed with the long lateral lobes forming a narrow tube around the column. The mid-lobe is white in the centre and edged with a wide frilly band of dark magenta.

This attractive species appreciates bright light. It needs an intermediate environment, plenty of water while in growth and a dry spell in winter. We hang ours in pots of coarse material and place them where air movement is good.
Actual flower size: 3–4 cm across.

Laelia pumila (Hook.) Reichenbach (f.)

First described by Hooker as *Cattleya pumila* in 1839, this species was transferred to the genus *Laelia* by Reichenbach in 1853. *Cattleya marginata*, *C. pinelii* and *C. spectabilis* are synonyms. It occurs in the Brazilian states of Minas Gerais and Espirito Santo, where it grows as an epiphyte in relatively open forests at 600–1,300 m above sea level. Mostly it occupies positions low down on trees near water courses, where the air is cool and fresh. This species is very closely related to *Laelia dayana** and *L. praestans*, so much so that plants of the three species are indistinguishable when not in flower.

The 3–8 cm pseudobulbs are about 1 cm apart on a stout rhizome. They are pencil shaped and have a single rather fleshy leaf 10–12.5 cm long. One or two showy flowers are borne on short spikes mostly in summer, but occasionally at other times through the year. The flat lavender flowers are 7–11 cm across and last well on the plant. The acute sepals and the broader petals are 3.5–5.5 cm long. The 4.5 cm lip is white or yellow within the wide tube and has a wide dark purple band around the undulating edge. There are three to five prominent keels down the centre of the lip.

Like *L. dayana*, this species flowers best if given as much bright light as possible. We have found that treefern slabs make the ideal mount. It grows fairly quickly into a large plant, so a mount of good size is needed. Intermediate temperatures are ideal, and plenty of water when in growth followed by a dry rest.

Actual flower size: 7–11 cm across.

Laelia rubescens Lindley

Known as the 'flor de Jesus' by the inhabitants of Guatemala, this species was discovered there by Hartweg. Lindley described it in 1840. It is a common epiphyte in Central America from Mexico to Panama, occurring from near sea level on the Pacific slopes in Mexico to 1,700 m altitude. It grows in dry wooded regions or in dense tropical forests, often fully exposed on tree trunks. Bright light gives the plants a purplish hue.

The 1.5–7.0 cm pseudobulbs are quite distinctive. They are strongly flattened, 1.5–4.0 cm wide, glossy when young, but often becoming wrinkled with age. Each pseudobulb bears one, or occasionally two, leaves at its apex. The stiff leathery leaves are 4–15 cm long (sometimes longer) and 2.0–4.5 cm wide. The arching flower spike is produced usually from the apex of the pseudobulb, but may appear from the base of a developing pseudobulb. It is 20–30 cm long, carrying between two and twelve fragrant flowers near its tip in autumn or winter. The white or pink-to-lavender flowers are up to 7 cm across. The three-lobed lip has a dark blackish-maroon blotch edged with yellow in the throat. The rounded lateral lobes enclose the column, while the broad mid-lobe has undulating edges. A velvety callus comprises two to four ridges, which are minutely hairy, near the apex.

L. rubescens does well potted or mounted on paperbark, treefern or cork. A bright position with intermediate conditions is ideal. Water freely in summer, and give a drier rest when flowering has finished.

Actual flower size: 4–7 cm across.

Laelia sincorana Schlechter

This beautiful Brazilian species is closely related to *L. pumila*.* It was discovered early this century and described by Schlechter soon afterward. In nature it is restricted to the tablelands of the Serra da Sincora in central Bahia state at elevations of 1,200–1,500 m, where it grows on vellozia bushes exposed to full sun, or on rocky ledges. The sparse vegetation is bathed each night in dew. The clustered pseudobulbs are almost globular when the plant is grown in the bright light of its native habitat, reaching a height of little more than 2 cm. In cultivation, however, with less light, they generally become more elongated and may reach a height of 5 cm. The stiff fleshy leaf is 6–11 cm long. It is boat shaped, and protects the flower buds which develop with it. From mid-spring to summer one or two, rarely up to four, flowers are borne on a short spike. The typically rose-purple flowers are large for the plant — about 7–10 cm across. They have narrow, slightly reflexed sepals and broad rhomboidal petals with wavy edges. The 5 cm lip embraces the column. The exterior is the same colour as the sepals and petals, but the inner surface is yellow in the throat, and dark rose-purple on the mid-lobe and around the edges of the lateral lobes. The frilly lip has five central keels.

We find this species does best when mounted on quick-drying material such as paperbark or cork. It likes a bright airy position and intermediate temperatures.

Actual flower size: 7–10 cm across.

Lanium avicula (Ldl.) Bentham & Hooker

Belonging to a small genus from northern South America, this creeping epiphyte with its dainty flowers is closely related to the epidendrums. Indeed, it was first described by Lindley as *Epidendrum avicula* in 1841. Bentham and Hooker, who created the genus *Lanium*, transferred this species to it in 1881. A relatively little-known species, *L. avicula* is native to Brazil and Amazonian Peru, growing in tall forests at about 1,800 m above sea level.

Its branching rhizomes form quite extensive patches. Mid-green pseudobulbs are set at 2 cm intervals and are 1–3 cm tall, narrow, with two spreading leaves at the apex. Typically 1.5–3.2 cm long, the leaves may be acute to rounded at the apex. Flowering in autumn to winter, this species produces terminal spikes 6–12 cm long carrying several well-spaced flowers about 1.2 cm in diameter. Both the spike and the outside of the sepals are covered with microscopic white hairs. The translucent yellow-brown to yellow-green or pink flowers sometimes carry red spotting. The narrow petals are shorter than the broad 0.7 cm sepals, and are slightly reflexed. The shovel-shaped lip with its upturned edges is about 0.5 cm long by 0.4 cm broad.

Because of its rambling habit, *L. avicula* is best mounted on treefern or similar material. It may also be grown in very shallow pans of coarse material such as chopped treefern chunks. Give medium to bright indirect light with water all year round. Although preferring intermediate to warm temperatures, it will grow cool once well established.

Actual flower size: approximately 1.2 cm across.

Lemboglossum cervantesii (LaLl. & Lex.) Halbinger

L a Llave and Lexarza discovered this species and in 1825 described it as *Odontoglossum cervantesii* in honour of Cervantes, a Mexican professor of botany. In 1983, Halbinger proposed the new genus *Cymbiglossum* for this and the *Lemboglossum* species on the following pages. However, a technical error rendered the proposal invalid, and it was too close to Brieger's *Cymboglossum* section of the *Dendrobium* genus. Therefore, in 1984, Halbinger created the generic name *Lemboglossum*. This species comes from the central highland forests of Mexico, where it grows as an epiphyte at 1,400–3,200 m elevation, favouring oaks in mixed forest as hosts. The tightly clustered pseudobulbs are dark green with brown spots, compressed, and 2–7 cm tall by 1–4 cm wide. There are two or three sheaths at the base of the pseudobulbs and a single strap-like leaf at the apex, which may be from 3 cm to 15 cm in length. It is folded at the base and has an acute tip. In late autumn to early spring between two and six fragrant flowers are produced on an erect or arching spike 12–32 cm long. They are 3.5–7.0 cm across, and last for several weeks. Their colour is white or lilac-pink with concentric circles of brown bars on the basal third of the tepals and occasionally on the lip. The broad rounded lip has a claw at its base, covered by a fleshy yellow callus.

Plants of this species prefer intermediate to cool conditions with partial shade, high humidity and good ventilation. A small pot is best, with a freely draining medium. Keep fairly dry in winter.

Actual flower size: 3.5–7 cm across.

Lemboglossum cordatum (Ldl.) Halbinger

C losely related to *Lemboglossum maculatum*, this species was introduced into England by Baker in 1838 and was described in the same year by Lindley as *Odontoglossum cordatum*. Halbinger transferred it to *Lemboglossum* in 1984. *Odontoglossum hookeri* and *O. lueddemannii* are conspecific. Although relatively uncommon, this species occurs from southern Mexico to Venezuela, growing as an epiphyte in the humid cloudforests at 1,900–3,000 m above sea level.

The closely set ovoid pseudobulbs are compressed, 4.5–7.5 cm tall, and are partially covered by three to five sheaths, with between two and four of these developing into leaves. The single strap-like apical leaf is 9–30 cm long (usually less than 20 cm), and is folded at the base. From five to twelve showy flowers 4–7.5 cm across appear in spring or early summer on a 30–60 cm spike from the base of the pseudobulb. The spreading sepals and petals, which taper to long narrow points, are white, yellow or yellowish-green heavily blotched with red-brown. The sepals are recurved and have a prominent keel on the back. The 1.8–2.5 cm lip has a fleshy callus on the short claw at its base. The semi-circular basal section is white with wavy red-brown edges and one or two blotches near the base. It ends in a sharply tapered point which is the same colour as the tepals.

L. cordatum is a generally easy subject for cool to intermediate conditions. It needs fairly high humidity and semi-shade. High summer temperatures must be avoided. It may be potted, but we grow ours on small treefern slabs.

Actual flower size: 4–7.5 cm across.

Lemboglossum majale (Rchb. (f.)) Halbinger

Described by Reichenbach in 1886 as *Odontoglossum majale*, this species was transferred to the new genus *Lemboglossum* in 1984. Weathers' *Odontoglossum platycheilum* is synonymous. It comes from the Sierra Madre de Chiapas in southern Mexico, where its habitat is threatened by logging, and in neighbouring areas of Guatemala. It grows on trees in pine and oak forests on cloud-shrouded mountains from 2,100 m to 3,000 m above sea level.

The compressed oval pseudobulbs are 4–7 cm tall and set up to 1 cm apart on the rhizome. They are smooth when young, becoming slightly wrinkled with age. They have three or four sheaths at the base and a single fleshy strap-shaped leaf at the apex. This leaf is 12–18 cm long, folded at the base and more or less rounded at the apex. Spikes of from 10 cm to 14 cm long are produced in spring from the developing new growth. Each spike carries two starry flowers 4.5–6.0 cm across. They are white or rosy-lilac, with violet blotches at the base of the tepals and on the rounded lip. The acute sepals and petals have several nerves, with the former having a conspicuous keel on the back. The lip, which is minutely warty or hairy, has a 1 cm claw which ends in two diverging yellow calli. The wavy sides of the lip are raised and the apex is recurved.

This is a small and fairly fragile plant, and is sometimes slow to establish. It should be grown in a cool to intermediate environment. Provide semi-shade and high humidity with good air movement. We mount our plants on treefern slabs and never let them dry out completely.
Actual flower size: 4.5–6 cm across.

Lemboglossum rossii (Ldl.) Halbinger

Ross, for whom this species is named, first collected it for Baker of England. Lindley described it in 1838 as *Odontoglossum rossii*. Halbinger transferred it to *Lemboglossum* in 1984. Its many synonyms include *Odontoglossum coerulescens*, *O. rubescens* and *O. warnerianum*. Although found in southern Mexico, Guatemala, Honduras and Nicaragua, this is not a common species. It grows as an epiphyte in the mixed cloudforests between 2,000 m and 3,000 m above sea level.

The compressed pseudobulbs are 3–6 cm tall, often yellowish, and become wrinkled with age. There are two sheaths at the base and a single strap-like leaf at the apex. The slightly fleshy leaf is 5–20 cm long, is folded at the base and has an acute apex. From late winter to early spring a 6–20 cm spike rises from the base of the newly matured growth, and carries up to four long-lasting flowers 5–8 cm across. They are pale yellow, white or pinkish with variable red-brown blotches on the sepals and at the base of the petals. The narrow sepals taper to sharp points with keels on the back of the laterals. The broad petals have wavy margins and are reflexed at the tips. The whitish skirt-like lip has darker veins and wavy sides which sometimes curl up. The boat-shaped callus on the claw of the lip is usually yellow, sometimes white, with brown spots.

A lovely cool-growing species, *L. rossii* may be mounted or potted and grown in moderate light. Good air movement is essential. It responds badly to hot humid summers.
Actual flower size: 5–8 cm across.

Lemboglossum stellatum (Ldl.) Halbinger

Lindley based his 1841 description of this species as *Odontoglossum stellatum* on plants collected by Hartweg and sent to the Royal Horticultural Society. Halbinger transferred it to *Lemboglossum* in 1984. Richard and Galeotti's *Odontoglossum erosum* is conspecific. It grows as an epiphyte in humid forests at 1,700–3,000 m altitude in southern Mexico, Guatemala, El Salvador and Venezuela.

Plants form dense clumps of slightly flattened pseudobulbs 1–6 cm tall, which may be egg shaped or elongated. They are partially covered by a few basal sheaths. From 6 cm to 15 cm long, the single strap-like leaf has a prominent keel and is conspicuously narrowed and folded at the base. One or two showy flowers are produced from late autumn to spring on an 8–15 cm spike. The very narrow sepals and petals may be yellow-green barred with reddish-brown or completely reddish-brown with yellow edges. They all taper to long points. Sepals are keeled on the back. The dorsal sepal is concave, while the laterals and the petals are recurved at the apex. The lip has a narrow claw at the base and a roundish irregularly indented skirt, which is white or pink with darker veins. The boat-shaped callus, usually white with brown marks, extends beyond the claw as a short bilobed plate.

We find *L. stellatum* does well mounted on small treefern slabs and hung in an intermediate to cool environment with high humidity, good ventilation and semi-shade. In winter, allow to dry out thoroughly between waterings.
Actual flower size: approximately 4 cm across.

Leochilus carinatus

Introduced into England in 1837 in a shipment of orchid plants from Mexico, this species was described soon afterwards as *Oncidium carinatum*, and was later transferred to Knowles and Westcott's *Leochilus*, created in 1838. We have, unfortunately, been unable to find details of its original author or who made the later transfer. It grows in the eastern part of the Sierra Volcanica Transversal on small branches and twigs in scrub-like vegetation, and is also found in coffee and citrus groves.

The 1.0–1.5 cm compressed pseudobulbs are oval and somewhat wrinkled and bear a single apical leaf about 7 cm long. At the base of the pseudobulb are one or two leaf-bearing bracts. In late summer an erect to arching spike about 15 cm long rises from the base of the pseudobulb and bears several to many 2 cm long flowers. After flowering is finished, plantlets are often formed at the nodes of the spike so that in time plants may become tangled masses. The sepals and petals are yellow-green with red-brown stripes along the edges of the petals. The sepals are suffused with brown and the spreading lateral sepals sometimes have a central stripe. The concave dorsal sepal hoods the column. The lip has red-brown or pink spots on and around the several finger-like projections on the crest.

This species dislikes sodden conditions about its roots, and is best mounted. We find cork or paperbark best. It likes a lightly shaded intermediate to warm environment with good air movement.
Actual flower size: approximately 2 cm long.

Leochilus scriptus (Scheidw.) Reichenbach (f.)

Described by Scheidweiler in 1843 as *Cryptosanus scriptus*, this species was transferred to the genus *Leochilus* by Reichenbach in 1854. Synonyms include *Oncidium scriptum*, *Leochilus major* and *L. powellii*. It is a native of Guatemala, Honduras, Costa Rica and Panama and grows from sea level to 900 m elevation. It may also occur in Mexico and Cuba. It grows usually in dense clumps on twigs and branches in wet or open pine forests. It is also common on coffee and citrus trees.

The wrinkled pseudobulbs are rather compressed, 1–5 cm tall, and may be oval or oblong. They carry two leaves and several bracts at the base, and a single leathery leaf at the apex. This is rounded or unequally bilobed at the tip, 3–14 cm long and narrowed at the folded base. The erect 4–25 cm spike rises from the base of the pseudobulb in spring, with up to twelve flowers 1.5–2.0 cm across. The sepals and petals are greenish-white to greenish-yellow with purple or red-brown marks, and both are keeled, as is the lip. The acute dorsal sepal is concave, while the subacute laterals may be reflexed. The petals are held forward and curve inward. The lip is narrow at the base with a cup-like hairy depression, in front of which is a fleshy slightly hairy two-peaked callus. The broad apex of the lip is bilobed.

L. scriptus does best for us when mounted in a humid warm to intermediate environment with good ventilation. It needs moderate shade and a drier rest once pseudobulbs are fully matured, but should never be allowed to dry out completely.

Actual flower size: 1.5–2 cm across.

Leptotes bicolor Lindley

The seed capsules of this species were once used to flavour ice-cream and sherbet. It was discovered by Harrison near Rio de Janeiro and described by Lindley in 1833. Synonyms include *Bletia bicolor*, *Leptotes glaucophylla*, *L. serrulata* and *Tetramicra bicolor*. It is a native of southern Brazil from the coastal mountains to subtropical rainforests at 500–900 m above sea level. It is also found in Paraguay.

The clustered cylindrical pseudobulbs are only 1–2 cm tall with one very succulent leaf which is usually 4–8 cm long, but may reach 12 cm. Almost terete, the leaf is green, more or less spotted with purple, acutely pointed, and has a groove on the upper surface. The 2 cm spike rises from the base of the pseudobulb in winter and spring, with up to three fragrant flowers which open successively and last from four to six weeks. The fleshy flowers are 3–5 cm across, with narrow sepals which are sharply curved inward at the acute apex and whose margins are somewhat deflexed. The 1.5–2.0 cm lip has white or greenish lateral lobes which are erect on each side of the column, and a convex magenta-rose midlobe with a white upturned apex ending in a sharp point.

This delightful little species is an easy subject in cultivation, doing well when mounted on treefern or in a shallow pan of fibrous material. Intermediate temperatures suit it well. Give it moderate shade and a humid spot. Plants should never be allowed to dry out completely for any length of time.

Actual flower size: 3–5 cm across.

Leptotes tenuis Reichenbach (f.)

This species, which was originally described by Reichenbach, belongs to a small genus closely related to cattleyas and laelias. *Leptotes minuta* and *L. pauloensis* are synonyms. It comes from the cool humid mountains in the southern Brazilian states of Espirito Santo, Sao Paulo and Santa Catarina. These mountains are subject to nightly mists.

The very slender 2 cm pseudobulbs are densely clustered on a creeping rhizome. Covered with papery bracts, they bear a very narrow leaf 2–6 cm long, which is minutely dimpled, almost terete and sharply pointed. It is dark green, sometimes tinged with purple, and has a narrow groove along the upper surface. Flowers, 1.5 cm across, are borne on a 3–5 cm spike which rises from the apex of the pseudobulb in winter or spring. The colour is variable. The sepals and petals may be a creamy translucent white or yellowish-green, while the lip may be cream to pinkish with or without a maroon blotch in the centre. The lateral sepals are narrowly triangular, while the dorsal sepal and the petals are oblong with an acute apex. The sepals have a pale mid-vein. The white to pale pink lateral lobes of the lip are erect and rounded, while the broad mid-lobe is rather convex with fringed edges.

L. tenuis does well when mounted on a good-sized treefern slab. It needs intermediate to cool conditions with light shade and fairly high humidity. It may also be grown in small pots of chopped treefern fibre. Give year-round moisture, which should be reduced a little in winter.

Actual flower size: approximately 1.5 cm across.

Liparis coelogynoides (Muell.) Bentham

The smallest of the Australian liparis, this species was first described by von Mueller in 1860 as *Sturmia coelogynoides*, and was transferred to the genus *Liparis* by Bentham in 1873. Other synonyms include *Leptorchis coelogynoides* (Kuntze) and *Liparis mowbulana* (Bailey). This is a fairly common species, sparsely distributed from the coast to the tablelands between central New South Wales and southeast Queensland. It is usually found only in small clumps, growing predominantly as an epiphyte, but also occasionally on rocks. It favours protected positions in rainforest and humid gullies and along stream banks.

The apple-green pseudobulbs are up to 1.5 cm tall, quite succulent, with deep grooves. They are often almost covered by sheathing bracts. Mature pseudobulbs bear two narrow leaves 5–15 cm long, which are slightly channelled and have five nerves, although only the central one is pronounced. Flowering in late spring to summer, this species has a semi-erect spike 10–25 cm long carrying between five and twenty pale green flowers with orange tips. The very narrow sepals and petals are 0.6–1.0 cm long, while the wedge-shaped lip is the dominant feature. At its apex it is 0.6–0.7 cm wide with irregular indentations. Slightly bent, this lip has a raised callus on the disc.

L. coelogynoides should be mounted or potted in a coarse well-drained medium and given cool to intermediate conditions. It does best in a humid spot, and should be kept moist all year round. It needs fairly bright light to flower well.

Actual flower size: approximately 1 cm across.

Liparis elegans Lindley

This species was first described by Lindley in 1830 and later by J. J. Smith as *Liparis stricta* and by Hooker (f.) as *Liparis gracilis*. The two latter names were eventually reduced to synonymy with *L. elegans*. This pretty species has a wide distribution, occurring in peninsular Thailand, Malaysia, Sumatra, Borneo and the Philippines. In Malaysia it is quite common on rocks and trees, and occasionally on sandy ground, from the lowlands to the 900 m mark. In the Philippines it grows, often as a terrestrial, on the damp shady forest slopes of Agusan on Mindanao and on Basilan Island at about 400 m elevation, where humidity is always high.

The pale green pseudobulbs are clustered and up to 3.5 cm long, with two shiny pale green leaves to 18 cm. The erect flower spike is produced from the young pseudobulb in winter and is up to 11 cm in length with many small flowers. These are translucent, and up to about 0.8 cm across. The upturned petals and sepals, along with the contrasting orange-brown lip, make this an attractive species.

L. elegans grows and flowers well in intermediate conditions and fairly bright light. It does best for us potted in a mixture of treefern fibre, leaf mould, sphagnum moss and coarse sand, and suspended from the greenhouse roof. Moderate water should be given all year round except for a short dry rest in the cooler part of the year.

Actual flower size: approximately 0.8 cm across.

Liparis nutans Ames

The genus *Liparis* is often overlooked by collectors, having an undeserved reputation for dowdy flowers. Most *Liparis* species are easy to grow, flower regularly, and present in fact a very attractive picture when in flower. Nowhere is this demonstrated better than in the case of *L. nutans*. This species, one of the most attractive of the genus, was described by Ames in 1915. It occurs on the southern Philippine island of Palawan and on Mindanao, where it is found in Agusan, Bukidnon, Lanao and Surigao provinces. The plant grows as both an epiphyte and a lithophyte in the shady forests where it receives some protection from prevailing high temperatures. Rain falls all year round, which ensures constant high humidity.

The clustered pseudobulbs are pear shaped with an orange-pink hue, and from 3 cm to 5 cm tall. The leaves are about 17 cm long, with bronze edging and bronze undersides, making it an attractive plant even when not in flower. The flower spike, which is up to 30 cm tall, is produced in summer or autumn from the apex of the pseudobulb. It bears many quite densely packed flowers which may be brick-red to coppery-brown. The thick fleshy lip is slightly darker than the rest of the flower and is bent sharply downward from the middle.

Despite its tropical origin, this species is an easy grower, and does well in intermediate conditions. We grow our plants in suspended pots of treefern fibre, leafmould, fine bark and coarse sand. Give good light and year-round moisture.

Actual flower size: approximately 1 cm long.

Masdevallia abbreviata Reichenbach (f.)

Masdevallias enjoyed great popularity with 19th century collectors, but fell gradually out of favour. Now this delightful genus is making a deserved comeback, and is becoming more frequent in collections. *M. abbreviata* is one of the smaller flowered masdevallias. It originates in northern Peru and Ecuador, and was described by Reichenbach in 1878. It grows with many other epiphytes in cloudforest and evergreen woods between 1,400 m and 2,800 m above sea level.

The long-stalked erect leaves, which form dense clumps, are 5–15 cm long by 1–2 cm wide, and three-toothed at the apex. Flowers appear in winter and spring on arching or erect spikes 12–25 cm long. Each spike has up to eight flowers which all open at the same time. About 1 cm across, their basic colour is white, with or without purple or crimson spotting. The sepals, which as in all masdevallias are by far the largest floral parts, have minutely serrated edges. They are joined to form an arching tube, then contract to more or less thickened greenish tails about 1.0–1.5 cm long. The concave dorsal is hooded over the petals, lip and column. The white petals are 0.3–0.4 cm long with a three-toothed apex and minutely toothed edges. The light yellow lip is fiddle shaped, 0.4–0.5 cm long, with two keels and erect rounded edges.

This species grows well in cool to intermediate conditons with moderate humidity and good air movement. It may be mounted or grown in a small pot, placed in a shaded spot and kept moist at all times.

Actual flower size: approximately 1 cm across.

Masdevallia aenigma Luer & Escobar

Discovered by Schlim more than 150 years ago, this species was previously known as either *M. auropurpurea* (Rchb. (f.)) or *M. bicolor* (Poeppig & Endlicher), two species to which it is closely related. Luer and Escobar gave it separate specific rank in 1982. The species is confined to the wet forests of the Eastern Cordillera in Colombia, where it has been found at about 2,500 m above sea level, growing in association with *M. encephala*, *M. corniculata* and *Dracula diabola*. Its coarse roots anchor it firmly to the trees on which it grows.

The fleshy 12–18 cm leaves are rounded at the apex. The erect flower spike, which is triangular in cross-section, is 8–17 cm tall with up to three flowers (most commonly two) set 1–1.5 cm apart. They open together or successively in winter or spring. The sepals form a 0.4 cm tube before spreading. The yellow dorsal is keeled and, as with the lateral sepals, has tiny warts inside. Its orange-yellow tail is about 3 cm long, while those of the lateral sepals are about 2 cm. The deep velvety maroon-purple of the laterals makes this a most attractive species. The small white petals and the hinged lip, which is dark purple or cream with purple spotting, are about 0.7 cm long.

M. aenigma has the reputation of being a little more difficult to grow than many others. It seems to do well potted in a freely draining mixture and placed in an intermediate environment. It must be kept moist all year round and never allowed to dry out completely.

Actual flower size: approximately 5 cm long.

Masdevallia agaster Luer

Although not credited with its discovery, Walter Teague reportedly collected this species on one of his many visits to his homeland in 1976. It was for some time called by Teague the 'white tubulosa' after a species to which it is closely related. Luer officially described it as a separate species in 1979. It grows on mossy trees in the cloudforests of southern Ecuador, where it receives year-round moisture.

The pointed leaves are 6–9 cm long, dull green below and dark green on the upper surfaces. A free-flowering species, *M. agaster* produces delightfully coconut-scented flowers for two or three months in winter. These are borne singly on an arching inflorescence up to 3 cm long. The sepals are golden-yellow on the outside with cream towards the apex. The inner surface is yellow within the 1–2 cm tube, then covered with fine white hair on the broader part of the sepals, while the 2.5 cm long tails are yellow-orange. The dorsal sepal is joined to the laterals for almost its entire length, but the rounded laterals open out and show a yellow vein down the centre. The flower is about 2 cm across the widest point. The petals and the lip, which is white suffused with purple along the edges, are hidden.

M. agaster requires cool humid conditions at all times and should be potted in a mixture of pine or fir bark, perlite, chopped sphagnum moss and treefern. Alternatively, it may be mounted on treefern with a little moss about the roots.

Actual flower size: approximately 2 cm across.

Masdevallia angulifera Reichenbach (f.)

Justifiably popular, this species has been a favourite in orchid collections for over fifty years. A native of the cool moist cloudforests of Colombia, it was described by Reichenbach in the latter part of the 19th century.

The mid-green glossy leaves are up to 12 cm long, including the 3–4 cm stalk. They are broadly oval and slightly reflexed at the apex. The inflorescence is slightly shorter than the leaves and bears a single flower in winter. The flower is shaped somewhat like a periscope with all sepals joined to form an angular tube about 2 cm long with a slightly swollen pouch like a 'belly' in the middle. The free ends of the sepals are triangular and open outward so that the overall length is 2.5 cm with the opening 1.5 cm across. The tiny petals and lip are completely concealed within the tube, which is glossy on the outside and velvety on the inner surfaces. Colour varies from yellow-brown to red-brown to the deep red specimen pictured here, with yellow at the base of the tube and the tips of the sepals. Each flower lasts up to three months, adding to the other obvious attractions of this plant.

This is a robust species and will do well in intermediate to cool conditions with good light and humidity. Any fibrous well-drained medium will serve. The plant should be kept moist at all times.

Actual flower size: approximately 2.5 cm long.

Masdevallia campyloglossa Reichenbach (f.)

This species has been in cultivation for more than a century. Described by Reichenbach in 1878, it is a native of Colombia, Ecuador and Peru, where it grows in the Andes between 700 m and 2,800 m above sea level.

The thick leathery leaves are 7.5–12 cm long, including the slender stalk, and are somewhat rounded at the apex. This species appears to flower at any time during the year on spikes which are slightly shorter than the leaves. *M. campyloglossa* belongs to the subsection *Coriaceae*, which is characterised by fleshy flowers, and the single flower of this species is no exception. It is about 2.5 cm in diameter, with a very short sepaline tube. The sepals are white with three purple veins and a few spots along the edges. The free parts of the sepals are triangular, spread well and taper to narrow points. The white petals have a sharp terminal point. The tongue-shaped lip is bent, as indicated by the specific epithet, which is taken from the Greek for 'bent lip'. White with three purple streaks, of which the central is the longest, the lip is minutely hairy.

M. campyloglossa is more warmth tolerant than many other masdevallias, coming as it does from a wide range of habitats and elevations. So, while temperature is not a critical factor for this species, good air movement and year-round humidity are. It may be potted in a fibrous well-drained material or mounted.

Actual flower size: approximately 2.5 cm across.

Masdevallia caudata Lindley

One of the first masdevallias to be described, this popular species was originally discovered by the French botanist Goudot and described by Lindley in 1833 based on dried specimens received in 1831. However, living plants of the species were not introduced into Europe until Bull did so after Shuttleworth — one of his collectors — rediscovered it in Colombia in 1874. *M. shuttleworthii* and *M. klabochorum* (both Reichenbach (f.)) are synonyms. This species is a native of the cool moist cloudforests of Venezuela, Colombia, Ecuador and Peru between 2,000 m and 2,500 m elevation, where it grows as an epiphyte.

A vigorous grower, with leaves from 9 cm to 12 cm long, this species soon forms sizeable clumps. The large flowers are borne from early spring to summer on 12–13 cm erect spikes, and last well. The pale yellow to orange dorsal sepal is marked with between five and seven deep rose longitudinal stripes and tiny rose spots in the outer half. The lateral sepals are creamy-yellow, so heavily suffused that they appear to be of a solid uniform rose colour. The long slender yellow-to-green tails are about 6 cm long, making the overall length of the flower about 15 cm, with the main body 3–4 cm. The white petals are only 0.5–0.6 cm long, while the 0.5 cm lip has two keels and is pale mauve or white spotted with purple. An unusual pure yellow form exists.

M. caudata does well in a cool humid environment with good air movement and moderate light. A potting mixture of treefern, perlite, sphagnum and fir bark is ideal. Keep moist.

Actual flower size: approximately 15 cm long.

Masdevallia decumana Königer

Closely related to *M. caudata**, this species was originally discovered in Peru in 1982 and described in the same year by Königer. It has since also been found in Ecuador. An inhabitant of the cloudforests at 1,500–2,500 m above sea level, it is not common in either location, being confined to small areas.

The dark green spoon-shaped leaves are 5–7 cm long, about 2 cm wide and notched at the apex. The plant is dominated by the huge flowers which are borne in winter — and occasionally at other times — on spikes 5–6 cm tall. The flowers are 4–6 cm wide, with a short concave dorsal sepal which is almost completely crimson and has an erect yellow-green tail about 6 cm long. The broad lateral sepals open widely and are heavily blotched with crimson on a cream or lavender base, and contract to gracefully curving tails. The tiny petals and lip are visible within the shallow tube.

M. decumana is not as vigorous as other members of the subsection *Caudatae* to which it belongs, multiplying vegetatively only slowly. It may be mounted or potted in a well-drained medium which must however be kept moist all year round. It is sensitive to excessive heat, and should be kept in a cool to intermediate environment with good air movement.

Actual flower size: 4–6 cm across.

Masdevallia erinacea Reichenbach (f.)

This species, with its most extraordinary flowers, is found in Colombia, Costa Rica and Ecuador at up to 1,400 m above sea level. It was described by Reichenbach (f.) in 1877 and has also been known by its synonym, *M. horrida*. It is now reportedly rare in its natural habitat.

Belonging to the subsection *Pygmaeae* of the subgenus *Amanda*, this species forms a dense clump of mid-green narrow leaves 2.5–5 cm long, which are quite fleshy but not stiff. The almost round flowers are held well clear of the leaves at blooming time in summer. As indicated by its specific name (which means 'like a hedgehog'), the flowers of this species are covered with spiny bristles on the outer surfaces and along the edges of the sepals (though not on the tails). The bristles form ridges along the veins of the sepals, with smaller ones in between. The flowers are 1.0–1.5 cm across, and the sepals form a short tube at their base. The dorsal is slightly hooded with its tail hanging down, while the swollen ends of the lateral sepals' tails look like 'tear-drop' earrings when the flower is viewed from the front. The sepals are heavily blotched with dark red or chocolate. The petals, about 0.3 cm long, have a callus at the base and toothed apices, while the 0.4 cm hinged lip has irregular margins.

M. erinacea grows well in intermediate humid conditions with good ventilation. It may be either mounted or potted and should never be allowed to dry out completely.

Actual flower size: 1–1.5 cm across.

Masdevallia estradae Reichenbach (f.)

This Colombian species was discovered in 1873 by Patin, a Belgian collector for Williams in England. Williams flowered it in 1874, and it was described in the same year by Reichenbach, who had received from Wallis dried specimens of plants found in a Colombian garden. Reichenbach's later description of *M. ludibunda* is generally regarded as being synonymous, although Luer considers it may be a separate species. Growing as an epiphyte in cool misty cloudforests from 2,000 m to 2,500 m altitude, *M. estradae* forms dense clumps.

It has deep green leaves keeled beneath and notched at the apex. The single, pleasantly scented flowers are produced freely at various times throughout the year on 7.5–12 cm spikes. The sepals form a short bent tube 0.8 cm long before opening out. Colour is variable from very pale flowers, white at the base with violet-purple on the outer half of the dorsal, to pure lavender, to the colour in the flower pictured. The helmet-shaped dorsal is rich magenta with yellow-orange margins and tail. The 1.0–1.5 cm long lateral sepals are similarly coloured and almost flat with recurved edges. The tails may be up to 5 cm long, while the pale petals and lip are both 0.8 cm long.

This species appreciates cool to intermediate conditions with good ventilation or air movement and fairly high humidity. It may be mounted or potted in a well-drained mixture which still retains some moisture. It should never be allowed to dry out completely.

Actual flower size: approximately 6 cm long.

Masdevallia floribunda Lindley

The only masdevallia found in Mexico, this species was first collected near Vera Cruz in 1840 by the French botanist Galeotti. Lindley described it as *M. floribunda* in 1843. Richard's *M. galeottiana* (1845) and Morren's *M. myriostigma* (1873) are now regarded as being conspecific with *M. floribunda*. Apart from Mexico, this species is also found in Guatemala, Belize, Honduras and Costa Rica, where it grows epiphytically on trees in damp forests between 900 m and 1,500 m above sea level.

It is a densely tufted plant with fleshy leaves 4–14 cm long. The wiry, semi-pendent to horizontal flower spikes are 2.5–10.5 cm long. The single bell-like flowers develop quickly in spring and summer; in some clones the spike may bear a second flower. Plants may flower several times in a year. The pale yellow flowers are dotted with brownish-purple or crimson, and have slender reddish tails. The dorsal sepal is ochre-yellow at the apex and contracts to a 1.2–2.0 cm long tail. The tails of the 1–2 cm lateral sepals are only 0.6 cm long. The 0.4–0.5 cm petals are white with a tooth towards the base, while the lip, about the same length, is white with a reddish-brown blotch at the reflexed tip and has toothed edges. The flowers of this species are variable, particularly in regard to the length of the tails.

One of the few warmth-tolerant members of this genus, this species has been used in a number of hybrids. It grows well potted or mounted, and needs intermediate to warm conditions, moderate light and high humidity.

Actual flower size: approximately 4 cm long.

Masdevallia gilbertoi Luer & Escobar

This striking masdevallia from Colombia is still rather a rarity in collections. Described by Luer and Escobar in 1978, it grows as an epiphyte on mossy trees between 1,400 m and 2,000 m altitude in its native habitat. Here the rainforest and cloudforest of the Andes is frequently bathed in mist, providing constant high humidity and cool temperatures.

The broad oval leaves of this species are approximately 10 cm long, including the stalk. They are quite fleshy, arch outwards, and have a prominent keel underneath. Single flowers are borne in winter and spring on erect to suberect spikes which are only slightly longer than the leaves. The glistening white flowers with their maroon bands and orange tube are most attractive. Each flower is 3–4 cm across at the lateral sepals, which project forward and then bend sharply downwards before contracting to slender tails. As with the erect tail of the hooded dorsal sepal, these are up to 7.5 cm long. Both the small petals, which have a distinct tooth near the base, and the lip are concealed within the tube.

M. gilbertoi thrives in intermediate to cool conditions with constant high humidity and moderate light. It does well grown in small pots of pine or fir bark, treefern fibre, perlite and chopped sphagnum moss, a mixture which helps to retain moisture. Good air movement is also important, especially in summer, when overheating may become a problem.

Actual flower size: 3–4 cm across.

Masdevallia herradurae Lehmann & Kraenzlin

Another Colombian masdevallia, this species was described by Lehmann and Kraenzlin in 1899, and named for the river near which it was discovered. It inhabits the cool damp cloudforests of the Central and Western Cordilleras where it grows on mossy trees at up to 2,100 m above sea level.

The strap-like mid-green leaves are 7–12 cm long. This species multiplies very rapidly, soon forming a specimen plant, and is very floriferous, producing flowers from the base of the same leaf year after year. These are borne in autumn on spikes 2.5–5.0 cm long. The flowers, usually dark crimson, contrast vividly with the green leaves. As well as this typical flower colour, blooms may be red and yellow in varying combinations, and even pure yellow, although this is rare. The sepals form a 0.4 cm long tube, then open widely. The paler tails are about 2 cm long. The spreading lateral sepals are about 1 cm long, excluding the tails. The greenish-white petals are 0.4 cm long and have a longitudinal callus which forms a short tooth near the base. The strap-shaped maroon lip is nearly 0.4 cm long and has some tiny warts.

M. herradurae flourishes in an intermediate humid environment with year-round moisture and moderate light. An open potting mix of treefern fibre, chopped sphagnum, perlite, and pine or fir bark is ideal. It may also be grown on a slab of treefern with a pad of sphagnum moss about the roots.

Actual flower size: approximately 5 cm long.

Masdevallia hirtzii Luer & Andreetta

This species was discovered almost simultaneously at different locations in Ecuador by both Hirtz and Andreetta. It was described in 1989 by Luer and Andreetta from material collected the previous year, and named after Hirtz, a mining engineer from Quito who has discovered many new species. It grows epiphytically in the cloudforests of the Cordillera de Condor at about 1,550 m altitude, and in some places is quite abundant.

The erect leathery leaf is 5–10 cm long including the 2.0–3.5 cm stalk, and is 1.5–2 cm wide. It is pointed at the apex, satiny green above and silvery-green beneath. This species flowers freely on 4–6 cm spikes and, over time, several spikes are produced from the base of each leaf. Flowering occurs in late autumn and winter. The bright orange to orange-red sepals form a cylindrical tube which is slightly curved forward with an erect or reflexed tail 2.5–3.0 cm long. The 2.7 cm lateral sepals are joined for 1.7 cm, then reflex at the mouth, contracting to form 2 cm slender tails. The fleshy petals and lip are both orange and about 0.6 cm long. This species is closely related to M. *mendozae** and M. *limax*,* but has a wider opening and longer tails.

M. *hirtzii* is a vigorous grower, and likes intermediate to cool conditions with constant humidity and moisture. Pot in a well-drained moisture-retentive medium or mount on a slab of treefern or similar material with a little moss about the roots. Grow in moderate shade.

Actual flower size: approximately 6 cm long.

Masdevallia hymenantha Reichenbach (f.)

Reichenbach described this species in 1855. It is a native of northern Peru where it grows on mossy trees in the cloudforests of the Andes at 2,100–2,800 m above sea level, where it receives year-round moisture. Often it is found sharing habitat areas with M. *replicata*.

The mid-green leaves are densely clumped and 6–10 cm long, including the 2–3 cm stalk. They are broadest at the rounded apex — up to 2 cm wide. In spring, a single delicate to bright pink flower is borne on an erect spike which is slightly longer than the leaves. The triangular flower is about 3 cm long excluding the tails. The sepals form a tube about 1 cm long which is quite pale on the inside. The free section of the dorsal sepal is about 1 cm long, contracting to an upright tail about 2.5 cm long. The lateral sepals are both broader and longer than the dorsal, with three darker veins each. They are approximately 2 cm long, with relatively short tails to about 1.5 cm. All tails are tipped with yellow. The oblong petals and lip are 0.8 cm long. There is a well-developed tooth at the base of each petal and the lip is thickened at the apex. The anther cap is dark maroon.

M. *hymenantha* appreciates shady, moist conditions with intermediate to cool temperatures with good air movement and high humidity. Being a species that forms clumps easily, it is an ideal subject for potting. As with all masdevallias, a well-drained but fibrous medium is required, and it should never be permitted to dry out completely.

Actual flower size: approximately 6.5 cm long.

Masdevallia limax Luer

This species was only introduced into cultivation by Andreetta in the late 1970s. Luer described it in 1978, naming it — rather unkindly — for its reputedly slug-like appearance. It appears to be quite rare in nature, having been found only in two isolated populations in central and southern Ecuador at about 2,000 m above sea level. Plants from the southern population are reported to have flowers almost twice the size of those from further north.

The mid-green leaves arch outward and may reach 12.5 cm. This species grows quite rapidly into specimen plants. The erect to almost horizontal spikes are slightly longer than the leaves and are borne in profusion in late winter and early spring. Like *M. hirtzii*,* this species bears a single flower with a swelling below the middle. In this case the swelling is quite pronounced, and the arching orange tube has a definite bend above the 'belly' and does not open widely at the apex. The waxy long-lasting flowers are 2 cm long with the downward-pointing tails about 1 cm long. The petals and lip are hidden in the tube.

Plants of *M. limax* grow well in intermediate to cool temperatures. Pains should be taken to keep summer temperatures as low as possible as this species reacts adversely to summer heat. Providing additional air movement by the use of fans will help to hold temperatures down, as will extra shading. Apart from its dislike of high temperatures, this species is undemanding.

Actual flower size: approximately 2 cm long.

Masdevallia mendozae Luer

First discovered in the Ecuadorean Andes in 1979 by Mendoza, an Ecuadorean national, this species was named in his honour soon after by Luer. It favours the cool moist cloudforests at about 1,850 m altitude where it is found growing low down on mossy twigs and branches or sometimes as a terrestrial in the leaf litter of the forest floor.

It is a vigorous species, with glossy mid-green to light green leaves 6–12 cm long, and is very free flowering over an extended period of time — usually from autumn to spring, but occasionally at other times also. The glossy flowers last for several weeks, and a second flower is sometimes produced on the same spike after the first one is finished. The spike is 4–6.5 cm long. The sepals are joined for almost their entire length to form a waxy brilliant orange to deep yellow tube 3 cm long and 0.6 cm across the opening. The curved tube has nine distinct ridges and short pointed tails 0.6 cm long. Completely hidden within the tube are the tiny petals, which have a small tooth and dark orange edges, and the small red or red-purple lip.

Closely related to *M. limax** and *M. hirtzii** this species appears to be tolerant of a variety of conditions. Although found in quite shady positions it will tolerate medium to bright light, and although happiest in intermediate to cool temperatures, will tolerate summer day temperatures as high as 29°C provided it is given adequate ventilation.

Actual flower size: approximately 0.6 cm across.

Masdevallia pandurilabia Schweinfurth

From central Peru, this species was described in 1942 by Schweinfurth, who has published a detailed study of Peruvian orchids. It inhabits the shrubby slopes of the Andes at about 2,700 m above sea level, where there is a constant supply of moisture in the form of rain, mist or dew.

The long-stalked leaf is about 12–15 cm in length and up to 2.5 cm wide. It may be subacute to rounded at the apex, which is three-toothed. The flower spike, which may be erect or arching, is up to 19 cm long and bears a single flower from 1.0 cm to 1.5 cm across. The yellow-brown flowers, which have a dark red lip, appear in winter and early spring. The widely spreading sepals are joined for about 0.5 cm to form a shallow tube which is covered with tiny hairs. They narrow abruptly to gracefully curving tails about 3.5 cm long. The 0.5 cm petals are irregularly notched at the apex and have a prominent more or less triangular projection at the base. The slightly smaller recurved lip is sickle shaped and has two fleshy calli at the base.

Cool to intermediate temperatures suit this species, which may be mounted or potted. It should be kept moist at all times and placed in a humid but airy position in moderate light. As in the cultivation of all masdevallias, good air circulation is important.

Actual flower size: approximately 1–1.5 cm across.

Masdevallia persicina Luer

This relatively new species was first collected in southern Ecuador by Walter Teague about 1975 and was originally described as *M. wageneriana* var. *ecuadorensis* by Braas in 1977. In 1978 it was elevated to specific status by Luer and renamed *M. persicina*. It is reported to be found scattered through a small area of Ecuador at 1,500–1,600 m above sea level, and is possibly quite rare in nature. It shares its habitat with other pleurothallids and with comparettias.

The glossy mid-green leaves are up to 5 cm long and 1.5 cm wide. They are quite fleshy and are rounded at the apex. The stem and underside of the leaf tend to blacken with age.

Flowers are produced freely throughout the year on spikes about 6 cm long. The flowers, 2.0–2.5 cm across, may be quite dull in hue or may display a most enticing peach colour. The smallish dorsal is yellow, while the spreading lateral sepals are suffused with a pale glistening pink. The 5 cm long tails are swept backward. The petals, as usual in the genus, are quite small. This species belongs to the subsection *Oscillantes*, which is characterised by a highly mobile lip that is attached by a very fine hinge. In this species the lip is very dark brown.

M. persicina grows quickly into a good-sized plant. It may be either potted or mounted, and should be given intermediate to cool conditions. It prefers moderate light but will tolerate brighter and drier conditions than most other masdevallias. Despite this, moist and shady conditions are recommended.

Actual flower size: 2–2.5 cm across.

Masdevallia polysticta Reichenbach (f.)

The well-known Czech collector Benedict Roezl discovered this species in northern Peru in the early 1870s. He sent plants to Ortgies in Zurich, and in 1874 Reichenbach described it. It flowered in England for the first time in 1875 at Veitch's nursery. This pretty epiphyte is a native of the temperate areas of northern Peru and Ecuador, where it is found in the Andes between 2,000 m and 2,500 m above sea level.

The spoon-shaped leaves, which are minutely three-toothed and recurved at the apex, are 10–15 cm long. They are dark green above with pale undersides. This species flowers in winter and spring with between three and nine flowers on a pale green spike which is more or less spotted with purple. The erect spike may reach 25 cm, while the hooded flowers, which all open at the same time, are about 3.5 cm long including the 1.5–2 cm long tails. The white to pale yellow sepals are spotted with purple, with a yellow mid-line on the lateral sepals. They are keeled on the outside and edged with very fine white hairs. The 0.3 cm petals are spoon shaped and toothed on the upper edges. The lip, which is the same length as the petals, is channelled and has longitudinal keels near the apex.

M. polysticta grows well in a small pot or mounted on a small treefern slab with a pad of moss about the roots to aid moisture retention. Cool to intermediate temperatures are appropriate, with moderate light. The plant should never be allowed to dry out completely.

Actual flower size: approximately 3.5 cm long.

Masdevallia prodigiosa Königer

This Peruvian masdevallia was discovered in 1978, and described soon afterwards by Königer. It grows among mosses on small scrubby trees at 2,000 m elevation in the cloudforests of Peru, along with *M. wurdackii* and several species of telipogon.

The broad arching leaves with their short stems are about 7 cm long and coloured a distinctive bluish-green. This is a very free-flowering species and may bloom several times a year. The wide open flowers, which are about 4 cm long without the tails, are borne on horizontal spikes 4–6 cm long, and last for three to four weeks. This species is very popular for its unusual colour — the flowers are a translucent pale apricot with darker areas of burnt orange on the sepals. The large concave dorsal sepal is shaped rather like a firefighter's helmet and is almost transparent at the base. It has three prominent ribs; the two outer ones are a darker apricot while the central one is cream. The yellow to green tail is swept backwards. The lateral sepals are joined, with three veins each and a darker patch in the centre. Their tails hang down or sweep backwards and are curled at the end. The petals are tiny, while the fleshy pale yellow lip pokes out like a tongue.

M. prodigiosa grows and flowers well in cool to intermediate conditions. Pot in a well-drained potting mix and keep moist all year.

Actual flower size: approximately 6–8 cm long.

Masdevallia pteroglossa Schlechter

Originally known as *M. wageneriana* var. *colombiana*, this Colombian masdevallia is smaller and opens more widely than that species. Schlechter gave it specific rank in 1920. It is found around the 1,800 m mark on the Western Cordillera of Colombia in the state of Antioquia where it grows epiphytically on the mossy trunks of forest trees.

The fleshy oval leaves are only 2.5–4.0 cm long, making the plant a real miniature. They are channelled above and pointed at the apex. This species grows quite vigorously, soon reaching specimen size. The flower spikes appear in winter and spring and are about the same length as the leaves, or slightly longer. The sepals form only a shallow tube, opening to present a flat flower about 2 cm across the lateral sepals. These broadly oval lateral sepals, which are joined for most of their length, are a translucent pale yellow dotted with crimson and have crimson streaks at the base. The dorsal sepal has fewer dots, but a central crimson stripe instead. The tiny petals are toothed at the apex. A unique feature of the subsection *Oscillantes*, to which this species belongs, is the hinged highly mobile lip that moves at the slightest provocation. In this species, the apex of the lip is bright red.

M. pteroglossa may be mounted or potted in a fine well-drained medium and grown in intermediate to cool conditions. It does best in moderate light levels with year-round moisture. *Actual flower size: approximately 2 cm across.*

Masdevallia purpurella Luer & Escobar

This species was discovered in 1974, but not described until 1982. To date it has been reported only from a small area of northeastern Colombia where it is abundant in the cool damp cloudforest. Also found in this area are dryadellas, oncidiums and telipogons.

The mid-green leaves of this species are 4–6 cm long and 1–2 cm across. They are oval with an acute tip. The 4.0–4.5 cm spikes are produced at irregular intervals throughout the year. Suberect to horizontal, they each bear a single pink flower about 2 cm across the lateral sepals. *M. purpurella* belongs to the subgenus *Masdevallia*, subsection *Caudatae*, and has the characteristic long tails and wide-spreading sepals of the subsection. The sepals join to form a shallow 0.4 cm tube within which the fleshy 0.45 cm lip and white notched petals are clearly visible. The hooded dorsal sepal, about 1.2 cm long, is pale on the outside, but almost entirely claret coloured on the inside, with a pale yellow area at the base. The colours are reversed on the 1 cm lateral sepals, which have three darker veins. As with the dorsal, they contract to greenish-yellow tails about 2.5 cm long.

Closely related to *M. caudata** and *M. triangularis*, this species grows well when potted in well-drained fibrous material and placed in an intermediate environment with moderate light and good ventilation. It appreciates year-round humidity.
Actual flower size: approximately 2 cm across.

Masdevallia rolfeana Kraenzlin

This brilliantly coloured species was introduced into England by Sander in 1891 and described in the same year by Kraenzlin. It was named in honour of Rolfe, the founder of the *Orchid Review*, and of the Royal Botanical Gardens at Kew, England. This species is a native of Costa Rica, where it is found growing as an epiphyte in the cloudforests of the Central Cordillera at 1,800 m above sea level. It has been found growing in association with *M. calura* and *M. reichenbachiana*, to both of which it is closely related.

The fleshy clustered leaves are typically 10–13 cm long by 2 cm broad. They are keeled below and notched at the apex. The flowers, which appear in summer and last for several weeks, are borne on spikes up to 7.5 cm long. The dark purple-crimson or claret-coloured flowers are about 6 cm long, including the 2–5 cm green or yellow tails. The sepaline tube is 1.2 cm long with yellow at the base. The 1 cm lip is red or rose coloured, spotted with crimson. It has two ridges and the recurved apex is crimson. The 0.8 cm long petals have smooth edges.

A very desirable species, it is not difficult in cultivation if given cool to intermediate conditions, moderate light, and good air movement. It may be mounted or potted in well-draining material. Year-round humidity is recommended. *Actual flower size: approximately 6 cm long.*

Masdevallia sanctae-inesae Luer & Malo

Closely related to *M. caudata** and *M. decumana,** this relatively new species was discovered by Malo in southern Ecuador near the city of Cuenca. Luer and Malo described it in 1978, and named it after Malo's orchid farm in Ecuador. It is a native of the eastern slopes of the Andes at about 2,500 m above sea level, where it grows on mossy trees in the cool cloudforest.

The mid-green leaves are 6–14 cm long and slightly recurved at the pointed apex. This species' propensity for almost continuous flowering, as each leaf produces successive spikes, makes it a most desirable addition to any collection. The suberect to almost horizontal spikes are 2.5–3.0 cm long and bear single flowers with widely spreading sepals and long tails — characteristics of the subsection *Caudatae* to which the species belongs. The creamy-yellow sepals are joined at the base to form a 0.8 cm tube, at the centre of which the 0.6 cm long petals and lip are clearly visible. The slightly concave dorsal sepal shades to yellow at the apex, while the lateral sepals have a pale orange patch. All sepals have a crystalline texture and three nerves, with those on the dorsal being most prominent. The flower is about 2.5 cm across at its widest point, with 3.0–3.5 cm yellow-green tails. The orange apex of the erect yellow-green lip provides a nice focal point to the flower.

Growing well in cool to intermediate conditions with moderate light and year-round humidity, this species may be potted or mounted. *Actual flower size: approximately 2.5 cm across.*

Masdevallia schroederiana Veitch?

Originally imported into England in a batch of plants purporting to originate in Peru, this species may be a native of Costa Rica at about 1,900 m above sea level. It is very closely related to the Colombian species *M. fulvescens*, which some believe may only be a smaller form. *M. schroederiana* was first exhibited in England in 1890 by Schroeder, for whom it is named, and was awarded by the Royal Horticultural Society. Luer believes that it was named by Veitch.

The 15 cm long leaves form dense clumps. Single flowers are borne on erect spikes in late winter to early spring, with the occasional flower in summer. Each flower, which is 3.5–4.0 cm long excluding the 5–8 cm orange-yellow tails, lasts four to five weeks. The sepals unite to form a 1.5–2.0 cm tube which is orange at the base. The 3 cm lateral sepals are the most striking feature of the flower, with a broad white band on the inner half contrasting with the maroon outer half. Concealed within the tube are the fleshy 0.8–0.9 cm lip and petals. The lip is recurved at the apex and has two keels in the centre.

M. schroederiana is easy to grow if temperatures are not allowed to rise too high, but is one of the first of the masdevallias to react adversely to hot weather. It prefers a cool to intermediate environment and should be kept moist at all times. Give moderate shade, and be sure to provide adequate air movement and ventilation in summer.

Actual flower size: approximately 8–12 cm long.

Masdevallia strobelii Sweet & Garay

This most enchanting species was described by Sweet and Garay in 1966. It was originally discovered in Ecuador in the late 1950s at an altitude of 1,400 m, and has since also been found in Peru. It prefers moist humid positions and is often found on the lower branches of trees along or near river banks. However, it has been found in fairly open positions as well.

M. strobelii grows into a specimen plant very quickly, with a compact clump of 4–6 cm leaves. It is a free-flowering species, which makes it a desirable plant for collectors. The single flowers appear on 4–6 cm spikes in winter. The orange tube formed by the sepals is 1 cm long, with the outward-facing part of the sepals yellow with white areas near the apex. Flowers measure 1.5 cm across the 'mouth'. A remarkable feature is the large number of stiff white finger-like protuberances which stand erect on the inner surfaces of the sepals, imparting a cool sparkling appearance. The yellow and orange tails are curly and twisted, curving sideways and backwards. The tiny petals and lip are visible at the centre of the flower.

Doing well either mounted or potted and grown in a moist intermediate environment, this species should never be allowed to dry out. It tolerates moderate light to fairly heavy shade.

Actual flower size: 2–2.5 cm across.

Masdevallia ventricularia Reichenbach (f.)

Although this species was first collected in Ecuador by Jameson, Reichenbach based his 1878 description on a plant from the collection of Consul Lehmann who had found it near Quito in 1877. It is a native of both Ecuador and Colombia. In Ecuador it is found growing low down on the mossy trunks of cloud-forest trees between 1,800 m and 2,200 m above sea level.

The suberect to spreading leaves are 12.5–15.0 cm long including the long stalks. They are quite fleshy and usually slightly longer than the flower spikes which each bear a single glossy flower. Appearing in mid-winter and spring, the cylindrical flowers are deep maroon or brownish with maroon blotches and streaks. The curving upright tube is up to 6.2 cm long with a slightly swollen middle and a yellow base. The free parts of the sepals spread widely to give the tube a broad mouth. The erect dorsal tail and hanging lateral tails are 2.5–7.5 cm long. The longer tailed form from Colombia is known as *M. ventricularia* ssp. *filaria* (Luer & Escobar). The small white petals have a few crimson spots, while the two-keeled lip is dull purple.

M. ventricularia may be potted or mounted. It needs intermediate to cool temperatures, constant moisture, and a damp shady position. *Actual flower size: approximately 8 cm long.*

Masdevallia xanthina ssp. *pallida* Luer

The type species, *M. xanthina*, was first described by Reichenbach (f.) in 1880 from plants imported into England by Veitch and Sons. The subspecies *pallida* was first described by Luer as *M. pallida*, but in 1988 he decided that it should be reduced to its present classification. The subspecies comes from Ecuador and Peru, while the type species inhabits the cool shady cloudforests of Ecuador and Colombia between 1,800 m and 2,500 m above sea level.

In both the species and the subspecies, the 6.5–7.5 cm long leaves are up to 2 cm wide but are completely dwarfed by the large flowers which are borne singly in spring and summer on erect spikes up to 8 cm tall. *M. xanthina* has pale honey-coloured flowers with mauve-purple at the base of the lateral sepals and orange-yellow tails. Subspecies *pallida* is white, with dark red spots at the base of the sepals and yellow veins on the dorsal, which also occasionally has a dark red central stripe. The long yellow tails give an overall length to the flowers of up to 17 cm. The rounded concave dorsal is about 3.5 cm long, with the lateral sepals slightly shorter. The white petals and fleshy lip are about 0.4 cm long. The beautiful cultivar 'Snowy Morn' pictured here is an awarded clone and was grown by Mrs Phyl Nicholas of Hobart, Tasmania.

Both the type and the subspecies are very spectacular and much sought after. Both appreciate cool to intermediate conditions in moderate shade, and should never be allowed to dry out completely. *Actual flower size: up to 17 cm long.*

Maxillaria juergensii Schlechter

Discovered in 1922 by Juergens, after whom Schlechter named it in 1925, this species grows on mossy trees in the mountains of southern Brazil at above the 350 m mark.

Each plant is a cluster of branching rhizomes covered with papery bracts, which also partly cover the 1–2 cm pseudobulbs. Roots are produced only towards the base of each rhizome, so that plants tend to become pendulous. Set 0.25–1.0 cm apart, the ridged pseudobulbs are more or less spindle shaped and bear two suberect leaves 3–4 cm long. These are dark green, sharply acute, and have a prominent keel. In spring, single flowers are borne on erect spikes 1–2 cm long rising from the base of the pseudobulbs. The fleshy 2.5–3.0 cm flowers are globular, with maroon sepals and petals that are paler towards the base. The dorsal sepal, which is slightly shorter than the 1.2–1.5 cm lateral sepals, is concave and hoods the column. The 1 cm petals are parallel to the column and turned up at the apex. The base of the broad lip is pale yellow-green heavily spotted with maroon. The rest of the lip is maroon. There is an elongated glossy callus on the basal section, and a rounded apical half which is bent at a 90° angle. The whole flower is highly glossy.

M. juergensii does well on a treefern mount, but may also be grown in a suspended pot, allowing the plant to trail over the edges. We use a mixture of treefern, pine bark and a small amount of sphagnum moss. It should be kept moist all year round. Intermediate to cool conditions in semi-shade suit it well.

Actual flower size: 2.5–3.5 cm across.

Maxillaria lindleyana Schlechter

This Brazilian species was first described as *Maxillaria crocea* by Lindley. However, Poeppig and Endlicher had used the name for a Peruvian maxillaria in 1836, thus making Lindley's name invalid. Schlechter later renamed the species in Lindley's honour. It is a native of southern Brazil, growing in cool mountainous areas where it experiences nightly dews.

The somewhat compressed pseudobulbs are oval, yellowish-green, 1.5–2.5 cm tall and up to 1.5 cm across at the widest point. They have several sheaths at the base and bear a single matt green leaf 11–20 cm long and 3–4 cm wide. This leaf is folded at the base, but is otherwise more or less flat and has an uneven apex and a prominent mid-vein beneath. The erect spike is 5 cm or more long and carries a single yellow flower. The sepals and petals all taper sharply to acute tips, with the 2 cm dorsal sepal hooded over the column. The spreading lateral sepals are 2.5 cm long. The petals, about 1.7 cm long, project forward and curve inward at the tip, sometimes even meeting and crossing. The 1 cm oval lip is marked with reddish-brown and has a long raised callus which is covered with minute hairs at its apex. The apex of the lip is irregular.

Intermediate to cool conditions and semi-shade suit this species. We grow our plants in suspended pots of treefern fibre, pine bark and sphagnum moss. Pots are well crocked with broken polyurethane pieces to reduce weight. Plants may also be mounted. Keep moist all year round.

Actual flower size: approximately 4 cm across.

Maxillaria notylioglossa Reichenbach (f.)

More commonly known as *Maxillaria meirax*, this species was described by Reichenbach in 1854. It occurs throughout most of Venezuela at altitudes of 1,000 m or more, and also in Brazil, where it inhabits the cool mountains of Sao Paulo and Rio de Janeiro and the savannah country of Minas Gerais.

The 2–3 cm tall pseudobulbs are set about 2 cm apart on a creeping rhizome covered with several sheaths. The flattened pseudobulbs, 2–4 cm long, curve upward and become wrinkled with age. The two narrow leaves are 5–12 cm long, flat and bilobed at the ends. The erect 3.5–5.0 cm spike carries a single pale green flower which does not open widely. The 1.0–1.2 cm sepals have sharp protruding points at the somewhat rounded apices. The lateral sepals, which form a shallow chin at the base, are projected forward. The narrow 0.7 cm petals are acute and lie alongside the column. The obscurely three-lobed lip has a short claw with a raised ridge. The erect lateral lobes are rounded, whereas the mid-lobe is triangular. It has a rounded callus near the base, in front of which is a dark brown spot. A frosty white V-shaped ridge extends from midway along the sides to near the apex. The dark purple anther cap provides an interesting contrast.

Plants of this interesting little species grow well in a suspended pot or wire basket filled with treefern chunks, pine bark and leafmould or moss. It prefers intermediate conditions with moderate shade and all-year-round moisture.
Actual flower size: approximately 1.5–2 cm across.

Maxillaria parahybunensis Cogniaux

This little-known species was described about the end of the 19th century by Cogniaux. It is found in the cool shady mountain forests of the Brazilian states of Sao Paulo and Minas Gerais, where it grows on mossy trees at moderate elevations.

The dark green to purplish-green pseudobulbs are closely set on a very short rhizome which produces roots only near the base, so that the plant is suberect to pendent. The 1 cm long pseudobulbs are cylindrical with prominent ribbing and basal sheaths. The single fleshy leaf is keeled beneath and more or less flat above with a central groove. From 3 cm to 5 cm long, it tapers to a sharp point. The flowers are very similar to those of *M. juergensii*,* and are borne on a very short spike in late spring or early summer. The 1.2 cm sepals and 0.9 cm petals are pale yellow-green and very heavily suffused with pinkish-brown. All have rounded or obtuse apices. The concave dorsal sepal is hooded over the column and forward-pointing petals, while the partially spreading lateral sepals are broadly triangular. The oblong 1 cm lip is bent halfway along its length, with small erect lateral lobes and a broad rounded mid-lobe. The longitudinal callus at the base is a very glossy dark brown.

M. parahybunensis does well mounted on small blocks of treefern or placed in small pots of treefern fibre or similar material. It prefers an intermediate to cool environment with semi-shade and year-round moisture.
Actual flower size: approximately 1 cm across.

Maxillaria seidelii Pabst

A relatively recent discovery, this species was named by Guido Pabst in honour of Alvim Seidel, proprietor of one of the oldest orchid nurseries in Brazil, who has collected a number of new species. Confined to the state of Rio de Janeiro, this species inhabits the cool shady mountain ranges at moderate altitudes. The area of its habitat, where it grows on mossy trees, is subject to nightly mists as the warm air rises and the moisture it carries condenses.

The mid-green pseudobulbs are densely clustered on a short creeping rhizome that may be erect or pendent, as it roots only on the basal portion. The oblong pseudobulbs, which are partially hidden by brown sheaths, are up to 1 cm tall by 0.4 cm wide. They have several very shallow grooves and bear two sharp-pointed needle-like leaves 3–4 cm long. Single flowers are borne on very short spikes from the base of the pseudobulb in spring or summer. These yellow bell-shaped flowers are about 1 cm long. The oblong sepals are 1 cm in length and curved at the acute apex, while the petals are slightly shorter. The 0.75 cm lip is oblong with a blunt point. The area near the base of the callus is suffused with reddish-brown.

M. seidelii grows well mounted on small treefern slabs, but may also be grown in small pots of fairly fine material. It prefers intermediate to cool conditions with year-round moisture, good air movement and semi-shade.
Actual flower size: approximately 1 cm long.

Microcoelia exilis Lindley

The type for its genus, this species was described by Lindley in 1830. It has also been known as *Angraecum chiloschistae*. A completely leafless epiphyte, this species occurs throughout the province of Natal in South Africa, Malagasy, the Comoros Islands, Mozambique, Zimbabwe, Zambia, Malawi, Tanzania and Kenya at low altitudes. It is found in the hotter coastal forests and valleys.

This curious orchid is little more than a mass of thin branching roots that radiate from a short stem which may occasionally reach 10 cm. The silvery-white roots, which appear green when wet, often have only a tenuous hold on the host tree and are easily dislodged. Several spikes rise from the crown of the plant in midsummer and autumn. These spikes, which may reach 17 cm, bear from twenty to eighty very tiny (0.2 cm) white flowers. While not opening fully, they are quite pretty, each with a tiny balloon-like spur. As the flowers open successively, the plant remains in flower for an extended period.

We have found that this species grows best when placed on a cork or paperbark mount and hung in a shady position. It likes intermediate to warm temperatures with generally high humidity, especially in summer. If grown cool, then it should be kept a little drier in winter. Once established, this is not a difficult species to grow, and makes an unusual addition to any collection.
Actual flower size: approximately 0.2 cm across.

Microcoelia stolzii (Schltr.) Summerhayes

Found in eastern Zambia, Tanzania and Malawi, this species inhabits the misty forests of the higher mountain areas. Although rain falls mostly in summer, year-round mist means that there is always some moisture available to the plants.

Like other members of the genus, this species is completely leafless at all times. It is a mass of unbranched roots, radiating from a central stem, which hang freely in the air, providing little in the way of support for the plant. These silver-white roots perform the function of photosynthesis normally carried out by leaves (when damp, the roots show a green tinge). The arching spikes rise from the crown of the plant and bear up to fifteen flowers each. The flowers are considerably larger than those of its relative, *M. exilis*, and are very attractive, especially when a large plant produces numerous spikes. A distinctive feature of the flowers, which are about 0.3 cm across, is the spur and the long lip.

Sometimes regarded as only of interest to the most fanatical of miniature collectors, this species is in fact an easily grown and attractive addition to any collection, flowering regularly and demanding little attention. Best mounted on cork or a rough-barked branch, it should be grown in a shady position with high humidity during the warmer months, and less moisture at other times. Intermediate temperatures are adequate.

Actual flower size: approximately 0.3 cm across.

Micropera rostrata Roxburgh

This is one of our favourite species, and although in its native habitat in the mountains of eastern India and northern Thailand the plant often exceeds 20 cm in height, we have included it because in cultivation it is easily maintained as a miniature. *M. rostrata* had its first European flowering in 1839 at Loddiges' nursery and became very popular in collections. However, by the end of the 19th century it was already scarce in cultivation, and remains so today. Until recently this species was known as *Camarotis purpurea*, and you may find it still under that name in some nurseries.

It is well worth taking a little trouble to find it, if only because of the superb colouring. It has the added appeal of a long flowering period. The flowers, a most unusual shape, are the largest in the genus and are borne in long trusses. Being a monopodial, it can be pruned if it grows a little too tall; just cut off the top, and it will branch below the cut. The top cutting will throw out new aerial roots and may be grown on as a separate plant.

M. rostrata appreciates intermediate to warm conditions with plenty of bright light. We grow our stock plants in small teak baskets of chopped treefern and they produce their arching spikes during autumn and winter. The plants have no pronounced resting period, and may be watered all year round unless grown under cool winter conditions when watering should be reduced.

Actual flower size: approximately 2 cm long.

Microsaccus wenzelii Ames

Belonging to a genus with fewer than ten species, all of which have the tiny sac-like spur for which the genus is named, *M. wenzelii* was described by Ames in 1915. This Philippines species is found growing as an epiphyte on mossy trees from 60 m to 1,200 m above sea level on Leyte Island, in central and central northern Luzon, and in Surigao province on Mindanao. We have seen plants growing in association with *Hymenorchis javieri** at Santa Fe on Luzon. These areas receive rain all year round and the atmosphere is generally humid. This species is rarely seen in collections, being regarded mostly as of botanical interest only, but for lovers of true miniatures it is a charming little species with an attractive compact habit.

It is a monopodial with flat stems that can reach 11.5 cm in length and are curved at maturity, when the base of the stem is usually leafless but covered with sheathing bracts. The highly succulent leaves are only 2 cm long by 0.5 cm wide. They are very closely set on the stem and overlap at the base. The tiny white flowers, which are about 0.5 cm long and almost sessile (stemless), appear from the leaf axils. There is usually only one flower from each axil, whereas many other members of the genus have paired flowers. The flowers do not open widely, and the lateral sepals are joined to the tiny spur.

M. wenzelii grows well for us in a semi-shaded position on a mount of paperbark with a little moss about the roots. Intermediate to warm conditions and good humidity are needed.
Actual flower size: approximately 0.5 cm long.

Mystacidium caffrum (Bolus) Bolus

Also known as *Angraecum caffrum* — as originally named by Bolus before he transferred it to the genus *Mystacidium* — this delicate miniature is widely distributed throughout South Africa, being found in eastern Cape Province, Natal, Transvaal and Transkei at altitudes up to 1,800 m. It is an epiphytic species, growing on the twigs, branches and trunks of understorey trees in cool temperate forests as well as on the lianas that twine about the trees. Here there is plenty of humidity in the summer when the area receives most of its rainfall, and low humidity in winter with its long intervals of dry weather.

The most noticeable feature of this plant is its mass of greyish roots which are prominently streaked with white. These roots often extend for long distances over their host, and assume a greenish tinge when wet. Each plant carries between two and four narrow leaves up to 6 cm long, but usually shorter. Flower spikes appear from below the leaves from spring to summer and carry eight to twelve closely set flowers. The green anther cap makes a nice contrast to the white almost bell-shaped blooms, which are 1.2 cm across and have a 2.5 cm spur.

Grow this species on twigs, cork or a similar mount, with plenty of water in summer and a distinct dry rest in winter. It will tolerate semi-shade or fairly bright light. Intermediate to cool conditions suit it best.
Actual flower size: approximately 1.2 cm across.

Mystacidium capense (Linn. (f.)) Schlechter

The first African epiphyte to reach Europe, this species was first described as *Epidendrum capense* by Linnaeus, based on material collected by Thunberg, who later redescribed it as *Limodorum longicorne*. In 1837 Lindley created the genus *Mystacidium* and called it *M. filicorne*. In 1918 Schlechter resurrected its original specific epithet. Found in large areas of South Africa, it is one of the few epiphytes to inhabit both the dry savannah regions and the evergreen forests, up to 700 m altitude. It occurs in large colonies both on rough-barked trees, particularly acacias, and on the smooth euphorbias. It is also reputed to be a nuisance in some orchards.

The short stems have several pairs of stiff leaves occasionally up to 13 cm long, which cap a mass of greyish roots with white streaks. The leaves fall off with age. Several pendulous spikes arise from the lower part of the stem from late spring to early autumn, each carrying between six and twelve scented flowers. The prominent feature of these flowers, which are about 2 cm across, is the tapering spur up to 6 cm long. The narrow pointed segments have a crystalline texture.

M. capense grows in areas with hot humid summers that have alternating wet and dry periods. In winter both temperature and humidity are lower with an accompanying prolonged dry period. We mount this species on cork or paperbark mounts and hang them in semi-shade. Intermediate to cool conditions suit the plant. It should be allowed to dry out thoroughly between waterings and given a dry winter rest.

Actual flower size: approximately 2 cm across.

Mystacidium venosum Harvey ex Rolfe

First described in 1912, this African species has a wide variety of habitats in eastern Cape, Natal and Transvaal provinces of South Africa and in Swaziland, up to 700 m above sea level. It occurs in both the humid coastal forests and the cooler misty temperate forests inland. It grows on a variety of host trees in either exposed or sheltered shady positions. The plant is almost stemless, with numerous thick white-streaked roots which travel for long distances both over and through the upper layers of bark on its host.

It has two to five leaves up to 6 cm long, but is occasionally leafless for prolonged periods.

Leaves may be shed during long dry winters or eaten by slugs in the wet summers. Several arching spikes appear below the leaves from late autumn to early spring, when the areas it inhabits are experiencing dry cool weather. The four to eight crystalline white flowers are 1.5–2.0 cm in diameter, with a spur 3–5 cm long. It is night-perfumed, the scent becoming obvious about dusk.

This tiny and attractive miniature is an easy grower once established. It should be mounted, and although cork may be used, paperbark is the ideal host as the roots are able to penetrate the thin multilayered bark which traps small quantities of moisture. It is happy in intermediate to warm conditions, but should be given a cooler dry rest in winter. Plants do well in semi-shade or moderately bright light.

Actual flower size: 1.5–2 cm across.

Nageliella purpurea (Ldl.) L. O. Williams

Lindley first described this species as *Hartwegia purpurea* in 1837 in honour of Hartweg, who discovered it. However, the name *Hartwegia* was already in use for a genus of the lily family, invalidating Lindley's name. L. O. Williams created the new genus *Nageliella* in 1940, in honour of Otto Nagel, one of Mexico's foremost collectors. Native to Central America, it is common on oaks at up to 1,500 m elevation, where it grows mostly among mosses on horizontal branches.

Even out of flower the plant is quite attractive with its slightly twisted pseudobulbs, 1.5–8.0 cm long, which are tipped with a single leaf. This tough rather leathery leaf is very fleshy with a rough texture and is heavily mottled with reddish-purple. The erect to arching spikes rise in summer from the apex of the pseudobulb, reaching up to 48 cm with a cluster of about ten purplish-red flowers — rarely white or pink — at the tip. About 0.7 cm wide, the nodding flowers open only one or two at a time, so that each spike flowers for several weeks. The spike should not be removed until completely dead as it extends and produces several more clusters of flowers. The sepals are 0.7–0.9 cm long, the narrow petals with minutely hairy edges a little shorter. The concave lip has three keels and is partly joined to the column to form a small sac.

We find that this species prefers to be mounted on treefern or cork, or potted in a coarse medium to which some live sphagnum moss has been added. It needs intermediate to cool conditions, moderate light and year-round moisture.

Actual flower size: approximately 0.7 cm across.

Nanodes discolor Lindley

This widespread species was described by Lindley in 1832, based on a plant from Amazonian Brazil. Bentham later renamed it *Epidendrum discolor*, while Ames called it *E. schlechterianum* in 1924. Garay and Dunsterville resurrected the genus *Nanodes* in the 1970s. It occurs from the Pacific coast of Mexico at up to 1,000 m above sea level, through Central America and northern South America, Brazil and Peru. It also occurs in Trinidad and Jamaica. It grows on either trees or rocks in humid oak forests, drier more open areas, or dense rainforests.

The branched stems are 2.5–8.0 cm long and form dense mats. They are covered by the bases of the broad succulent leaves, which are 1–3 cm long with a bilobed apex. Succulent and often suffused with red, they have a dark red mid-vein, are channelled above and keeled below. The flowers, which may appear from spring to autumn near the apex of the stem, may be yellow-green, red-green, bronze-green, or pale pink to purple. The up to three stemless flowers nestle in the foliage and are about 2.5 cm long. The translucent sepals and petals are acute, while the broad lip is joined to the column for half its length with the remainder having upturned edges.

N. discolor can be difficult to establish from small pieces: it rather resents disturbance and division. Once established, though, it is not a difficult subject. It grows well for us when mounted on cork and hung in an intermediate environment where it receives frequent misting, good air movement and moderately bright light.

Actual flower size: approximately 2.5 cm long.

Neofinetia falcata H. H. Hu

For pure elegance this Japanese miniature is probably without rival. Formerly known as *Angraecum falcatum*, it is one of the most widely grown orchid species in its country of origin. It was popular with the ruling classes in the 17th century, and at one time as many as three hundred and fifty varieties were said to be in cultivation. Political unrest and changing fashions took their toll, but there are still about one hundred and fifty forms under cultivation. Flower form does not vary much, and most of the varieties consist of degrees of leaf variegation. One very worthwhile form, however, the 'Amami' cultivar has plain green leaves but stouter growth than the type, and larger flowers.

N. falcata is the sole member of the genus, and originates in the cooler areas of Japan, the Ryukyu Islands and Korea. In its native habitat it grows on rocks or deciduous trees where it gets full winter sun but shade in summer. It will tolerate low temperatures, and may be grown out-of-doors in frost-free areas. The main attraction of this elegant species, apart from its pure white long-spurred flowers, is its delicate fragrance, most obvious on summer and autumn evenings. Called in Japan 'fu-ran' or 'wind orchid', this species likes good air movement, particularly around the roots. While it may be grown on a small mount, we prefer to use small pots suspended from the greenhouse roof. To allow plenty of air to reach the roots we fill the pots with coarse chunks of treefern.

Actual flower size: approximately 6 cm long.

Neolehmannia porpax (Rchb. (f.)) Garay & Dunsterville

This species was originally described as *Epidendrum porpax* by Reichenbach in 1855, based on plants collected in Nicaragua by Oersted. Garay and Dunsterville transferred it to the genus *Neolehmannia* in 1976. Other synonyms include *Nanodes mathewsii*, *Epidendrum gnomus* and *E. porphyrophyllum*. This epiphyte is found growing in pine and oak forests to 2,000 m above sea level, and ranges from Mexico to Panama and into Venezuela and Peru.

N. porpax has no pseudobulbs, but comprises a number of stems to 8 cm covered with alternating leaves. It branches freely and soon forms an attractive specimen plant. Its succulent leaves are often suffused with purple when the plant is grown in bright light. The beetle-like flowers appear at the apex of each stem from summer to late autumn. The main feature of the flower is its large fleshy lip, which is very glossy and ranges in colour from pale to very deep maroon with green edges, contrasting nicely with the pale green sepals and petals.

This is a species that grows well in intermediate to cool conditions with bright light to full sun. We find that it does best when mounted on some coarse-barked material which drains well. We use cork, which does very well. Provide plenty of water when in growth and a misting on bright winter days. It may be potted in very coarse material and the stems encouraged to trail over the pot's edge.

Actual flower size: approximately 2.5 cm long.

Nidema boothii (Ldl.) Schlechter

Often mistaken for a maxillaria, this species was first recorded as *Maxillaria boothii* by Lindley in 1838. In 1922 Schlechter created the genus *Nidema*, of which this species remains the sole member. Other synonyms include *Dinema paleaceum, Epidendrum paleaceum, Epidendrum boothii* and *Encyclia boothii*. It is a widely distributed species, being recorded from Mexico, Panama, Surinam and Cuba. It grows at altitudes up to 1,400 m above sea level as an epiphyte, favouring both open areas and dense forests.

The creeping rhizome bears many closely set apple-green pseudobulbs, each 3–5 cm long. These are somewhat flattened and have a short basal stalk. The usually single narrow leaf is typically 10–15 cm long, but may occasionally be longer. From autumn to spring up to five flowers are borne on a spike about 10 cm long. These are pleasantly fragrant and may be cream to greenish-yellow, and are about 3 cm across. All segments are narrow and taper to an acute point except the lip, which is rounded at the apex. The sepals are approximately 1.5 cm long, and the petals slightly shorter. The lip has two raised yellow calli, one on either side of a central channel, and a ridge on the underside which forms a protrusion at the apex.

Because it tends to ramble, *N. boothii* does best when mounted. We use treefern, but the plant is not choosy. It grows well when given intermediate conditions with moderate to bright light and lots of water when in growth, with a gradual reduction as winter approaches. *Actual flower size: approximately 3 cm across.*

Notylia barkeri Lindley

First described in 1838 by Lindley, this species has numerous synonyms including *N. trisepala, N. bipartita* and *N. guatemalensis*. In the 1970s it was proposed that this variable species be split into two separate entities, *N. trisepala* and *N. tridachne*, depending on whether the lateral sepals were free (*N. trisepala*) or joined (*N. tridachne*), but this proposal has never been widely accepted. This epiphytic species grows throughout Central America from Mexico to Panama in dense humid deciduous or mixed forest, shady ravines, swamps and coffee or citrus groves from the lowlands to 1,600 m above sea level.

The clustered pseudobulbs are compressed, wrinkled, 1.0–1.3 cm tall, and are partly obscured by several bracts and one or two leaves at the base. The single apical leaf is 3.5–20 cm long and folded at the base. It is leathery, strap-like and more or less three-toothed at the broadly rounded apex. Flowers are produced from late winter to summer on pendent spikes rising from the base of the new pseudobulbs. From 5 cm to 32 cm long, they carry many 0.5–0.7 cm long flowers. These are faintly fragrant, greenish-yellow to white, with a few orange spots on the curving petals. The 0.3–0.7 cm lateral sepals are joined to about midway, or free with recurved apices. The dorsal is recurved. The clawed lip is white, spear shaped with an acute apex.

N. barkeri likes humid intermediate to warm conditions in light shade. Water copiously while the plant is in growth, less in winter. Small pots or mounts of treefern or cork suit this species. *Actual flower size: approximately 0.8 cm long.*

Notylia cordiglossa Reichenbach (f.)

Closely related to *Notylia barkeri,** and *N. hemitricha*, this Brazilian species was described by Reichenbach in the latter half of the 19th century. It is a native of the northern states of Amazonas and Para at less than 500 m above sea level, where it grows on trees along forest edges, near streams, on open slopes or in clearings — anywhere it can find relatively fresh air in these hot humid habitats far from the cooling influence of the sea. It has also been reported from the warm lowland areas of Rio Grande do Sul in the far south of Brazil.

The small clustered pseudobulbs are wrinkled and partially hidden by bracts and leaves at the base. The broadly oval leaf at the apex of the pseudobulb is about 15 cm long. The pendent spike rises from the base of the pseudobulb with twenty-four or more pale green to yellowish-green flowers. The oblong concave dorsal sepal is 0.6 cm long and bent forward over the horizontal column. The 0.6 cm lateral sepals are joined for almost their entire length and are slightly recurved. The 0.5 cm petals curve down and forward, tapering to an acute apex. The lip is whitish with a keel on the claw at its base and a spear-shaped blade.

N. cordiglossa grows well when mounted on a piece of natural cork, or placed in a small pot of well-drained fibrous material. It prefers a warm to intermediate environment with high humidity and good air movement. Moderate shade is preferred, with plenty of water while in growth. Reduce watering in winter, when regular mistings are useful.

Actual flower size: approximately 0.8 cm long.

Oberonia palmicola Mueller

Von Mueller described this species in 1860 as *O. palmicola*, but there is still some uncertainty as to whether or not it is synonymous with Lindley's *Oberonia titania* of 1859. Von Mueller's name remains in general usage. This attractive miniature ranges over a wide area of eastern Australia, from northeastern New South Wales to southeastern Cape York Peninsula. Although it occasionally grows as a lithophyte, it is predominantly epiphytic on trees in moist gullies or gorges in rainforest or open forest. In the tropics it occurs from the coastal mangrove swamps to 900 m above sea level, showing a decided preference for the cooler tablelands. The smallest of the Australian oberonias, it grows into clumps of several fan-like growths with between four and ten succulent flat leaves 1–6 cm long. The tapering pale green leaves are often suffused with pink or bronze, especially when grown in strong light. This species flowers in spring in the southern part of its range, six months earlier in the tropics. Rising from the centre of the fan of leaves, the gracefully arching spike is 5–15 cm long and is covered with up to three hundred minute flowers only 0.15 cm across. These are an attractive translucent red with a darker lip.

An easy species to grow, it does best when mounted on treefern or cork with moss about the roots. Place it in semi-shade in intermediate to cool conditions. It needs year-round moisture, but if grown cool it is best only to mist in winter. Make sure air movement is good, as in stagnant conditions it is subject to fungal infections.

Actual flower size: approximately 0.15 cm across.

Octomeria decumbens Cogniaux

One of several genera closely related to *Pleurothallis*, the genus *Octomeria* was so named because of the eight pollinia that all of its members possess. *Octomeria decumbens* was described by Cogniaux, curator of the Brussels herbarium. A native of Brazil, this species occurs in the states of Rio de Janeiro, Sao Paulo, Parana and Minas Gerais. It is found growing on mossy trees in the cool damp mountain ranges which are subject to nightly mists and fogs.

The very narrow leaves are borne on a creeping rhizome. Together with their rather long slender stalks, which are covered with papery bracts, the pale to mid-green leaves are 10–18 cm long with an acutely pointed apex. They are fleshy, and may be slightly curved. The upper surface is flat with three shallow longitudinal furrows, while the underside is rounded. The leaves are thus semi-circular in cross-section. Flowers are produced in clusters from the top of the leaf stalk. They are a translucent pale creamy-yellow with darker tips, and have a sparkling crystalline texture. The sepals and petals, which are quite free of each other, are approximately 0.75 cm long. The dark 0.4 cm lip is hinged, three-lobed and has two keels on the disc.

Like most of the octomerias, this species is floriferous and of easy culture. It may be potted or mounted and grown in a cool to intermediate environment. Semi-shade and year-round moisture are needed. It is an ideal companion plant for masdevallias, but is not quite so heat-sensitive.

Actual flower size: approximately 1 cm across.

Oncidium barbatum Lindley

This species was discovered by Swainson who sent plants to the Glasgow Botanical Gardens, where they flowered in 1819. Lindley described the species shortly afterwards. It is closely related to O. *ciliatum*, with which it is often considered to be conspecific, and O. *micropogon*.* It can be distinguished from both by the minute beak-like mid-lobe of the lip. It is endemic to Brazil, occurring at moderate elevations in Ceara, Pernambuco, Bahia and Minas Gerais.

The waxy compressed pseudobulbs are somewhat quadrangular and 3–6.5 cm tall by 2–3.5 cm wide. They have one or two leaf-bearing sheaths at the base and a single leaf 6–10 cm long at the apex. This is erect to spreading, dark green and usually paler underneath. Several flowers, each 2.0–2.5 cm wide, are borne on a spike 30–60 cm long. The acute sepals and rounded petals are yellow, blotched and barred with red-brown, while the lip is bright yellow with some markings on the callus. The more or less oblong tepals are very wavy, and the lateral sepals are joined for one-third of their length. The flat lip is about 2 cm wide with large rounded lateral lobes and a tiny mid-lobe. The callus has several rounded protuberances and the disc is toothed.

Not a difficult species in cultivation, O. *barbatum* prefers intermediate temperatures with moderate to bright filtered light and good air movement. Water copiously in summer and allow a drier cooler rest in winter.

Actual flower size: 2–2.5 cm across.

Oncidium bifolium Sims

This species was described in 1812 by Sims, based on a specimen from Uruguay, which flowered at Loddiges' nursery in England. *Oncidium vexillarium* and *O. celsium* are conspecific. *Oncidium bifolium* grows as an epiphyte in southern Brazil, Uruguay, Argentina and Bolivia in a variety of habitats — from the hot lowlands, where it favours shady streamside positions, to the cold mountain areas up to 1,000 m altitude or more.

The clustered ovoid pseudobulbs are 3–4 cm long (occasionally to 7 cm), and become furrowed with age. At the apex are usually two rather fleshy strap-like leaves 6–15 cm long with an acute apex. The 20–35 cm spike, which may be branched, appears in summer with between five and twenty flowers 2–2.5 cm across. The sepals and petals are yellow, barred and spotted with red-brown, while the broad three-lobed lip is yellow with red-brown markings on the callus. The concave dorsal and fiddle-shaped petals have undulating edges, with the petals curved inward at the rounded or notched apices. The 1 cm lateral sepals are joined to the middle, have pointed tips, and are obscured by the lip, which is about 2 cm long and 2.0–2.5 cm wide. The small lateral lobes are rounded, while the skirt-like mid-lobe dominates the flower. At its base is a fleshy callus with several finger-like protuberances.

A very adaptable species, *O. bifolium* is tolerant of a range of conditions. We grow ours in intermediate temperatures with moderate shade and generally high humidity. Allow the plant to dry out a little in winter.

Actual flower size: 2–2.5 cm across.

Oncidium concolor Hooker

Although described about 1839 by Hooker, based on plants sent to England by Gardner in 1837, this beautiful species was not commonly cultivated until about 1876. Among its synonyms are *O. ottonis* and *Cyrtochilum citrinum*. It grows in the mountains of southern Brazil and Argentina, sometimes in areas that experience frequent frosts in winter.

The clustered dull green pseudobulbs are rather egg shaped, and become wrinkled as they age. They may be from 2 cm to 5 cm tall and 1.0–2.5 cm in diameter. Two acute strap-like leaves are borne at the apex of the pseudobulb. They may be 9–15 cm long and have a prominent mid-vein beneath. An arching to pendulous spike carries up to twelve well-spaced flowers about 5 cm long in spring or summer. The pointed, more or less concave sepals are yellow to yellow-green, with the laterals joined for about half their length. The more rounded oblong petals, which are held upright in front of the dorsal sepal, are yellow with some green on the back. The sepals and petals are 1.4–2.0 cm long. The dominant feature of the flower is the broad more or less ruffled lip, which is up to 3.5 cm long. The 1 cm claw has two parallel keels tipped with orange and a short protuberance on either side at the midway point. The column has two very broad wings at its apex.

O. concolor may be mounted or potted. We use treefern for both purposes. It likes a cool to intermediate environment with moderately bright light and good ventilation. Allow the plant a dry rest in winter.

Actual flower size: approximately 5 cm long.

Oncidium dasystyle Reichenbach (f.)

Belonging to the same section as *O. concolor,** this species was introduced into cultivation by B. S. Williams in 1872. Reichenbach described it the following year. Its distribution is limited to the state of Rio de Janeiro in Brazil, where it grows in the cool coastal ranges. The latitude here is roughly on the Tropic of Capricorn, and the mountains experience bright days and cool nights with heavy dews.

The clustered pseudobulbs are compressed and become furrowed with age. About 3 cm tall, they bear two rather thin leaves 12–15 cm long. Flowers are borne in winter on a slender arching to pendulous spike 30–45 cm in length. There are usually three to six flowers on the spike, each to nearly 4 cm across. The 2 cm pointed sepals and petals are pale yellow, blotched with red-brown. The concave dorsal sepal is hooded over the column. The petals are sometimes twisted at the base. The lateral sepals are joined for half their length and are obscured by the large skirt-like lip, which is pale yellow to almost white except for the large glossy two-lobed callus, which is almost black. There are no distinct lateral lobes, but two tiny ears near the base of the 3 cm lip. The conspicuous column wings are almost square.

This beautiful species is fairly easy to cultivate although not as strong a grower as many of the other Brazilian oncidiums. Intermediate temperatures suit it best, with moderate to fairly heavy shade and high humidity.
Actual flower size: 3–4 cm across.

Oncidium fuscopetalum (Hoehne) Garay

Described by Hoehne as *Oncidium macropetalum* var. *fuscopetalum*, this species was later elevated by Garay to specific rank. It differs from *O. macropetalum** in the colour of its petals and the configuration of the callus. It is native to Brazil, growing in the hot lowlands of Mato Grosso on the edges òf the forests and along stream banks.

The clustered pseudobulbs are 2.5–5.0 cm tall and become wrinkled with age. They are slightly flattened and ridged with one or two leaf-bearing bracts at the base and one or two dark green strap-like leaves at the apex. These leaves are 6–15 cm long, strongly arching and acute at the tip. Several flowers are produced in winter on an arching spike up to 30 cm long. The wavy sepals and petals are dark brown, occasionally with some yellow mottling. The erect 0.75 cm dorsal sepal and 1 cm lateral sepals, which are joined for about half their length, are elongated with blunt slightly recurved apices. The irregularly edged petals are 0.75 cm long and about 0.5 cm wide, with a very narrow claw at the base. The 1.2 cm lip is yellow with red-brown blotches on and around the callus, which comprises several raised glands. The lateral lobes are acute with rounded upper edges. The broad mid-lobe is skirt-like, and the isthmus is irregularly serrated.

An attractive species, *O. fuscopetalum* grows well mounted on treefern or similar material and given intermediate to warm conditions with moderate light and good air movement.
Actual flower size: approximately 1.5 cm across.

131

Oncidium gracile Lindley

Belonging to the same section as *O. concolor** and *O. dasystyle*,* this species was described by Lindley in the 19th century. From the hot dry savannah country of Minas Gerais in Brazil, it grows as a semi-terrestrial among grasses in sandy soil or in rock crevices amid stunted vegetation. It is found usually between 500 m and 1,000 m above sea level.

The tightly clustered pseudobulbs are pale yellow-green to mid-green, and sometimes produce small plantlets at their apex. From 2 cm to 5 cm tall, these plump pseudobulbs have papery bracts at the base, and two stiff more or less erect leaves at the apex. Folded at the base, these leaves are 6–10 cm long with a prominent mid-vein and edges which are slightly curled back. The spikes, which are 30 cm to 1 m or more in height, thus rising above the surrounding grasses, bear between six and twelve long-lasting well-spaced flowers. The sepals and petals are about 0.8 cm long, and curve slightly at the apices. They are chestnut-brown edged with olive-green. The 1.6 cm lip is yellow, long and narrow at the base, with a single orange-yellow callus ending in two prominent points. The kidney-shaped outer section of the lip is about 1.6 cm wide.

This is one of the 'terrestrial' oncidiums, which deserve to be more widely grown than they are. Easy to manage, they flower regularly and prolifically. We grow our plants in suspended pots of coarse treefern chunks with a little broken sandstone. They do well in intermediate conditions with moderate light and plenty of water when in growth.

Actual flower size: approximately 1.5 cm across.

Oncidium harrisonianum Lindley

Described by Lindley in 1832, this species was named after its discoverer, who had sent plants to a relative in England. Its synonyms include *O. pallidum*, *O. pantherinum* and *O. pentaspilum*. It is endemic to Brazil, where it grows in the cooler ranges of Rio de Janeiro, Sao Paulo and Espirito Santo, or on the inland tablelands of Minas Gerais up to 1,000 m elevation.

The almost round pseudobulbs are compressed, with a prominent ridge on either side. They are 2.0–2.5 cm in diameter and bear a single very fleshy leaf 6.5–15 cm long. This suberect to curved leaf is dull green, and covered with minute grey spots. It has a prominent keel below and is more or less acute. The erect to arching spike is 12–30 cm long with branches on the lower half. Flowers are borne on the branches and the terminal half of the spike. They are about 1.6 cm across, with yellow or orange-yellow sepals and petals blotched with red-brown. The yellow lip has red-brown spots or stripes on the small lateral lobes and about the callus. The concave dorsal and spreading lateral sepals are more or less oblong with subacute apices, while the oar-shaped petals have slightly reflexed margins. The wide mid-lobe of the lip is often curved upward at the apex. At the base is a cushion of hairs and five finger-like calli.

O. harrisonianum grows well for us on a treefern mount when hung in a semi-shaded position and given intermediate to cool conditions. It appreciates good ventilation or air movement, and plenty of water when in growth with a drier winter rest.

Actual flower size: approximately 1.6 cm across.

Oncidium hians Lindley

This Brazilian species was introduced into England in 1838 and was described later the same year by Lindley. It is synonymous with O. *leucostomum*, O. *quadricorne*, and O. *maxilligerum*. It is restricted to the cool mountains of Parana and the inland tablelands of Minas Gerais, where it grows in areas of stunted vegetation at up to 1,000 m above sea level.

The almost round pseudobulbs are 1–2 cm tall and somewhat flattened. At the apex a single leathery leaf rises. It is 5–10 cm long and about 2.5 cm wide, spreading or strongly curved, folded at the base and with a keel beneath. In late spring or summer a more or less erect branched spike 12–30 cm long rises, carrying numerous well-spaced flowers from 1.0 cm to 1.5 cm across. The oblong sepals and petals are typically reddish-brown with yellow edges, but may be completely yellow-brown, or yellow with red-brown longitudinal stripes. They curve slightly forward at their rounded apices. The obscurely three-lobed lip is pale yellow with or without red-brown spots. It is 0.6–0.8 cm long with tiny rounded lateral lobes and a spreading mid-lobe which is narrow at the base and about 0.45 cm at the apex. The large crest is whitish, with four upward-curving finger-like calli.

An easily grown species if given even moderate care, the plants take up little space. It appreciates intermediate to cool conditions with moderate shade, and does best for us when mounted. A relatively small treefern slab will accommodate a plant for many years.

Actual flower size: 1–1.5 cm across.

Oncidium hookeri Rolfe

Very closely related to O. *loefgrenii** and O. *raniferum*, this species was first collected by Gardner somewhere near Rio de Janeiro in 1837. It was originally mistaken for O. *raniferum*, and so remained undescribed until 1887. The differences between the two species are fairly minor, and indeed O. *raniferum* var. *majus* is a synonym for O. *hookeri*. It is confined to the cool mountain ranges of southern Brazil, where it grows as an epiphyte at moderate elevations.

The 1.5–3.0 cm pseudobulbs are narrowly conical and distinctly ridged, with one or two leaf-bearing sheaths at the base. There are one or two erect or arching leaves at the apex of the pseudobulbs. They are 8–20 cm long, narrow, and more or less rounded at the apex. In autumn or winter an erect to suberect spike 15–20 cm long carries up to about sixty flowers, each 0.7–1.0 cm long. The oblong sepals and petals are creamy-yellow with some brownish tinges, while the three-lobed lip is yellow with reddish-brown markings on and about the callus. The dorsal sepal and the petals curve inward at the tips, while the lateral sepals extend behind the relatively large lateral lobes of the lip. The 0.6 cm mid-lobe is fan shaped and has a very fleshy concave callus at the base. This callus comprises about five rather flattened lobes.

An undemanding species, O. *hookeri* appreciates a position in moderate shade with intermediate to cool conditions. It grows well for us when mounted on treefern. Allow to dry out a little in winter.

Actual flower size: 0.7–1 cm long.

Oncidium hydrophyllum Barbosa Rodrigues

A Brazilian species, O. *hydrophyllum* was described in the late 19th century by Barbosa Rodrigues. It grows both in the cooler mountains of several southern states and in the drier savannah country of the interior, where it experiences a continental climate. It is found growing in humus-filled rock crevices or on sandy soil among tall grasses, as well as in the cooler misty forests.

The tightly clustered pseudobulbs are dull yellow-green, slightly compressed with acute edges, and they sometimes produce new plantlets at their apices. They are ovoid, typically 3–6 cm tall and up to 3 cm wide, with papery bracts at the base and two strap-like leathery leaves 6–20 cm long at the apex. The erect spike rises from 30 cm to 1 m or more, bearing several 2–3 cm flowers. The sepals and petals are greenish-yellow, heavily blotched with reddish-brown or purple-brown with a few paler spots. The concave 0.8 cm dorsal sepal lies almost along the column, while the 1 cm ovoid lateral sepals are spreading. The very crisped, broad petals have a narrow base. The 1.6 cm lip is bright yellow with brown marks on the callus, which has several finger-like protrusions. The lateral lobes are ear shaped, while the 2 cm wide mid-lobe is skirt-like. The rhomboid column wings are held well forward.

Like O. *gracile*,* this is an easily grown and attractive species. It may be mounted, but we prefer to grow it as we do O. *gracile*: in suspended pots of treefern fibre in moderate light and intermediate conditions.

Actual flower size: 2–3 cm long.

Oncidium limminghei Morren ex Lindley

This species was first collected in Venezuela by van Lansberg, who sent plants to Morren in Belgium in 1855. Morren sent the type material to Lindley who described it in that year. O. *echinophorum* is conspecific. The species is reported only from Venezuela and from the state of Rio de Janeiro in Brazil.

It is a curious little plant with flat, almost heart-shaped pseudobulbs 1–2 cm long, which often overlap on a branching rhizome. Each pseudobulb bears a single leaf which is also heart shaped and lies flat against the host. The leaf is about 3.5 cm long, and light grey-green with maroon-purple veins. The erect to horizontal spike rises from the base of the new pseudobulb in summer or autumn and bears one flower at a time, continuing to lengthen until up to five flowers, each 3–4 cm across, have been produced. The concave dorsal sepal and slightly incurved petals are dark reddish-brown, more or less barred with yellow-green, while the ovoid sepals are generally duller in colour. The three-lobed lip is yellow, spotted with orange-brown or red, with rounded lateral lobes that narrow at the base and curve inward at the tips. The mid-lobe has a long narrow isthmus and may be turned up or slightly incurved. The callus comprises three ridges and the large column wings are deeply fringed.

O. *limminghei* should be mounted on cork or paperbark. It prefers moderate light in intermediate to warm conditions with relatively high humidity.

Actual flower size: 3–4 cm across.

Oncidium loefgrenii Cogniaux

Cogniaux named this species, which is very similar to O. *hookeri** and O. *raniferum*, in honour of Loefgren, the Swedish botanist and explorer who became head of the botany section of the Botanical Gardens in Rio de Janeiro. O. *mellifluum* is synonymous. This species comes from the southern half of Brazil, growing in both the cool mountain ranges and the hot dry savannahs.

The slightly flattened pseudobulbs are closely set on the rhizome. From 1.5 cm to 2.5 cm tall, they are narrow, dark green with some purple spotting, and are strongly ribbed. They bear two narrow strap-like leaves 7–13 cm long, which have a prominent mid-vein and are sub-erect to arching. The branched spike is up to 15 cm or more in length and in autumn or winter carries many 1 cm long flowers. The tiny sepals and petals are yellow with a few reddish markings. The petals are swept upward with the dorsal sepal, which is hooded over the column. The pointed lateral sepals are joined for about half their length before spreading out. The three-lobed lip is yellow, with a bright red glossy callus made up of several very fleshy rounded lobes in three transverse rows. The tiny lateral lobes are rounded and often curved up at the ends. The 0.6 cm mid-lobe is narrow at the base, spreading to 0.45 cm at the more or less bilobed apex, which is often curved upward.

This unusual little species grows well when mounted and hung in moderate to fairly heavy shade. It prefers humid conditions and intermediate temperatures.

Actual flower size: approximately 1 cm long.

Oncidium longipes Lindley

Introduced into England in 1850, this species has been widely cultivated since that time. Lindley described it in 1851. Synonyms include O. *janeirense* and O. *oxyacanthosmum*. It is native to southern Brazil, where it grows in the cool, moist mountains as well as the warmer lowlands. In the latter areas it occurs on trees along river banks.

The elongated pale green pseudobulbs are more or less clustered on a stout rhizome. From 2.0 cm to 2.5 cm tall, they are furrowed and have two glossy green leaves at the apex. These are 10–15 cm long, strap-like, and sharply pointed. This species flowers freely on a zigzag spike up to 15 cm long from spring to early autumn. The two to five long-lasting flowers are 2–3.5 cm across, with yellow sepals and petals streaked with reddish-brown. The bright yellow lip is spotted with dull red on and about the whitish callus. The oblong sepals are acute, while the broader petals are more or less rounded. The lateral sepals are joined for about one-third of their length. The ear-like lateral lobes of the lip have wavy edges, as does the broad mid-lobe. The callus at the base of the lip has many wart-like projections. The claw of the mid-lobe is more or less fringed.

A popular and easily grown species which grows quickly to specimen size, O. *longipes* does very well for us mounted on treefern in intermediate to cool conditions with moderately bright indirect light. Water freely when in growth, followed by a drier winter rest.

Actual flower size: 2–3.5 cm across.

Oncidium macronix Reichenbach (f.)

escribed by Reichenbach in the second half of the 19th century, this attractive and unusual species — along with *O. longicornu* — belongs to the section *Rhinocerontes*, a name that refers to the unusually elongated callus shaped like the horn of a rhinoceros. It is a native of Argentina, Paraguay and the far south of Brazil, where it grows as an epiphyte both in the cool mountain areas and in the hotter lowlands.

The dark green pseudobulbs, set about 1 cm apart, are 4–5 cm tall, quite narrow, compressed, strongly ridged, and sometimes curved. They usually bear two narrow tapering leaves 10–14 cm long. In autumn, branched 40 cm spikes bear many 1.0–1.5 cm flowers. The widely spreading sepals and petals are predominantly pale to dark purplish-brown with some yellow-green mottling, especially near the apex. The more or less erect dorsal sepal is slightly recurved, and the relatively broad wavy petals curve inward at the apex. The three-lobed lip is yellow with a large orange-red blotch around the callus, which is usually orange-red but may be yellow. The lateral lobes are rounded, as is the broad mid-lobe. The column is white.

A distinctive species which is easily cultivated, *O. macronix* does well for us when mounted on small treefern slabs and hung in moderate light in intermediate to cool conditions. Give copious water when in growth, with a slightly drier rest after flowering.

Actual flower size: 1–1.5 cm long.

Oncidium macropetalum Lindley

his species, described by Lindley in the 19th century, comes from inland Brazil, Paraguay and possibly also from Bolivia. Its habitat is the hot lowland and savannah country up to 1,000 m altitude.

The plump pseudobulbs, from 2.5 cm to 5.0 cm tall, are ridged and slightly compressed. They have one or two leaf-bearing bracts at the base and one or two arching leaves about 10–15 cm long at the apex. An arching spike bears a few to many well-spaced flowers about 3.2 cm long in winter. The short wavy sepals are pale yellow with or without red-brown bars. The dorsal sepal is erect or slightly recurved and the lateral sepals are joined at the base. The 1.5 cm long petals, together with the lip, dominate the flower. They are bright yellow with or without dark red markings at the narrow base. Shaped like a rounded square, they have undulating edges and may be indented. The three-lobed lip is yellow with red-brown blotches on and around the callus, which has several finger-like projections at the rear and three diverging rounded ones in front. The lateral lobes are rounded, as is the bilobed mid-lobe. The isthmus is serrated and the relatively large column wings are more or less rounded.

O. macropetalum does best in an intermediate environment with moderate light and good air movement. It needs plenty of water when in growth with a drier resting period.

Actual flower size: approximately 3 cm long.

136

Oncidium micropogon Reichenbach (f.)

Although first grown in Europe as early as 1853 and described by Reichenbach a year later, this species did not come into general cultivation until reintroduced by Sander in 1886. Closely related to *O. barbatum** and *O. ciliatum*, it is synonymous with *O. dentatum*. It is reported from the hot lowlands of Bahia in Brazil, where it favours riverside trees, and from the cooler mountain areas of Santa Catarina and Rio Grande do Sul.

The clustered ovoid pseudobulbs are compressed with acute edges and several ribs. From 3.0 cm to 6.5 cm tall, they bear one or two strap-like leaves. These are suberect, 10–15 cm long and more or less rounded at the tips. This species flowers from summer to autumn on 30–45 cm spikes which carry from three to ten or more flowers about 4 cm long. The oblong sepals are yellow with red-brown bars, and the acute laterals are joined for about half their length. The dorsal sepal is more or less rounded. The bright yellow 2 cm petals are spotted at the narrow claw-like base. They are almost round with wavy irregular edges and a sharp point at the apex. The almost equally three-lobed lip is yellow, with spots on and around the fleshy callus which has several conical projections. The lateral lobes are roundish, while the mid-lobe is fan shaped with undulating edges and a sharp point. The edge of the isthmus is toothed.

We find that this species does very well if given intermediate conditions with moderate light and fairly high humidity. We grow our plants on treefern mounts.

Actual flower size: approximately 4 cm long.

Oncidium pubes Lindley

Descourtilz discovered this species in the early years of the 19th century, but it was not described until 1826, after Douglas sent plants to London from Brazil. Its synonyms include *O. bicornutum* and *O. pubescens*. This species comes from the cooler mountain regions of southern Brazil, Paraguay and possibly Argentina.

The clustered dark green pseudobulbs are almost terete, tapering slightly near the apex. From 5 cm to 7 cm long and 1.0–1.5 cm in diameter, they usually have a pair of very dark green strap-like leaves 7–12 cm long and up to 3 cm wide with an acute apex. This species usually flowers in autumn on an arching to pendulous spike carrying many 2 cm flowers on short branches. The sepals and petals are glossy yellow, more or less barred and spotted with red-brown — sometimes to such a degree that little yellow is visible. The 1.2 cm petals and dorsal sepal are paddle shaped, with the petals curved inward at the apex and the concave dorsal hooded over the column. The lateral sepals are joined for most of their length. The three-lobed lip is yellow with red-brown markings around the ridged callus, which is minutely haired, and toothed in front. The small lateral lobes are oblong, and the clawed mid-lobe is kidney shaped.

O. pubes grows easily and flowers regularly in cultivation, and with its bright glossy flowers makes a nice show. It needs intermediate conditions, moderate light and plenty of water when in growth. It does very well for us mounted on treefern slabs.

Actual flower size: approximately 2 cm across.

Oncidium pulchellum Hooker

Discovered by Parkes, this species was described by Hooker in 1827. It belongs to the 'variegata' group of oncidiums, more commonly known as 'equitant' oncidiums. This species grows as an epiphyte in Jamaica, Cuba and Guyana between 300 m and 800 m above sea level, where it is exposed to both wind and bright sunlight. The plant comprises a few fleshy rigid leaves arranged in a flat fan. The leaves, V-shaped in section, are often slightly toothed along the edges. In bright light the leaves assume a red-bronze colour. Flowering is mostly from late spring to summer on an erect, sometimes branched, spike 30–60 cm tall bearing from twelve to twenty or more flat flowers. These are variable in size, but are typically about 2.5–3.0 cm long. Colour ranges from white, more or less tinged with rosy-pink or lilac, to deep pink or rose. The 0.6–1.0 cm petals are narrow at the base, rounded, with undulating edges. The oval dorsal sepal is slightly smaller, concave and acute. The lateral sepals are joined for most of their length and are obscured by the large skirt-like lip. The large lateral lobes are rounded, and the veined mid-lobe has wavy margins. The crest, with three calli, has orange-brown blotches edged with white.

Plants of this species may be grown in small pots or baskets, but we have found that it does best mounted on small pieces of cork and hung in fairly bright light. It likes high humidity, but prefers to dry out between waterings. Warm to intermediate conditions are best. Plants appreciate a light misting on bright winter days.

Actual flower size: approximately 2.5–3 cm long.

Oncidium pumilum Lindley

This species, which is similar to *O. nanum* and synonymous with *Epidendrum ligulatum*, was described by Lindley in 1825. It occurs in Uruguay, Argentina and through much of Brazil, where it grows in a wide range of habitats from hot humid lowlands to the cooler mountain ranges.

O. pumilum is a miniature 'mule ear' oncidium, with clustered insignificant pseudobulbs only 0.3–0.5 cm tall. These are flattened and bear a single fleshy leaf 5–12 cm long and 1.6–3.5 cm wide. Often suffused with pinkish-brown and spotted with purple, the stiff leaf is more or less erect, pointed, and folded at the base. The erect spike is 8–15 cm long and carries many densely packed flowers on short branches in winter and spring. The sepals and petals are yellow with red-brown markings, while the 0.5 cm lip is pale yellow with a brown line on either side of the callus. The dorsal sepal is concave and the petals curve forward. All tepals have blunt apices. The large lateral lobes of the lip are rounded on the upper edges and curve downward. The concave mid-lobe is more or less oval. The fleshy callus comprises two pairs of diverging ridges. The column has large curved wings.

A delightful and compact species, it does well for us mounted on sections of paperbark trunk or cork and hung in a moderately bright position. It is tolerant of a wide range of temperatures. Water all year round, with a dry winter rest if grown in cool conditions.

Actual flower size: approximately 0.8 cm long.

Oncidium tetrapetalum (Jacq.) Willdenow

Described by von Jacquin in 1763 as *Epidendrum tetrapetalum*, this species was transferred to the genus *Oncidium* in 1805 by Willdenow. It remains unclear whether or not Linnaeus' *Epidendrum guttatum* of 1753 is conspecific, so we have retained here the commonly accepted name. Synonyms include *Oncidium quadripetalum* and *O. tricolor*. This species grows as an epiphyte in Cuba, the West Indies, Colombia and Venezuela from the lowlands to 300 m or more above sea level.

Another of the 'equitant' oncidiums, it has no pseudobulbs, each growth comprising between three and five leaves 5–20 cm long and 0.3–0.6 cm wide. These are fleshy and acutely three-edged with a channel on the inner side. The edges are sometimes minutely serrated. In summer an erect 30–60 cm spike bears many 2–2.5 cm flowers. These open successively over an extended period. Colour is variable. The 0.8 cm sepals and petals may be brownish with purple or rose markings, yellow with bright chestnut bars, or white, green and crimson. They are oblong and have wavy edges and a keel on the back, with the joined lateral sepals held behind the lip. The 1.0–1.3 cm lip may be white tinted with pink, or white with a red-brown blotch in front of the complex crest. The small lateral lobes are oblong, while the many-nerved mid-lobe is kidney shaped.

O. tetrapetalum likes warm to intermediate conditions with plenty of bright light and high humidity. Cork mounts are excellent, but small well-drained pots or baskets may be used.

Actual flower size: approximately 2–2.5 cm long.

Oncidium triquetrum (Sw.) R. Brown

Swartz described this species as *Epidendrum triquetrum* in 1788, and later transferred it to *Cymbidium*. It was introduced into England in 1793 by Bligh. Brown transferred it to the genus *Oncidium* in 1813. This 'equitant' oncidium is confined to Jamaica, where it often grows epiphytically in exposed conditions from 150 m to 300 m above sea level.

Each tufted plant has three or four fleshy leaves 3–20 cm long. As reflected in the specific name, these leaves are acutely pointed and three-angled. Flowers appear mostly in summer, but occasionally at other times, on a 7–18 cm spike which often produces flowers for more than a single season. The five to fifteen long-lasting flowers are usually fairly densely clustered towards the apex of the spike. Colour varies from white with dense reddish-purple or purple spots to rose-red edged with white and stained and spotted with crimson. The 1 cm sepals are slightly concave and have acute apices. The joined lateral sepals are hidden by the large oval to heart-shaped lip. The more or less diamond-shaped petals taper to long narrow points. The three-lobed lip has small rounded lateral lobes and a large mid-lobe, at the base of which is a small almost globular orange-yellow callus.

Cork mounts or small open baskets seem best for this species, which needs plenty of light, high humidity and good air movement. Warm to intermediate conditions are best. Allow the plant to dry out between waterings, but take care that it does not become desiccated.

Actual flower size: approximately 2 cm long.

Ornithocephalus inflexus Lindley

Described by Lindley in 1840, this charming little species has many synonyms, including *Ornithocephalus elephas*, *O. mexicanus*, *O. pottsiae* and *O. tonduzii*. Although ranging from southern Mexico to Belize and Costa Rica, this species is not common. Usually it grows hanging from the outer twigs of trees in tropical deciduous forests, often near clearings or pasture land. Habitat elevations range from 800 m to 1,100 m.

The plant has a few narrow tapering leaves which may be straight or curved, and which form neat fans. Leaves are 3–10 cm long. In spring and summer zigzag spikes 6–15 cm long rise from the leaf axils and bear between ten and thirty well-spaced delicate flowers about 0.6 cm long. The sepals and petals, whose edges are irregularly serrated near the apex, may be white, greenish-white or green. They are keeled on the back, with the keel on the sepals protruding past the apex as a distinct tapering point. The rounded sepals are smaller than the somewhat triangular petals, which are narrowed at the base. The greenish lip has a concave oval base with minute hairs on the short lateral lobes. The tongue-shaped mid-lobe is recurved at about 90°, with deflexed sides and a concave mid-section. The column projects forward.

O. inflexus does well for us mounted on paperbark or tea-tree (*Leptospermum*) twigs, or on small cork or treefern mounts. It prefers intermediate to cool temperatures with good air movement and year-round moisture.

Actual flower size: approximately 0.6 cm long.

Ornithocephalus iridifolius Reichenbach (f.)

This species was collected by Leibold in Mexico and described by Reichenbach in 1864. It is quite rare, occurring only in Nayarit, Jalisco and Vera Cruz in Mexico, and in Guatemala. It grows on trees in open oak forests, in deciduous tropical forests or in coffee plantations from 550 m to 1,000 m above sea level.

The flat leaves of these pseudobulbless plants are arranged like a fan. From 2.5 cm to 7.5 cm long but only 0.3–0.6 cm wide, the leaves taper to an acute point and are jointed near the base, which may be covered with old leaf bracts. In late summer or autumn a slender 4–8 cm spike carries several flowers about 0.5 cm across. The irregularly toothed sepals and petals are white or cream, while the lip has some green markings. The tips of the tepals curve inward, with the keel on the sepals protruding beyond the apex, and that on the petals producing a sharp independent point before the apex. The saucer-shaped lip has broad rounded lateral lobes which are partially covered with minute hairs. The mid-lobe is more or less rounded and has a green triangular callus between the lateral lobes with a central ridge. The lip is joined to the base of the incurved column.

O. iridifolius does best when mounted on a small twig — perhaps with a little moss about the base — or a piece of cork. It prefers a fairly shady intermediate environment with good air movement and year-round moisture.

Actual flower size: approximately 0.5 cm across.

Ornithocephalus myrticola Lindley

Descourtilz collected this species in the early 19th century in Brazil, where he found it growing on trees of the Myrtaceae family, hence its specific name. Lindley described it in 1840. Among its synonyms are *O. pygmaeum* and *O. reitzii*. It occurs in a range of habitats in southern Brazil and Bolivia, from cool moist mountain ranges to dry savannahs and hot lowlands.

The plant is without pseudobulbs and comprises a fan of very fleshy leaves which are jointed near the base. The leaves are typically 5–7 cm long and 0.5–0.7 cm wide, tapering to an acute point. The flowers are borne on zigzag spikes 4–8 cm long which rise from the leaf axils. The flowers — which are redolent of lemon — and the spikes are covered with relatively long hairs. There are about fifteen densely packed flowers on the spike, each measuring about 1 cm across. The irregularly edged sepals and petals are white with a central green stripe on the sepals and several stripes on the petals. The 0.5 cm lip is often held uppermost. Its edges are reflexed and its fleshy disc has five prominent yellow or green calli, the outer ones being hairy. There is a transverse green stripe in front of the calli. The narrow apex is white.

This species does well when mounted on cork or paperbark and placed in a semi-shaded intermediate environment with good humidity and air movement. Give it some water all through the year, and never let it dry out completely.
Actual flower size: approximately 1 cm across.

Ornithochilus difformis (Ldl.) Schlechter

Once included as a section of *Aerides*, *Ornithochilus* was elevated to generic status in 1883 by Bentham and Hooker. This species is still often known under the name of *Ornithochilus fuscus* (Wallich, 1833). However, this was published as a synonym for Lindley's *Aerides difformis* (1833) and as such the specific epithet becomes invalid. Schlechter renamed the species *O. difformis* in 1919. It grows in forests from India to southwest China, Indochina, Indonesia and Malaysia, at elevations of 700–2,000 m, favouring branches towards the top of its host trees.

Its very short pendent stem has between three and five closely set leaves 7.5–15 cm long. These are mid-green, oval, fleshy, and have a pointed apex. Flowering is mostly in summer but may occur in winter, on pendent spikes 10–30 cm long. The many well-spaced long-lasting flowers are about 1 cm long. The greenish-yellow sepals and petals are striped with red-brown, upswept, and curve inward at the apex. The lip dominates the flower with its deeply toothed and folded glossy reddish-brown mid-lobe, which is edged with greenish-yellow. The mobile lip has a short claw at its base and a glossy dark maroon or greenish-yellow 0.4 cm spur, which is bent at right angles and is almost completely closed by two calli near its entrance. The small lateral lobes are erect, and there is a raised keel on the mid-lobe. A number of colour variations are known.

O. difformis should be mounted and hung in light shade in intermediate to warm conditions and given year-round moisture.
Actual flower size: approximately 1 cm long.

141

Ornithophora radicans Garay & Pabst

A delightful miniature, this species was first described by Linden and Reichenbach in 1864 from material collected in the Rio Grande do Sul and Porto Allegre areas of southern Brazil. Originally classified as a sigmatostalix, it was reclassified by Garay and Pabst in 1951 when they created the new genus *Ornithophora*, of which it remains the only species. It is widespread in southern Brazil, occurring in the states of Parana, Espirito Santo, Rio de Janeiro, Sao Paulo, Santa Catarina and Rio Grande do Sul.

An extremely popular and easy-to-grow species, it has delicate thin apple-green pseudobulbs, each bearing a pair of narrow grassy leaves, spaced at intervals of 1–3 cm on the creeping rhizome. In late summer flower spikes emerge from the base of the pseudobulbs, each bearing about ten bird-like flowers (the generic name means 'bird bearing') which are pale lemon-green with a white and yellow lip and purple column.

The plant's rambling habit makes it ideally suited to slab cultivation, although flat pans may also be used. It needs a position in moderate shade and should be kept moist all year round except for a slightly drier rest after the new pseudobulbs have matured. Pseudobulbs, however, should not be allowed to shrivel. The plant thrives in intermediate to cool conditions.
Actual flower size: approximately 0.6–1 cm long.

Pabstiella mirabilis (Schltr.) Brieger & Senghas

Brieger and Senghas created this genus in 1975 to honour Guido Pabst, the Brazilian botanist. They regarded Schlechter's *Pleurothallis mirabilis* as being sufficiently distinct from all other pleurothallis to warrant its own genus. It is distinguished by the very long column-foot (about 0.5 cm) to which the 0.5 cm claw of the lip is attached. Luer did not accept this change, and in 1986 returned the species to *Pleurothallis*, creating the subgenus *Mirabilia* of which it is the only member. We have chosen to retain Brieger and Senghas's name. This unusual epiphyte inhabits the cool moist mountain ranges in the Brazilian states of Sao Paulo, Parana, Santa Catarina and Rio Grande do Sul.

The very fleshy leaves are held on long wiry stalks up to 5 cm long. The blade of the leaf is 2–5 cm long and 1 cm wide. In spring wiry spikes rise from the point where the leaf joins its stalk. The arching spikes are up to 5 cm long and carry about six delicate white flowers which may be faintly tinged with pink. They are about 1 cm long, including the spur formed by the lateral sepals to accommodate the long claw of the lip. The dorsal sepal is slightly hooded, while the narrow rounded petals point forward. The free parts of the lateral sepals curve outward under the lip. The minutely warty blade of the lip is held almost at right angles to the claw.

P. mirabilis should be given cool damp conditions with good air movement, moderate shade and relatively high humidity all year round.
Actual flower size: approximately 1 cm long.

Panisea uniflora (Ldl.) Lindley

This species belongs to a small genus which is closely related to *Coelogyne*. Indeed, Lindley originally described this species in 1830 as *Coelogyne uniflora*, later transferring it to his new genus *Panisea*. It grows as an epiphyte at 250–1,500 m above sea level in Nepal, Sikkim, Burma, Thailand and Laos.

The globose to pear-shaped pseudobulbs are clustered on a creeping rhizome. From 1.5 cm to 2.0 cm tall, they are an almost translucent green to yellow-green, and somewhat wrinkled, with loose papery bracts at the base. They bear two rather soft narrow leaves 5–10 cm in length. Very short erect spikes carry a single flower usually in summer or autumn. The 3 cm long flower, which has a crystalline texture, may be white to brownish-yellow, yellow-green or pale pink. The 2 cm sepals taper gradually from a broad base to sharp points. The dorsal sepal may be curved forward or slightly recurved. The petals have a narrow claw at the base and are broadly spade shaped with a blunt apex. The oval lip has small upright lateral lobes which are pointed on the front edge, and a wavy mid-lobe with three keels, each ending on an orange 'knob'.

We find that this species appreciates a warm to intermediate environment, with high humidity, moderate light and good air movement. It may be grown on cork or paperbark mounts or in shallow pans of fairly coarse well-drained material. It needs year-round watering, with only a slight reduction in winter, unless temperatures fall below 10°C, when it may be misted occasionally.

Actual flower size: approximately 3 cm long.

Paphiopedilum bellatulum (Rchb. (f.)) Pfitzer

Introduced into England in early 1888, this species was described later that year by Reichenbach as *Cypripedium bellatulum*. It was subsequently removed to the genus *Paphiopedilum* by Pfitzer. Found in the mountainous Shan states of Burma and in northern Thailand, it occurs predominantly between 300 m and 1,600 m altitude on moss-covered limestone cliffs. It has been reported as growing at sea level in thickly wooded areas where the high temperatures are moderated by shade. In most locations through its range temperatures range from 20–35°C in summer to 10–30°C in winter. Occasionally winter temperatures fall to 5°C or even 0°C. However, these low temperatures occur for only a few hours in the early mornings. The monsoon period from May to November brings high temperatures and humidity and is then followed by a cool dry season.

The leaves of this species may be up to 20 cm long and 6 cm wide, although they are usually smaller. The attractively mottled leaves are purple underneath. The short hairy spike barely clears the foliage and bears a single flower about 6 cm across in late spring or summer. As well as the typical 'freckled' example pictured here, there is an albino form and one with longitudinally arranged spots.

P. bellatulum does not thrive in truly tropical conditions, preferring intermediate temperatures with 60–75 per cent humidity and good ventilation. This species should be potted in fairly coarse material. Good drainage is essential. Give moderate indirect light.

Actual flower size: approximately 6 cm across.

Paphiopedilum concolor (Par. & Batem.) Pfitzer

This species was discovered by Parish in 1859 near Moulmein in Burma, and introduced into Europe in 1864. Described as *Cypripedium concolor* by Bateman in 1865, and as *C. tonkinense* by Godefroy, it was transferred to the genus *Paphiopedilum* by Pfitzer in 1888. It occurs across South East Asia from southern Burma, through southern Thailand, Cambodia and Laos to Vietnam. It is found growing in humus-filled hollows in limestone cliffs from less than 300 m to 1,000 m above sea level. The southwest monsoon prevails from May to September, bringing high temperatures and humidity, followed by a distinct dry period from October to February with milder conditions.

There are usually about four leaves 8–15 cm long with grey-green tessellations on a darker green background. The undersides are purple. The flower spike is short, only 5–8 cm tall, with up to three flowers about 6 cm across which last for over a month. This species flowers mostly in summer and autumn but flowers may appear at any time during the year. Having the only yellow flowers in the section *Brachypetalum*, this is a most desirable species.

It does best for us in shallow pans or trays of broken limestone or sandstone mixed with coarse chunks of treefern. Intermediate to warm temperatures are recommended, with fairly bright indirect light. Water heavily in the growing season and keep a little drier in winter. This species can be grown into a large specimen plant.

Actual flower size: approximately 6 cm across.

Paphiopedilum fairrieanum (Ldl.) Pfitzer

Described by Lindley in 1857 as *Cypripedium fairrieanum* (or *fairieanum*) and transferred to *Paphiopedilum* by Pfitzer in 1888, this species belongs to the section *Ceratopetalum*, members of which are characterised by petals that are so recurved that they resemble the horns of a water buffalo. This is the famous 'lost' orchid. As it had first arrived in England in a mixed batch of orchids, its precise habitat was a mystery and no collector seemed able to locate it. So in December of 1904 Sander offered a reward of one thousand pounds for its rediscovery and the exclusive details of its location. The offered reward did the trick, and in 1905 it was rediscovered near the border of India and Bhutan. It occurs on gneiss and sandstone ledges among tall grasses in southern Sikkim, Bhutan and Arunachal Pradesh between 1,200 m and 3,000 m above sea level. Summer rain saturates the air and temperatures range from 20°C at night to 30°C during the day. Winters are cool, dry and sunny with overnight dews and occasional frosts.

The leaves are 15–20 cm long with slightly wavy edges. The hairy spike, up to 26 cm tall, produces a single flower (rarely two) 6–8 cm across in autumn and winter. The flower lasts for six weeks.

Pot this species in a well-drained medium and give intermediate conditions with cooler winter temperatures, when the plant should be kept on the dry side. Conventional wisdom to the contrary, most paphiopedilums from northern India appreciate a dry winter rest.

Actual flower size: 6–8 cm across.

Paphiopedilum fowliei Birk

This popular and attractive species is a native of the Philippines where it grows generally above the 500 m level as a semi-terrestrial in pockets of leafmould in limestone rocks. It belongs to the *Phacopetalum* section of the paphiopedilums (literally, 'warty petals') and is closely related to *P. hennisianum* and *P. lawrenceanum*. It has very attractive grey-green to blue-green mottled foliage. The flower spike, which bears a single flower, is covered with dark hairs, and the lateral petals are edged with dark hairy warts, large on the upper edges, smaller on the lower.

This species does well in warm to intermediate conditions. The way it grows in its natural habitat provides clues for its satisfactory cultivation. Good drainage is essential, and we grow ours in plastic pots filled loosely with coarse chunks of sandstone and treefern. Give it moderate light and water throughout the year.

P. fowliei has an interesting history, being discovered originally in 1924 near Victoria Peak on Palawan Island. Ames confused it with *P. barbatum* from Malaysia and it was not given separate specific rank until 1981 when Fowlie corrected the earlier error. He knew that members of this section tend to have a high degree of endemicism to specific areas, and doubted that this species could be the same as *P. barbatum*, which originated a long way from Palawan. Like all the mottle-leaved 'slippers', this species is a worthwhile addition to any collection, and is an attractive plant even when not in flower.

Actual flower size: approximately 7 cm long.

Paphiopedilum glaucophyllum J. J. Smith

Introduced into England in 1900, this species was described by the Dutch botanist J. J. Smith in the same year. Belonging to the section *Cochlopetalum*, in which the petals are twisted like spiral sea shells, it is closely related to *P. chamberlainianum*, *P. liemianum*, *P. moquetteanum*, *P. victoriamariae* and other multiflowering species. It occurs in east Java on volcanic mountains at 200–750 m above sea level, where it is found growing in pockets of humus. The temperature is always warm, and the area is subject to the northeast monsoon during which humidity rises to almost 100 per cent. A much drier period occurs from July to September.

The bluish-green leaves are up to 20 cm long with purple spotting underneath. The flower spike is up to 40 cm tall, with between ten and twenty flowers opening successively over a long period from spring to summer. The first flower usually occurs when the spike is about 15 cm tall, followed by others at intervals of 2 cm. The twisted hairy petals of the 8 cm flowers have a soft appearance, and the rosy lip makes it a most attractive species.

P. glaucophyllum should be grown in a warm spot in light shade. Pot in a well-drained medium such as scoria (volcanic gravel) and treefern chunks. It appreciates a brief resting period during the winter months.

Actual flower size: approximately 8 cm across.

Paphiopedilum godefroyae (Godefr.) Pfitzer

Another member of the section *Brachypetalum*, this species was originally discovered about 1875 by Murton and brought to England by Godefroy who named it *Cypripedium godefroyae* in 1883. Pfitzer placed it in *Paphiopedilum* in 1888. This species, which is in many ways intermediate between *P. concolor* and *P. niveum*, is said to occur in Burma, Malaysia and Vietnam as well as in Thailand. In the latter country it is found on limestone cliffs on Birds' Nest Island off Champun on the eastern side of the Isthmus of Kra. Here it grows very close to sea level (up to about 35 m) only on the western side of the island, where it is in full shade until mid-morning and then fully exposed to the tropical sun for the rest of the day. It also occurs on the opposing limestone mountains on the isthmus.

The mottled leaves are up to 12 cm long and completely purple beneath. The short flower spike carries one or two white or cream flowers 5–7 cm across from late spring to summer.

Grow this species in bright light in warm intermediate conditions, with high humidity in summer. A well-drained medium is essential — we have found that broken limestone or sandstone mixed with chopped treefern is ideal. A short dry period in midwinter will imitate the plant's natural cycle and produce best results.

Actual flower size: 5–7 cm across.

Paphiopedilum javanicum (Ldl. & Paxt.) Pfitzer

Discovered by Reinwardt in 1823, this species was introduced into Europe by Thomas Lobb in 1840. However, it remained undescribed until 1850 when Lindley named it *Cypripedium javanicum*. Pfitzer removed it to the genus *Paphiopedilum* in 1888. It belongs to the section *Blepharopetalum*, the species of which are distinguished by the numerous hairs which resemble eyelashes along the edges of the petals. It is closely related to *P. virens*, a native of Borneo. Indeed, *P. javanicum* has been reported from Borneo, but Fowlie believes the reports to be incorrect and that the plants reported are in fact the endemic *P. virens*. *P. javanicum* is a native of Java and Bali (and possibly other islands at the eastern end of Java) on fine-grained volcanic rocks from 1,000 m to 1,500 m above sea level. The area is subject to the seasonal northeast monsoon.

The 15–20 cm long leaves are greyish-green sparsely mottled with darker green. It flowers in autumn or winter on a reddish-purple spike up to 30 cm tall. There is usually a single flower, or rarely two, up to 8 cm across, and covered with fine hairs on all parts except the lip. The rosy-purple tips of the petals make a nice contrast to the basic green ground colour of the flower. The dorsal is striped green and white.

This very pretty species requires intermediate to warm conditions with good humidity. Any well-drained fibrous potting medium will suffice. Grow in moderate shade and do not overpot.

Actual flower size: approximately 8 cm across.

146

Paphiopedilum leucochilum (Rolfe) Fowlie

First described as a variety of *P. godefroyae* by Rolfe in 1894, this species was not given specific status until Fowlie elevated it in 1977. It belongs to what is possibly the most popular section of the paphiopedilums, the *Brachypetalum*. Along with other members of this section — *P. bellatulum*,* *P. concolor*,* *P. godefroyae*,* *P. niveum** and the natural hybrid '*Ang Thong*' — it is distinguished by the inrolled edges of the lip and the lack of 'ears' on either side of the pouch. This charming species occurs on islands west of the Isthmus of Kra and in the area of the Gulf of Krabi, where its thick roots cling to limestone cliffs at low altitudes. This area receives its rain from the southwest monsoon during May to September, when it is accompanied by high temperatures and humidity. A dry spell occurs from October to February, with temperatures falling to a minimum of 13°C in December and January. These low temperatures are however brief, lasting only for a few hours in early morning.

The attractively tessellated leaves are about 15 cm long and have a satiny texture. The single flower is borne on a short spike in summer and is about 6 cm wide. It is a brilliant glossy white with wine-red spots which fuse into intermittent stripes on the dorsal sepal and petals.

P. leuchochilum is suited best to intermediate to warm conditions and moderate shade to fairly bright light. It may be grown in pots or shallow pans containing a coarse well-drained material. Provide plenty of water except for a short dry winter rest.

Actual flower size: approximately 6 cm wide.

Paphiopedilum niveum (Rchb. (f.)) Pfitzer

This species was 'accidentally' introduced into England in 1868, when plants imported as *Paphiopedilum concolor** by Veitch & Co. proved to be a new species. Reichenbach described it as *Cypripedium niveum* in 1869, and it was transferred to the genus *Paphiopedilum* by Pfitzer in 1888. A native of peninsular Thailand and Malaysia, it is also found on adjacent west coast islands, especially on the Langkawi Islands, a group shared by Thailand and Malaysia. Its habitat is similar to that of *P. godefroyae*:* the western sides of limestone mountains down to sea level. Here it often grows in pockets of decaying vegetation in crevices of sloping rocks, but seldom on perpendicular cliffs. Unlike *P. godefroyae*, this species does not favour positions which are fully exposed to the sun, preferring some shade during the hottest hours. The southwest monsoon is followed by a distinct dry period from October to February when the plants are, if not dormant, at least in less active growth.

The 10–15 cm long leaves, with their pretty tessellations and purple undersides, together with the delicate satiny white flowers minutely spotted with purple, make this one of the most popular paphiopedilums. The one or two flowers, about 6 cm across, are borne on spikes up to 15 cm tall in late spring or summer and last for about a month.

Intermediate to warm temperatures are recommended, along with light to moderate shade. Pot in an open well-drained mixture and water heavily when in growth; follow with a cool dry rest.

Actual flower size: approximately 6 cm across.

Paphiopedilum spicerianum (Rchb. (f.)) Pfitzer

This species was first flowered in Europe in 1878 by Herbert Spicer, after whom it was named. Originally described as *Cypripedium spicerianum*, it was transferred to the genus *Paphiopedilum* by Pfitzer in 1888. Formerly a relatively common species, *P. spicerianum* ranged from the Indian state of Manipur through Bhutan and into Burma. In Manipur it is now found only in isolated colonies and is probably extinct in Bhutan. It inhabits limestone cliffs, usually near waterfalls or rivers, at elevations of 750–1,300 m above sea level. It is usually found among grasses and ferns in shady positions. The roots often run over the surface of the cliffs and into cracks or pockets of humus. The months of July to September bring heavy rains to the area, when humidity rises to almost 100 per cent, and temperatures range from 18°C at night to 30°C during the day. From October to May the climate is cool, sunny and dry with night temperatures down to 10°C. Moisture during this season is provided by dew and mist.

The leaves of this species are usually from 10 cm to 20 cm long (occasionally longer) and are green spotted with red-purple at the base. One or two flowers to 6 cm across are borne on a 20–40 cm spike in autumn or winter. The most appealing characteristic of the flower is the beautiful white dorsal with its central purplish line. It is wide, flared and recurved.

P. spicerianum prefers a well-drained medium, a cool shady spot with plenty of moisture from late spring to autumn, and intermediate conditions.

Actual flower size: approximately 3 cm across.

Paphiopedilum venustum (Wall.) Pfitzer

Discovered in 1816, this was the first *Paphiopedilum* introduced to science. Described as *Cypripedium venustum* by Wallich in 1820, it was transferred to *Paphiopedilum* in 1888 by Pfitzer. It has been found in Sikkim, Bhutan, Nepal, Assam and the state of Meghalaya in India. A species of varying habitats, it has been found near coal mines, in dense jungle undergrowth near streams, among mosses and ferns on the forest floor, and in palm and bamboo thickets. In India it occurs predominantly from 300 m to 800 m above sea level in areas where the humidity is usually 90–100 per cent. During the monsoon season, day temperatures may reach 35°C, with slightly cooler nights. In the dry season day temperatures reach 25°C, dropping to 18°C at night. In other areas it occurs sometimes at altitudes up to 1,500 m with lower humidity and temperatures.

The leaves of this species, from 15 cm to 20 cm long, carry a very attractive grey-green mottling on a dark green background. The undersides are deep purple-red. The spike, which may reach 25 cm, carries a single flower (occasionally two) about 10 cm wide. It appears in winter. The attractively striped dorsal sepal and much-veined lip make this a popular plant in collections.

As the range of its native habitats suggests, this species will tolerate a variety of temperatures, from warm to cool. Humidity should be reduced when temperatures fall. Pot in any well-drained fibrous mixture and give moderate shade. Warmth tends to accentuate leaf markings, while coolness may produce more flowers.

Actual flower size: approximately 10 cm across.

Paphiopedilum venustum varieties

There are several named varieties of *Paphiopedilum venustum*,* including the var. *pardinum* pictured here. It was described as a separate species by Reichenbach in 1869, but in 1887 was recognised as a variety of *P. venustum*. The leaves of this variety are up to 15.5 cm long. The two or three flowers are larger than in the type. The sepals are a purer white with broader and deeper green stripes. The warts on the petals are larger and more scattered, and the lip has more prominent veins.

The var. *measuresianum* has no purple on the leaves, which are pale green with darker green mottling. The flower is yellow-white with green stripes on the sepals and petals, and green veins on the lip.

The var. *rubrum* (U. Pradhan) has leaves to 17 cm, and a flower scape to 11 cm tall. The dorsal sepal is the same as in the type. The petals are deep wine-red with green basally, and the lip is also wine-red with green veining.

The var. *teestaensis* (U. Pradhan) comes from the Teesta Valley and has light green leaves to 14 cm with olive mottling and light purple spotting underneath. The petals are a deeper brown-pink than in the type, with larger and more distinct warts.

P. venustum and its varieties are popular plants in collections, being easily grown in a variety of conditions and flowering regularly.

Papillilabium beckleri (Muell. ex Benth.) Dockrill

This tiny Australian species was described in 1873 by Bentham as *Cleisostoma beckleri*, named for its original collector. Since then it has enjoyed many names, including *Sarcochilus beckleri*, *Sarcanthus beckleri* and *Saccolabium virgatum*. In 1967 Dockrill created the genus *Papillilabium*, and transferred this species to it. The genus remains monotypic. Its range extends from southeastern New South Wales to southwest Queensland at usually less than 650 m above sea level. It prefers to grow on the outer twigs of rainforest trees, particularly near or overhanging running water. It also inhabits shrubs and small trees in humid gullies. Long wiry roots attach the unbranched stems of the plant to its host.

The stems may be up to 4 cm long, but are usually shorter. Arranged alternately, the two to six narrow leaves are 2–5 cm long, green in colour, with or without purple spotting. In spring up to four spikes are produced, each 1–4 cm long and carrying between two and eight flowers 0.5–0.7 cm across. The pale green flowers are sometimes marked with purple-brown or occasionally with crimson. The lip may be white, green or yellowish-green with a thick disc densely covered with minute 'bumps'. The intensely fragrant flowers have a long slender spur.

P. beckleri has a reputation for being difficult to keep in cultivation. We find it does best in a fairly shady protected position in a cool humid environment. Cork, paperbark or tea-tree sticks make a suitable mount. It needs to be kept moist and appreciates frequent misting. *Actual flower size: 0.5–0.7 cm across.*

Parasarcochilus spathulatus (Rogers) Dockrill

Like *P. weinthalii*,* this Australian monopodial has been the object of much discussion as to its true identity. First described by Rogers in 1927 as *Sarcochilus spathulatus*, it was transferred by Dockrill in 1967 to the genus *Parasarcochilus*. In 1972 Garay transferred it to *Pteroceras*, claiming that it has only two pollinia. Further investigation by Senghas in 1990 has revealed that it has in fact two pairs of pollinia, and it has now been returned to the genus *Parasarcochilus*. It grows epiphytically on the outer twigs of rainforest trees overhanging running water in the foothills from central eastern New South Wales to southeast Queensland. Usually found below 600 m, it is not a common species.

The pendent stem is up to 4 cm long and does not branch freely. The two to ten dull green leaves are 1.5–7.0 cm long, are sometimes spotted, and turn reddish in bright light. This species flowers in late winter or spring with one or two pendulous spikes 2–5 cm long, bearing up to five widely spaced flowers, each 1.0–1.5 cm in diameter. The greenish-brown sepals and petals are shallowly spoon shaped, while the cream lip is marked with purple and has a hollow spur about 0.4 cm long. The flowers are strongly perfumed.

Many growers find that this species does not respond well to cultivation, going into a steady decline. Some care in establishing the plant is called for, and in finding a suitable microclimate. Intermediate to cool conditions are best, with high humidity and good ventilation. It should be mounted on a small twig.

Actual flower size: 1–1.5 cm across.

Parasarcochilus weinthalii (Bailey) Dockrill

This rare and much-sought Australian species was first described by Bailey in 1903, who named it *Sarcochilus weinthalii* after its original collector. Bailey later described another specimen of the species as *S. longmannii*. In 1967 Dockrill removed it from the genus *Sarcochilus* because it has no calli on the lip — one of the distinguishing characteristics of that genus — and created the new genus *Parasarcochilus*. In 1972 Garay returned it to *Sarcochilus*, but it has recently been re-established as a *Parasarcochilus* by Dr Senghas of Germany. This temperate species is confined to the area between northeast New South Wales and southeast Queensland, where it grows as an epiphyte in isolated patches of scrub or in rainforest up to 700 m on the foothills of inland ranges.

The short pendent stems have between three and seven moderately broad leaves 3–9 cm long. They are sickle shaped, pale yellow-green and often slightly twisted. It is a spring-flowering species, with one or two pendent spikes 2–7 cm long. The three to twelve fragrant flowers are 1.2–1.5 cm across, with waxy sepals and petals which usually open widely. The flowers are cream or white, blotched or streaked with reddish-purple. The lip has two yellow spots at the base.

P. weinthalii is not an easy plant to cultivate, but we have had success by mounting plants on a piece of weathered hardwood paling, placing a little moss about the roots, and hanging it in fairly heavy shade. We give plants intermediate temperatures with high humidity and good air movement. They are slow growers at best.

Actual flower size: 1–1.5 cm across.

Phalaenopsis cornu-cervi (Breda) Blume & Reichenbach (f.)

This epiphyte was originally described as *Polychilos cornu-cervi* by Breda in 1827. Blume and Reichenbach transferred it to *Phalaenopsis* in 1860. *P. devriesiana* is conspecific. It occurs in Thailand, Burma, Malaysia and Indonesia from low elevations to about 1,000 m above sea level. It grows on stunted vegetation in moderately exposed conditions where dew sustains it during the dry season, or in dense forest.

The short stem has a few fleshy leaves 10–22 cm long and 2–4 cm wide. Narrowed at the base, they are sometimes bilobed at the apex. Flowers may be produced at any time on a simple or branched spike 9–42 cm long, which is flattened and carries two rows of distinctive alternating bracts. The seven to twelve flowers are fragrant, long-lasting, and 3–5 cm across. They are fleshy and very glossy, and open a few at a time. The more or less acute sepals and petals are yellow or greenish-yellow with red-brown spots or blotches. The sepals are keeled on the back. The fleshy white lip has red-brown stripes at the base of the column and on the erect lateral lobes. The horizontal mid-lobe is anchor shaped and irregularly indented. It has three pairs of forward-pointing appendages from the base to the mid-lobe.

A fairly easily grown species, it may be mounted or grown in pots or baskets of rather coarse freely draining material. It does best given semi-shade and high humidity. Temperatures should range from intermediate to warm, with plenty of water all year round.

Actual flower size: 3–5 cm across.

Phalaenopsis equestris (Schauer) Reichenbach (f.)

Described by Schauer as *Stauroglottis equestris* in 1843, this species was transferred to *Phalaenopsis* by Reichenbach in 1849. Both *Phalaenopsis rosea*, by which name the species is still commonly known, and *P. riteiwanensis* are synonymous with this species. It occurs throughout most of the Philippines, growing as a pendent epiphyte in moderately shady humid habitats from sea level to 300 m.

The very short stem is covered by the overlapping bases of the fleshy green leaves, which are occasionally suffused with pale purple beneath. There are up to five elongated oval leaves 10–20 cm long. Flowering occurs at any time, with between ten and fifteen delicate flowers on a slightly zigzag spike up to 30 cm long. The suberect to arching spike may be branched, and continues to grow for several months with two or three flowers open at once. The size and colour of the flowers is very variable. From 1.5 cm to 3.0 cm across, they range from white to pale rose with rose, purple or orange at the centre. The edges of the oblong sepals and the almost diamond-shaped petals are recurved. The fleshy lip is darker rose with yellow at the base of the somewhat spoon-shaped lateral lobes. The acute mid-lobe is slightly concave in the middle, with a two-lobed squarish yellow or white callus with red spots between the lateral lobes.

P. equestris may be mounted, potted, or grown in a hanging basket. It needs semi-shade, high humidity and copious water all year round. Temperatures should range from intermediate to warm.

Actual flower size: 1.5–3 cm across.

Phloeophila pubescens (Barb. Rodr.) Garay

This intriguing pleurothallid was originally described as *Physosiphon pubescens* in 1877 by Barbosa Rodrigues. In 1974 Garay transferred it to Hoehne & Schlechter's *Phloeophila*, a genus established in 1926. After renaming it *Sarracenella pubescens* in 1981, Luer has since transferred it to the genus *Pleurothallis*, renaming it *P. sarracenia* (Lindley had already used the name *P. pubescens* for another species). Despite this latest change, about which we have reservations, we have continued to use the most commonly accepted name. This species inhabits the cool misty mountains of Minas Gerais, Rio de Janeiro, Parana and Santa Catarina in Brazil.

The succulent leaves are closely set on a creeping branching rhizome, often growing away from its mount or host so that segments hang freely. Green to yellow-green with purple spots, the almost stalkless boat-shaped leaves are up to 2 cm long with an acute tip. The unusual 'slug-like' flowers are produced in late winter and early spring directly from the rhizome. The curved 1.5 cm flowers are dark reddish-purple, with all sepals joined to form a tube which is minutely hairy inside. The sepals contract to triangular points at the small opening. The narrow petals and tiny lip are hidden deep inside the tube. The lip is covered with minute warts, and the upturned sides at the base are edged with fine hairs.

An easy grower in intermediate to cool conditions, this species does well mounted on treefern, paperbark or cork. Provide semi-shade, with year-round moisture.

Actual flower size: approximately 1.5 cm long.

Pholidota species

This unnamed species arrived in our nursery some years ago in a batch of dendrochilums. Its flowers, however, are arranged spirally rather than in two rows as is the case with dendrochilums. We strongly suspect that this species comes from the mountainous areas of northern Luzon, as most of the highly endemic dendrochilums come from that area at about 1,500 m above sea level.

The dark green pencil-shaped pseudobulbs are up to 6 cm long by 1 cm in diameter, and are much wrinkled. Each one bears a single leaf up to 15 cm long. The arching spikes appear from the maturing pseudobulb in winter, and reach 20 cm in length. The twenty or more 1.5 cm flowers adorn the upper half of the spike, each with a 1 cm long salmon-coloured bract. They are faintly perfumed and most unusually shaped. The dorsal sepal and petals are swept up, with the upper third bent back sharply, while the lateral sepals are swept forward under the virtually hidden lip. Both sepals and petals are about 1.5 cm long. The lip is a little unusual, with two round wings (0.3 cm long) protecting the column and joined by a minutely pointed mid-lobe. The translucent creamy flowers have a green tinge and are salmon-coloured in the centre.

This species grows well for us in semi-shade with intermediate to cool temperatures. Our plants are mounted on slabs of treefern and receive year-round moisture, with a slight reduction in winter.

Actual flower size: approximately 1.5 cm long.

Phreatia baileyana Schlechter

A tiny plant, which will possibly appeal only to the most ardent collectors of miniatures, this delicate Australian species was first described as *Oberonia pusilla* by Bailey in 1889. It was later transferred to the genus *Phreatia* and in 1911 Schlechter gave it its present name in honour of Bailey. *Phreatia pusilla* (Rolfe) is a synonym. It is a tropical species, occurring only in northeastern Queensland from Townsville to Cooktown on the ranges and tablelands above the 600 m mark. Here it is quite common on mossy trees, or sometimes on rocks, in cloudforest or rainforest usually in protected positions.

It often grows in small clumps, with several tiny stems 0.5–4.0 cm long growing together. These stems, which may be erect or curved, have three to six succulent terete leaves 1–3 cm long and only about 0.25 cm in diameter. They are pale to mid-green, and sometimes have a very shallow groove or channel. The more or less erect spikes rise from the lower leaf axils, usually from autumn to spring. They are up to 3 cm long and bear between five and twenty microscopic flowers 0.1–0.15 cm across. The white to pale green flowers open widely and bear their lip uppermost.

Despite its fragile appearance, this species is relatively easy to cultivate. We grow ours on small slabs of treefern with a little moss about the roots. The plants are suspended in intermediate to cool conditions in fairly heavy shade. We keep them moist at all times, and ensure that air movement is good.

Actual flower size: 0.1–0.15 cm across.

Phreatia crassiuscula Mueller ex Nicholls

First described as *Oberonia crassiuscula* by von Mueller, this species was later described as *Phreatia limenophylax* in 1873 by Bentham. The Australian, Nicholls, resurrected the original specific epithet in 1945 to give this species its present name. It inhabits the same general area as *Phreatia baileyana,** that is, the mountain ranges and tablelands of northeastern Queensland; but it is not found below the 800 m level. It is a plant of the cloudforest and rainforest, where it grows on the trunks of trees.

The very short stems, about 1 cm long, are covered with the persistent bases of old leaves. They grow either singly or occasionally in groups of two or three. The pale to dark green, very succulent, leaves are deeply channelled on their upper surface and rounded below. Each plant carries between three and six leaves each 2–6 cm long, forming an imperfect fan. This species may flower at any time, but for us the main flowering period is late spring. The short arching flower spikes are up to 3.5 cm long and bear numerous minute flowers about 0.2 cm in diameter. The crowded cream, white or greenish flowers open widely, but a good magnifying glass is necessary to distinguish the floral features clearly. The lip is attached by a short broad claw, and its edges are turned upward.

P. crassiuscula prefers a cool humid environment in fairly heavy shade. It may be mounted, but we grow ours in suspended pots of fine treefern fibre and moss. Keep moist all year round.

Actual flower size: approximately 0.2 cm long.

Physosiphon tubatus (Lodd.) Reichenbach (f.)

Another species of disputed identity, *Physosiphon tubatus* was first collected in 1828 by Deppe in Guatemala. He sent plants to Loddiges in London, who called it *Stelis tubata* in 1830. However, this name was never validly published. Hooker described it as *Physosiphon loddigesii* in 1843; but in 1861 Reichenbach resurrected Loddiges' original specific epithet, so that the species became known as *P. tubatus*. It is still commonly known by that name today, although Luer recently proposed that it should be included in the genus *Pleurothallis*. It is a common plant both in Mexico at between 900 m and 2,500 m above sea level and in Guatemala up to 3,500 m. It grows in humid forest, with a preference for oaks as host.

The fleshy erect to suberect leaves are 4–15 cm long and 1–3 cm wide. Flowers are produced in spring or summer on an arching spike 8–25 cm long (occasionally up to 40 cm or more). The spike bears between ten and twenty-five or more tubular flowers 0.6–2.0 cm long. Both the size and the colour are variable. Colour ranges from greenish-yellow to apricot or bright orange-red. Both the sepals, whose free ends spread widely, and the three-lobed lip have three nerves, while the tiny petals have a single nerve.

A vigorous grower and a prolific flowerer, this species needs little attention and soon forms a good-sized clump. It does well mounted on treefern or in small pots of treefern fibre and sphagnum moss. A cool moist environment with moderate indirect light is ideal. Never allow it to dry out completely.

Actual flower size: 0.6–2 cm long.

Plectorrhiza brevilabris (Muell.) Dockrill

Since it was first described as *Cleisostoma brevilabre* by von Mueller in 1880, this species has had a number of name changes. Bailey called it a *Sarcochilus*, Rupp a *Saccolabium*, and finally Dockrill changed it again in 1967 when he created the new genus *Plectorrhiza*. A native of Australia, it is found from southeast Queensland to central Cape York Peninsula. In the south it grows at low altitudes, but in the tropics it is found up to 1,200 m or more above sea level. It grows as an epiphyte on small trees and shrubs and also on the outer twigs of larger trees in shady positions. The hanging stems are usually less than 10 cm long, attached to their host by long slender roots which are less inclined to tangle than those of the *Plectorrhiza tridentata*.*

The closely set leaves are arranged alternately and are 3–8 cm long with unequal notching at the apex. The flowers appear in summer on spikes which are reddish in colour, wiry, and slightly zigzag. Length varies from about 3 cm to 17 cm. The three to twenty very fragrant flowers are about 1 cm across, with contrasting dull red or brown patches on the greenish-cream sepals and petals. The short fleshy lip has a vertical spur 0.5–0.7 cm long and a long hairy appendage within.

This species does well on a treefern, cork or hardwood mount with a little fresh moss about the roots. It should be hung in a cool shady place with good ventilation and moderately high humidity.

Actual flower size: approximately 1 cm across.

Plectorrhiza tridentata (Ldl.) Dockrill

This little Australian monopodial has had many synonyms since it was first described as *Cleisostoma tridentata* by Lindley in 1838. These include *Saccolabium calcaratum*, *Thrixspermum tridentatum*, *Sarcochilus tridentatus* and *Sarcanthus tridentatus*. Dockrill placed it in his newly created genus *Plectorrhiza* in 1967. It is found in a variety of habitats from northeastern Victoria to northeastern Queensland. In the south it grows in the lowlands or in the low ranges, but in the tropics it occurs only at higher altitudes. It often grows on the outer twigs of rainforest trees, and is abundant in humid environments such as steep gullies, dense swampy areas and on protected slopes.

While the stems of this species are usually less than 20 cm long, they may occasionally reach 30 cm. The plant produces extensive mats of long contorted and tangled roots — hence its common name of 'tangle orchid'. However, most of these roots are aerial, and plants are often found hanging by one or two roots. From four to twenty green or purplish leaves are arranged alternately on the stem. They are 4–10 cm long and pointed at the apex. Pendent spikes appear in spring or summer and bear between three and fifteen long-lasting flowers having a lemon fragrance. They are about 0.8 cm in diameter, brown and green in colour with white side-lobes to the lip. The lip is deeply spurred.

Because of its pendent habit this species must be mounted, but it is not choosy about the material. It needs a cool and shady spot with high humidity and good air movement.

Actual flower size: approximately 0.8 cm across.

Pleione formosana Hayata

Pleiones were initially thought to belong to the genus *Coelogyne*, to which they are in fact closely related. *P. formosana* is regarded by many as a variety of *P. bulbocodioides*, which was first described (as a coelogyne) by Franchet in 1888 and transferred to *Pleione* by Rolfe in 1903. However, *P. formosana* is so well established in the horticultural world under this familiar name that it is doubtful if it will change. It occurs in the Himalayan area and in Taiwan at 1,500–2,500 m above sea level, often close to the snowline. Although essentially a terrestrial, it also grows on sunny rocks or mossy tree trunks, favouring moist and misty environments.

The round purplish-green pseudobulbs are 2–3 cm tall. The new growth appears each year in spring from the base of the old pseudobulb together with the flower spike. One or two flowers, which may reach 10 cm in diameter, are produced on the short spike. The colour is variable, ranging from pure white through pale mauve-pink to deep rose. The fringed white lip is heavily keeled and marked with orange-brown. After flowering the pleated leaves grow to a length of 10–20 cm. They are deciduous in winter when the plant becomes dormant.

An easy species to cultivate, *P. formosana* does well when grown in shallow pans or boxes with a mixture of peat, moss, coarse sand and leafmould. Be sure to make provision for good drainage. In winter water only enough to prevent the pseudobulbs from shrivelling. Give bright light, cool conditions. A garden subject in mild areas.

Actual flower size: approximately 6–10 cm across.

Pleurothallis ghiesbreghtiana Richard & Galeotti

Much confusion surrounds the true identity of this pretty species, with little agreement among commentators concerning its various synonyms. It is probably synonymous with one of the two species designated as *P. racemiflora*. While these predate Richard and Galeotti's 1845 epithet, the continued use of the name *P. ghiesbreghtiana* is probably the most satisfactory way to identify the species. Some botanists also believe that it is synonymous with *P. quadrifida* (Lex.) Lindley of 1842. A native of Central America, it is found from near sea level in Panama to 1,800 m on the Pacific slopes of Mexico. It grows as an epiphyte in dense evergreen forest or in mixed deciduous forest.

The glossy, very leathery, leaves are up to 17 cm long (occasionally longer), broad and notched at the rounded apex. A single spike 25–45 cm long rises in spring or summer, bearing between twenty and thirty well-spaced greenish-yellow to bright yellow flowers. The long-lasting fragrant flowers, about 1 cm in diameter, are open and nodding. The concave dorsal is recurved at the apex, while each of the almost entirely joined lateral sepals has a keel along the central nerve on the back. The 0.5–1.0 cm petals have a short narrow claw at the base. The short lip is rounded at the apex and often has irregular wavy edges.

This robust species grows well either potted or mounted on treefern and placed in a semi-shaded position. Cool to intermediate conditions are suitable, with year-round moisture and good air movement.

Actual flower size: approximately 1 cm across.

Pleurothallis grobyi Bateman ex Lindley

Bateman first imported this species into England from Guyana, and named it in honour of Lord Grey of Groby, a dedicated orchid grower. However, it was Lindley who first described it in 1835. Its many synonyms include *P. surinamensis* and *P. marginata*. It ranges from Mexico through Central America and the West Indies into South America as far as Peru and southern Brazil. It may be found from near sea level up to 1,500 m altitude.

The plants comprise neat clumps of paddle-shaped fleshy leaves from 1.5 cm to 7.0 cm in length. They are usually suffused or mottled with purple underneath. The erect to arching spikes are produced in spring or summer. About 5–15 cm long, they are thread-like and somewhat zigzag, carrying several well-spaced flowers which do not open widely. Normally, all flowers on a spike open at the same time. They are a translucent creamy-yellow or greenish-white with longitudinal reddish-purple stripes. The concave dorsal sepal is recurved at the apex, and the lateral sepals are joined for most of their length, with upturned sides forming a scoop. The petals are tiny, as is the tongue-shaped lip.

We find that this little species grows quite happily mounted on treefern or potted in a medium of pine bark, treefern fibre and sphagnum moss. It prefers a cool shady environment with good air movement and fairly high humidity. The plant should never be allowed to dry out completely.

Actual flower size: 0.5–0.75 cm long.

Pleurothallis hypnicola Lindley

This Brazilian pleurothallis was described by Lindley in 1842. Cogniaux's *P. cuneifolia* is a synonym. It inhabits the cool damp forests in the mountain ranges of southern Brazil, sharing locations with many other pleurothallids such as *P. sonderana** and *P. grobyi.**

The mid-green leaves are 6–12 cm long including the slender 2–4 cm stalk, which is covered with dark brown bracts. The acute leaves are minutely three-toothed and slightly reflexed at the apex. Flowers are produced in spring and at other odd times during the year on a spike that rises from the top of the leaf stalk. Over a period of time many spikes are produced from the same leaf stalk. Each one continues to elongate over an extended period, producing flowers on old spikes even after the leaves have dropped. The wiry somewhat zig-zag spike may eventually reach a length of 12 cm. The flowers, which may open simultaneously or in succession, are approximately 0.6 cm long. Colour is usually yellow, very heavily blotched with dark claret so that flowers may appear to be totally red. The lateral sepals are yellow at the base, and are joined for about half their length, forming a scoop under the 0.3–0.4 cm lip. The small petals have a thickened glossy apex.

P. hypnicola prefers a cool moist environment in fairly heavy shade. It may be mounted or potted, but should be kept moist all year round. Lacking pseudobulbs, like all pleurothallids, it can succumb quickly if allowed to dry out for long periods.

Actual flower size: approximately 0.6 cm long.

Pleurothallis johnsonii Ames

Described by Ames in 1923, this species comes from Guatemala and Honduras, where it is relatively rare. It is also reported from Mexico. It grows among the leaf litter of the forest floor or on moss-covered rocks at up to 2,800 m above sea level.

The leaf is up to 17 cm long, including the stalk, which is covered in loose bracts. It is mid-green, broadly oval to lance shaped, sharply pointed and often recurved at the notched apex. Flowering in winter or spring, this species is unusual in that it may produce flower spikes from both the base of the leaf and from the base of the stalk. In the former case the spike is up to 4 cm long, in the latter up to 7 cm long. The fleshy flowers are reddish, blotched with purple. The sepals are covered with tiny glands both inside and out, as well as along the edges near the thickened apex. The flowers are approximately 1 cm long. The dorsal sepal is concave at the base, while the lateral sepals are keeled along the back of the mid-vein. The petals are also covered with tiny glands and have long hairs along their upper edges. The tongue-shaped lip is 0.5–0.7 cm long with wavy edges at the apex, a V-shaped callus just above the claw, and fleshy warty calli along the lateral nerves.

P. johnsonii prefers a cool damp atmosphere and semi-shade. It may be potted, but does well for us when mounted on medium-sized treefern slabs with a little live sphagnum moss about the roots. The plant should never be allowed to dry out completely.

Actual flower size: approximately 1 cm long.

Pleurothallis ochracea Porsch

mountain ranges where the forests enjoy a cool humid climate.

The plants lack pseudobulbs, and the leaves are only 1.5–2.5 cm long, including the short stalk. Sometimes suffused with purple, they are moderately fleshy. Spikes rise from the point where the leaf meets the stalk, and bear several straw-yellow flowers. About 0.8 cm long, they do not open widely. Both the sepals and the 0.2 cm petals are pointed at the apex. The tiny lip is only 0.25 cm long.

Despite its small size, this is not a difficult plant to manage in cultivation. It can be grown in small pots, but there is always a risk that if drainage is not really excellent the pots may become waterlogged. If this happens the plants are subject to sudden collapse. We find it best to grow this species on small treefern mounts with a little moss about the roots. It prefers a cool to intermediate environment with fairly heavy shade and high humidity. Plants should never be allowed to dry out completely.

Actual flower size: approximately 0.8 cm long.

In a genus renowned for the number of miniatures it contains there are few smaller than *P. ochracea*. Rarely seen in collections, this species was described by the Austrian botanist Porsch about the end of the 19th century. The plants used by Porsch were supplied by Wettstein, who sent many herbarium specimens, as well as live plants, to the Botanical Gardens in Vienna. *P. ochracea* is very limited in range, being confined to the southern Brazilian state of Parana, growing as an epiphyte in the cool

Pleurothallis prolifera Herbert ex Lindley

Very closely related to *P. pectinata* and *P. tridentata*, this species was described by Lindley early in the 19th century. Barbosa Rodrigues' *P. litophila* is a later synonym. A native of the Brazilian states of Rio de Janeiro, Sao Paulo and Minas Gerais, it grows mostly as a lithophyte in rock crevices — together with *Laelia longipes*, *L. flava*, *L. crispilabia* and *Bifrenaria tyrianthina* — but also on trees. These cool mountain areas experience hot dry days and cool nights with frequent heavy dews.

The leaves of *P. prolifera* are borne at intervals on a stout rhizome. The leaf stalk is 3–15 cm long and the 3–7 cm leaf blade is bent

downward. The leaf is somewhat heart shaped with a prominent mid-vein and turned-up sides. It is rather leathery in texture, and mid-green in colour, suffused with purple, particularly in bright light. A spike is produced in spring or summer from the base of the leaf. Up to 2 cm long, it lies flat along the middle of the leaf, with several 0.5–0.6 cm long dark maroon flowers which do not open widely. The narrow 0.25 cm long petals and lip have serrated edges. The petals point forward, while the lip lies along the joined lateral sepals. Sometimes young plantlets are produced on the top of the leaf, instead of flower spikes.

A cool to intermediate environment suits this species. It does well in rather brighter light than most *Pleurothallis* species, and is a little more tolerant of dryness. We grow it on treefern mounts hung in moderate shade.

Actual flower size: 0.5–0.6 cm long.

Pleurothallis schiedei Reichenbach (f.)

Of all *Pleurothallis* species, this is deservedly one of the most popular with collectors. Reichenbach described it in 1850, naming it in honour of Schiede, who originally collected it in Mexico. Although occurring in Mexico, Guatemala and El Salvador between 1,500 m and 2,500 m above sea level, it is not particularly common in any of those countries.

It grows in neat clumps on mossy trees in humid montane deciduous forests, particularly oak forests. The olive-green leaves are 1.5–5.0 cm long and 0.5–0.9 cm broad. They are very fleshy, and rounded beneath. Plants continue to flower over several months at any time of the year as the zigzag wiry spike elongates until it reaches 8–14 cm. The up to five flowers — about 0.6 cm across — are tan or orange-brown, heavily spotted with dark brown or purple-brown. The feature of the flowers that fascinates most people is the 0.1–0.3 cm long white filaments which dangle from the edges of the sepals and make the plant unique, at least among Mexican species. The filaments move in the slightest breeze or in response to static electricity. The 0.4–0.5 cm long sepals have recurved edges and tips. The spoon-shaped petals are 0.3 cm long, while the trough-like lip is about 0.25 cm long. The pale brown lip is spotted with purple-brown and has two erect horns at the base and a recurved apex.

P. schiedei grows very well when mounted on small treefern slabs and hung in a cool damp spot with moderate shade and good air movement. Plants will tolerate short dry spells.

Actual flower size: approximately 0.6 cm across.

Pleurothallis sonderana Reichenbach (f.)

One of the better known and most popular of the genus *Pleurothallis*, this species was described over a hundred years ago by Reichenbach. In nature it is confined to Brazil, but it is very widespread there, occurring in the southern states of Minas Gerais, Espirito Santo, Rio de Janeiro, Sao Paulo, Parana, Santa Catarina and Rio Grande do Sul. It grows on branches and trunks of trees in the cool moist forests of the mountain ranges.

The fleshy erect leaves are 2–6 cm long, including the short stalk. They are narrow, with a central channel above and a rounded underside. The 3 cm long spike rises from the top of the stalk from summer to winter. It bears between three and five golden-yellow to burnt-orange flowers which last for several weeks. They do not open widely, and tend to nod on their stems. Both the acute dorsal sepal and the lateral sepals, which are joined for almost their entire length, are 0.6–0.7 cm long. The more or less oval petals are only 0.25 cm in length. The slightly longer lip is minutely serrated near the apex and has a spur on either side near the base.

Like most of the pleurothallis, this species is an easy one to maintain in cultivation once the right conditions have been provided. It may be potted in any freely draining fine mixture or mounted on a piece of treefern with a little moss about the roots. It prefers a fairly well-shaded position and cool temperatures with good air movement, and should never be allowed to dry out completely.

Actual flower size: approximately 0.7 cm long.

Pleurothallis strupifolia Lindley

Described in the 19th century by Lindley, this species has several synonyms, including *P. bicolor* and *P. hookeri*. It inhabits the cool mountain ranges of southern Brazil, where it grows epiphytically among mosses and lichens.

Leaves are borne at intervals on a creeping rhizome. The stalk, which is covered with papery bracts, is up to 7 cm long, topped by a very fleshy stiff leaf 5–10 cm long. The curved leaf points downward and is notched at the tip. This species flowers in spring or summer with the spike rising from the base of the leaf. Each 3–5 cm long spike has about five fleshy flowers and lies along the middle of the leaf. The flowers, approximately 1 cm long, do not open widely, and are cream or pale yellow heavily spotted with very dark maroon — almost black in some cases — and more or less suffused with pink. The hooded acute dorsal sepal is recurved at the apex and striped with pink on the outside. The joined lateral sepals form a broad rounded platform, and are minutely toothed along their edges, as is the dorsal sepal near its base. The pale 0.4 cm long petals are spoon shaped, with irregular indentations around the apex. The minutely spotted lip is 0.4 cm long and has several fleshy calli.

This very attractive species does best for us when mounted and allowed to sprawl over a treefern slab. It should be given cool to intermediate conditions and a damp semi-shaded position. Water copiously in summer, less often in winter.

Actual flower size: approximately 1 cm long.

Pleurothallis teres Lindley

This little-known species was described by Lindley, probably about 1842. Unlike most other pleurothallis, it does not inhabit the cool damp forests, but rather the dry inland areas of the Brazilian states of Rio de Janeiro and Minas Gerais. Here, on a plateau between 500 m and 1,000 m above sea level, it experiences a continental climate with large diurnal variations in temperature. The area is subject to cold very dry winters with dew as the only source of moisture. The vegetation is limited to grasses, stunted scrub and a few scattered trees. *P. teres* is a rock dweller in bright light, growing with the rupicolous laelias, *Bifrenaria tyrianthina, Oncidium spilopterum* etc.

In bright light the almost terete leaves become a darkish red-brown, while in shade they are green, tinged or mottled with red-purple. These leaves grow close together on a thick branching rhizome, which is anchored to the rocks with wiry roots. The pencil-shaped leaves are 4–12 cm tall with a single channel on top. *P. teres* flowers mostly in winter (though flowers may appear at almost any time) and sometimes twice a year. The erect spike rises from the base of the leaf channel. Up to 9 cm tall, it bears up to a dozen or more brick-red nodding flowers about 0.7 cm long.

A very adaptable species, *P. teres* does well in cool to intermediate conditions, in either bright light or semi-shade. It may be potted or mounted, but we grow our plants in shallow pans of coarse mixture suspended where ventilation is good. Reduce watering in winter.

Actual flower size: approximately 0.7 cm long.

160

Pleurothallis tribuloides (Sw.) Lindley

First described more than two hundred years ago as *Epidendrum tribuloides* by Swartz in 1788, this species was transferred by Lindley to the genus *Pleurothallis* in 1830. It has also been described as *P. fallax* (Reichenbach (f.)) and *Cryptophoranthus acaulis* (Kraenzlin). It is widely distributed throughout Central America from Mexico to Panama, and in the Caribbean on Cuba and Jamaica. It is epiphytic in dense damp forests and on oaks in open fields.

It grows into extensive masses of dark green fleshy leaves 2–7 cm long with rounded apices. Its main flush of flowers comes in spring or summer, but flowers may appear at any time of the year. A very short spike holds up to four fleshy flowers at the base of the leaves. Commonly orange to brick-red, these may occasionally be deep maroon. The dorsal sepal is joined to the united lateral sepals at the tip, with only a slit along each side. The 0.5–0.8 cm long sepals have three nerves each and are covered with tiny glands on the inner surfaces. Petals are 0.25–0.30 cm long with two nerves. The narrow lip, about 0.3 cm long, has three nerves, hairs along the edges, and one tooth on either side. The sides are turned downward and the apex is rounded. The seed pod of this species is covered with short 'spikes', making it unique among pleurothallis from this area.

P. tribuloides grows well mounted or potted in fine well-drained material. Cool conditions suit it best, with moderate to heavy shade and year-round moisture.

Actual flower size: 0.5–0.8 cm long.

Polystachya luteola (Sw.) Hooker

This species, originally described as *Cranichis luteola* by Swartz in 1804 and renamed *Polystachya luteola* in 1824 by Hooker, has a multitude of synonyms. Among them are *Polystachya minuta* (Britton), by which the species is still known in Jamaica, *Dendrobium flavescens* (Lindley), *Dendrorchis minuta* (Kuntze) and *Polystachya mauritiana* (Sprengel). The extremely wide distribution of this species probably explains the plenitude of synonyms. It occurs in the Philippines, where it is the sole representative of the genus, in Borneo, India, Sri Lanka, Indonesia, Malaysia, Madagascar, Mauritius, Central and South America and the West Indies. It grows both as an epiphyte and as a lithophyte, often forming large clumps. It inhabits both warm coastal areas and cloudforests up to 1,200 m above sea level.

The conical pseudobulbs are 3–5 cm tall and 1 cm in diameter at the base. There are between two and ten leaves 4–15 cm long and occasionally longer. The branched flower spike rises from the apex of the pseudobulb and can reach a height of 65 cm. The fragrant flowers, borne in loose racemes, are inverted (non-resupinate) with a prominent chin. They are about 0.6 cm across. The lip has a callus and many fine hairs on the disc. This species flowers mainly in winter, but can flower more than once a year.

P. luteola grows well mounted or potted in a coarse medium and placed in an airy position with bright indirect light. It is an adaptable species, and will be happy in either warm or intermediate conditions.

Actual flower size: approximately 0.6 cm across.

Polystachya ottoniana Reichenbach (f.)

Named after the German botanist Otto, this species was introduced into Germany in 1847 and described by Reichenbach in 1855. It has also been known as *P. glaberrima*, *P. pisobulbon* and *P. capensis*. Occurring in South Africa in eastern Cape Province, Natal, Transvaal and Transkei and in Swaziland, this species is found both near the coast and up to 1,800 m above sea level in areas which experience occasional frost and snow in winter. Most of the rainfall in these areas occurs in summer, and plants grow in sunny fairly open positions.

The conical pseudobulbs are clustered on a creeping rhizome, and measure 1–3 cm in height. The leaves, which reach a length of approximately 6 cm, are mostly deciduous in the cool resting season, leaving a mass of wrinkled pseudobulbs exposed. A spike bearing up to six flowers, each up to 2 cm in diameter, appears from the apex of the new growth in spring. They are quite showy. As in all polystachyas the flower is non-resupinate, the lip being held uppermost. The pink-suffused flowers have a pretty yellow stripe on the lip.

This species seems to do best for us when mounted or grown in open baskets filled with fairly coarse medium and hung in moderately bright light. It is happiest in intermediate to cool conditions, but will tolerate quite high summer temperatures. It needs a cool dry rest in winter, when watering should be reduced.
Actual flower size: approximately 1.5–2 cm across.

Polystachya pubescens (Ldl.) Reichenbach (f.)

This pretty species, which was introduced to cultivation in England in the mid-19th century, remains one of the most popular polystachyas in collections today. First described as *Epiphora pubescens* in 1837 by Lindley, it was renamed *Polystachya pubescens* by Reichenbach in 1863. Other synonyms include *Polystachya lindleyana* and *Lissochilus sylvaticus*. It is a widely distributed species ranging through the east and northeast of South Africa — eastern Cape Province, Natal, east Transvaal and Transkei — and Swaziland. It is fairly common on sandstone outcrops where shallow pockets of soil and humus have accumulated, and on trees in the coastal lowlands and in the warmer forests, in exposed positions where it receives full sun, and also in more protected shady areas. The prolonged dry winter with cooler temperatures and lower humidity ensures that the plants have a distinct resting period, which should be duplicated as far as possible in cultivation.

The dark green pseudobulbs are conical and from 2 cm to 6 cm tall, with two or three leaves 8–10 cm long which are often suffused with purple. The hairy inflorescence is produced from the apex of the new growth in spring to early summer. The spike, which may reach 24 cm, bears from eight to twenty-five fragrant flowers up to 2 cm across which open progressively over a period of several months, with ten or more open at any one time. The golden-yellow flowers are non-resupinate. The lateral sepals have contrasting red-brown stripes.

An easy species to grow, potted or mounted, in cool to intermediate conditions.
Actual flower size: 1.5–2 cm across.

Promenaea stapelioides (Link & Otto) Lindley

Link and Otto described this species early in the 19th century as *Cymbidium stapelioides*. The specific epithet refers to the resemblance of the flowers to the South African stapelias. In 1832 Lindley described it as *Maxillaria stapelioides*, transferring it to his new genus *Promenaea* in 1843. Reichenbach's *Zygopetalum stapelioides* is another synonym. Native to the cooler mountain areas of southern Brazil, it grows mostly on trees, but also on damp rocks in shady positions at moderate elevations.

The clustered pseudobulbs are compressed and more or less four-angled. From 2 cm to 3 cm tall, they are enclosed at the base by between two and four leaf-bearing bracts. Two soft grey-green leaves, 5–6 cm long, rise from the apex of the pseudobulb. They are spreading, with a prominent mid-rib beneath and an acute apex. In summer or autumn one or two long-lasting flowers almost 5 cm across are produced on short spikes from the base of the pseudobulb. The keeled, slightly overlapping sepals and petals are greenish-yellow, densely blotched and barred with dark purple-maroon. The velvety lip is mostly a dark purplish-black. The paler lateral lobes project forward. The concave mid-lobe is almost round with a raised keel on the rounded crest.

This unusual species may be mounted, but we grow it in well-drained suspended pots of treefern fibre, pine bark and sphagnum moss. It prefers moderate shade to bright indirect light in intermediate conditions. Plants should never be allowed to dry out completely, but water may be reduced after flowering.

Actual flower size: approximately 5 cm across.

Promenaea xanthina (Ldl.) Lindley

Still commonly known by its synonym, *P. citrina*, this species was probably first collected in Minas Gerais at the beginning of the 19th century by Descourtilz, who called it *Epidendrum jonquille*. However, this was not published, so Lindley's *Maxillaria xanthina* of 1839 is the earliest valid name. Lindley transferred it to *Promenaea* in 1843. It is a beautiful and popular miniature that originates in southern Brazil, where it grows as an epiphyte, and occasionally on rocks, in the sheltered mountain forests at up to 1,700 m elevation.

The obscurely four-angled pseudobulbs are clustered on a branching rhizome. About 2 cm long, they have one or two leaf-bearing bracts at the base, and two suberect to spreading leaves at the apex. From 5 cm to 7 cm long, they are soft, pale to mid-green, have an acute apex and a prominent mid-vein below. When not in flower, the plants are almost impossible to tell from those of *P. stapelioides*.* The one or two fragrant flowers are borne on an arching 5–10 cm spike which rises from the base of the pseudobulb in spring or summer. Lasting a month or more, they are clear yellow with reddish blotches on the base and lateral lobes of the lip and on the column. The sepals are about 2 cm long, the petals slightly shorter. The oblong 1.5 cm lip is more or less rounded at the apex. The lateral lobes are erect, and the broad mid-lobe is deflexed. The fleshy three-lobed callus has a raised protuberance inside the three-toothed apex of its mid-lobe.

In cultivation, we treat this species just as we do *P. stapelioides*.*

Actual flower size: approximately 3–4 cm across.

Psygmorchis pusilla (L.) Dodson & Dressler

Another species that has had a number of name changes over the years, this species was originally described by Linnaeus as *Epidendrum pusillum* in 1753. It was moved to the genus *Oncidium* by Reichenbach (f.) in 1863 under the name *Oncidium pusillum*. It has also been known as *Oncidium iridifolium*. It was finally removed from *Oncidium* when Dodson and Dressler created the genus *Psygmorchis* (meaning 'fan orchid') in 1972. This species is usually found in large colonies from Mexico to Panama, in the West Indies and in Brazil and Bolivia. It is quite commonly encountered growing on coffee and citrus trees in cultivated orchards. Its natural habitat is the hot humid forest up to elevations of 800 m above sea level, where it often grows on smaller branches and twigs overhanging streams.

As is indicated by the generic name, this species is fan shaped. It has no pseudobulbs, but instead a series of equitant fleshy leaves up to 8 cm long. Flower spikes appear from the leaf axils in spring or summer and bear a succession, usually two or three, of single flowers. At 2.5 cm in diameter, the flowers of this species are the largest of the genus.

This delightful little species has proved difficult to maintain in cultivation for any length of time. It has been suggested that the plant may in fact be quite short-lived in nature. For best results, grow it in warm to intermediate conditions with fairly bright light. Plants should be mounted on twigs or small cork mounts and placed where humidity is high and air movement good.

Actual flower size: approximately 2.5 cm across.

Pterostylis nutans R. Brown

This attractive deciduous Australian terrestrial species, widely known as the 'nodding greenhood', was described by Robert Brown in 1810. It is a very widespread species, occurring from Queensland to Tasmania and South Australia, and also in New Zealand. It inhabits the undergrowth of dry sclerophyll forest and open sandy woodland and heath. It has also been noted growing on boulders where pockets of humus have collected.

The small egg-shaped tubers are about 1 cm long and multiply freely, forming large colonies, and making it one of the easiest of the Australian terrestrials to cultivate. The pale green leaves form a basal rosette in autumn, after dormancy in the hot dry summer. The four or five leaves are 1.5–5 cm long, veined, and have wavy edges. The flower stem appears in winter or spring and carries a single translucent flower. The dorsal sepal and petals form a 'hood' 1.5–2.5 cm long which is curved so that the opening faces the ground. The petals have a few short hairs along the edges. The lateral sepals are joined below the labellum for one-third of their length with the free ends thrust out horizontally. The lip, which projects through the lateral sepals, has a red-brown ridge along the centre and is densely covered with short white hairs.

Tubers should be planted at a depth of about 2 cm in a container of sandy soil with a little leafmould added. A cool shady spot is preferred. Plants should be watered from early autumn, from the time the new growth emerges from the soil, and kept fairly dry once the leaves have fallen.

Actual flower size: 1.5–2.5 cm long.

Pterostylis pedunculata R. Brown

Robert Brown described this Australian terrestrial species, commonly known as the 'maroon hood' in 1810. Like *Pterostylis nutans*,* it is widely distributed from southern Queensland to Tasmania and into South Australia. It frequents coastal heathlands, open eucalypt forests, tea-tree scrub and ferny gullies at higher altitudes. In some areas it even colonises tree-fern trunks, and we have seen plants growing in thin layers of soil on exposed rocks.

The small almost round tubers are about 1 cm long, and lie dormant during the hot summer months, putting out between three and six mid-green leaves during the autumn. The leaves, which have long petioles and are 4–5 cm long, form a rosette at the base of the flower spike. There is a prominent network of veins on the leaves, which have wavy edges. The 10–25 cm flower spike normally bears a single flower, which is usually green shading to deep red-brown in the apical half, but is sometimes completely maroon. The 'hood' is formed by the dorsal sepal and petals and is 1.2–2.0 cm long, erect for two-thirds of its length, then bent forward at a right angle. The lateral sepals are joined for half their length and rise vertically so that the tip of the hood protrudes between them. The deep maroon lip is about 0.5 cm long, has a central ridge, and is covered with minute hairs. The flowers appear in late winter or spring.

In cultivation, this species should be treated in exactly the same way as *P. nutans*.* We grow our plants in white polyurethane boxes on the greenhouse floor.

Actual flower size: approximately 3 cm long.

Restrepia hemsleyana Schlechter

This species, which was described by Schlechter in 1918, is a native of the Venezuelan Andes, including the foothills and the Sierra de Perija. The latter forms part of the border with Colombia, so it is possible that this species also occurs in that country.

The tufted plants have no pseudobulbs and comprise long-stalked leaves about 8.5 cm long. They are broadly oval with a prominent keel beneath and the stalks are covered with several papery bracts. The single flower is borne in winter or spring on an arching spike which rises from the underside of the leaf. Over a period of time each leaf produces several spikes. These are longer than the leaves, so that the 5 cm long flower is held well clear. The almost erect dorsal sepal is only 0.3 cm wide and tapers sharply to a thread-like tail which has a thickened end, as do the 1.3 cm long petals. The dorsal sepal has three crimson stripes. The 3 cm long lateral sepals are joined for much of their length and are heavily spotted and/or striped with crimson. The relatively large lip (1.0 cm by 0.25 cm) lies along the connate lateral sepals. The sides of the lip are turned upward near the base with a sharp-pointed tooth on either side.

R. hemsleyana grows well in intermediate to cool conditions in semi-shade. It should be given year-round moisture and never permitted to dry out completely. It may be mounted or potted in a fine well-drained mixture. It requires much the same treatment as masdevallias and grows well with them.

Actual flower size: approximately 5 cm long.

Restrepia muscifera (Ldl.) Reichenbach (f.) ex Lindley

This attractive little species was originally described as *Pleurothallis muscifera* by Lindley in 1842 based on material from Guatemala. It was transferred to the genus *Restrepia* in 1859. Synonyms include *R. xanthophthalma* and *R. lansbergii*. It grows as an epiphyte in the humid forests of Central America from Mexico to Panama, and in northern South America, at elevations of 480–1,500 m above sea level.

It is without pseudobulbs. The leaves are 3–15 cm long including the flattened stalk, which is covered with several papery bracts. These are somewhat inflated, and spotted with purple. The green leaves may be suffused with purple underneath, especially in bright light. The blade of the leaf is broadly oval and prominently keeled beneath. The charming flowers may appear at any time of the year on 1.5 cm spikes from the underside of the leaf. Several spikes will eventually be produced by a single leaf. The single 2.0–2.5 cm long flowers are translucent yellow-green, spotted with maroon. The almost erect dorsal sepal tapers to a yellow-orange 'knob', as do the thread-like petals. The lateral sepals are joined for most of their length, and the minutely spotted, tongue-shaped lip lies along them. The lip has a spur on each side of the base. The column is pale, and there are two orange spots at the base of the sepals.

R. muscifera does well mounted or potted in a mixture of treefern fibre, pine bark and chopped sphagnum moss. A cool to intermediate environment is ideal, with semi-shade and fairly high humidity.

Actual flower size: 2–2.5 cm long.

Rhinerrhiza divitiflora (Muell. ex Benth.) Rupp

Bentham originally described this Australian species in 1873 as *Sarcochilus divitiflorus*. In 1951 Rupp removed it from *Sarcochilus* because of its distinctive roots and flowers, and created the genus *Rhinerrhiza*, of which this remains the sole species. It occurs from central New South Wales, where it grows in the lowlands and on the lower slopes of the ranges, to northeast Queensland, where it is found only on the ranges and tablelands above 600 m altitude. It inhabits rainforest trees and, in the south, trees in open forest.

An unusual feature of the plant is its thick roots, which look and feel like coarse sandpaper, giving rise to the plant's common name of 'raspy root'. In fact, the whole plant is dry and papery to the touch. The stems, up to 3 cm long, bear between two and six dark purplish-green leaves 5–15 cm long and 2–3 cm wide with wavy edges. In early spring from one to four pendent spikes 6–30 cm long bear up to sixty quite spectacular flowers which all open simultaneously, or occasionally in groups, and last for a maximum of two days. The narrow sepals and petals are 2–5 cm long and taper to fine points. The white cup-shaped lip provides a contrast to the pale orange of the tepals.

Rather notorious for its slow growth, this species is not difficult to cultivate but seldom puts out new growths, rather extending its monopodial stem. It does well in intermediate to cool conditions with moderate shade, and should be mounted. Water all year round with a slightly drier spell in winter.

Actual flower size: 4–10 cm long.

Rhyncolaelia glauca (Ldl.) Schlechter

Lindley originally described this species in 1839 as *Brassavola glauca*, by which name it is still commonly known. Although it was discovered by Henchman, Lindley based his description on plants sent to him from Mexico by Hartweg. Bentham transferred it to *Laelia* in 1880, where it remained until Schlechter moved it to his new genus *Rhyncolaelia* in 1918. It occurs in Mexico, Guatemala and Honduras, growing predominantly on stunted trees in relatively dry areas and on oaks in open mountain forest at up to 1,500 m above sea level.

Plants are generally about 15 cm in height, with the compressed spindle-shaped pseudobulbs from 3 cm to 10 cm, though usually 7 cm or less. Each pseudobulb bears a single fleshy leaf 6–12 cm long. This rigid leaf is somewhat boat shaped with a rounded apex. The flower spike rises from the apex of the pseudobulb and is up to 10 cm tall, bearing a single long-lasting flower which is usually about 12 cm across. It is fleshy, fragrant, and mostly olive-green to white with a white or yellowish lip that has a rose-pink spot or several reddish stripes in the throat. The spreading sepals and petals are 5.5–6.5 cm long. The petals are wider than the sepals, pointed, and slightly wavy. The lateral lobes of the broad lip enclose the column at their base. The spreading mid-lobe has a blunt apex.

R. glauca is a very rewarding species, and not a difficult subject. It needs plenty of bright light, and intermediate to warm conditions. It grows well mounted or in a hanging basket. Give plenty of water, but allow to dry out between waterings.

Actual flower size: approximately 12 cm across.

Robiquetia fuerstenbergiana (Schltr.) Schlechter

This vandaceous monopodial was originally described by Schlechter in 1912 as *Saccolabium fuerstenbergianum*. The following year he transferred it to *Robiquetia*, a genus established in 1826 by Gaudichaud. Found only in Thailand, this species grows as an epiphyte in the north of the country at elevations of about 1,800 m above sea level.

The stem is about 6 cm long, covered with old leaf bracts on the lower part. There are about five leaves at any one time, arranged alternately and fairly closely set. From 8 cm to 15 cm long and 2.5–3.0 cm wide, they are very fleshy, stiff, dark green above and heavily suffused with purple below. The apex has two unequal rounded lobes, and there is a prominent keel below, with a groove on the upper surface. The 7–9 cm spikes appear in late spring to summer, with several to many pink to vivid amethyst flowers about 1.5 cm long. The 0.4 cm concave dorsal hoods the column. The 0.3 cm petals, also concave, point forward. The lateral sepals spread slightly with their edges curved inward. The lip, which is joined to the column, forms a swollen spur about 1 cm long with a wide opening and a small raised callus within. The spur is paler than the tepals. The white anther cap forms a distinct 'beak'.

Plants of this species need bright indirect light and humid intermediate temperatures. They grow well in slat baskets or pots of a freely draining coarse medium. Water copiously when in growth, with a pronounced dry resting period in winter.

Actual flower size: approximately 1.5 cm long.

Sarcochilus ceciliae Mueller

Commonly known as 'fairy bells', this delightful Australian species was first described by von Mueller in 1865. Synonyms include *Thrixspermum ceciliae* (Reichenbach (f.)) and *Sarcochilus eriochilis* (Fitzgerald). In nature it ranges from northeastern New South Wales to the Atherton Tableland in north Queensland. It is seldom found below 450 m altitude, and grows almost exclusively as a lithophyte on volcanic rocks or sandstone in rainforest or open eucalypt forest. It favours rocky ledges with a loose covering of leaf litter in sheltered to moderately exposed positions where dew forms regularly.

It grows either in clumps of densely packed tufts or as single growths. The four to eight narrow fleshy leaves are brownish-green more or less spotted with purplish-red, becoming a decided red in exposed conditions. The erect spikes, up to 20 cm long, appear in late spring or summer and carry from three to fourteen delicate pink flowers. About 0.5–0.7 cm long, the cup-shaped flowers face upwards. The short fleshy lip has a densely hairy callus. There is a pure white form with clear yellow calli on the lip.

Many growers have some difficulty with this species. The key to good results lies in the fact that it will not tolerate 'wet feet', yet it likes a humid atmosphere about its roots. Good results can be obtained by mounting on horizontal pieces of cork set in a pot or tray of moss. But we grow our plants in small pots of broken Sandstone and moss suspended in moderate light with good ventilation. Give moderate water, but do not allow the plant to become waterlogged.

Actual flower size: approximately 0.5–0.7 cm long.

Sarcochilus falcatus R. Brown

The most common of the Australian sarcochilus, this species was described by Brown in 1810. Synonyms are *Thrixspermum falcatum* (Reichenbach (f.)) and *Sarcochilus montanus* (Fitzgerald). Known widely as the 'orange blossom orchid', it extends from eastern Victoria in the south to Cape York Peninsula in north Queensland. In the south, it occurs from the lowlands to 1,200 m altitude, but in the tropics it is found only above the 800 m mark. It is predominantly epiphytic on rainforest trees in moist habitats — cool gullies and gorges in the mountains. The semi-pendulous stems are 1–8 cm long with between three and eight pale green to yellow-green fleshy leaves 5–16 cm long. As indicated by the specific epithet, the leaves are rather sickle shaped. The flower spike appears in late winter to spring in temperate areas, two or three months earlier in the tropics. Up to 18 cm long, it bears three to fifteen crystalline flowers 2–4 cm across. These heavy-textured flowers are very strongly vanilla scented. The lateral lobes of the lip are usually stained with orange and have red stripes. The small yellowish mid-lobe has several calli. The spur is sometimes stained with purple. The plants we have seen from the northern mountains are much smaller in all parts, with fewer and smaller flowers, than those from further south.

S. falcatus does well in cultivation, and is best grown on mounts of treefern, cork or weathered hardwood with a little moss. It prefers cool shady conditions with good air movement. It should be kept moist at all times.

Actual flower size: approximately 2–4 cm across.

Sarcochilus fitzgeraldii Mueller

Known locally in Australia as the 'ravine orchid', this lovely species was named in 1870 by von Mueller, then Director of the Melbourne Botanical Gardens, in honour of Fitzgerald, who sent him plants. A relatively large species for the genus, this monopodial branches readily and can form good-sized colonies. However, in cultivation the stems are usually less than 15 cm high. A species from temperate northeastern New South Wales and southeastern Queensland, it grows mostly on cliffs or rocks in moist gullies on the eastern slopes of the Great Dividing Range. It is occasionally found growing terrestrially at the base of trees such as the brush box *Tristania conferta*. It is always found in well-shaded moist positions.

The four to eight leaves are from 6 cm to 20 cm in length (often shorter in cultivation), dark green and channelled. This species flowers in spring from the leaf axils, with erect to pendulous spikes 10–20 cm long. These bear between four and fifteen showy fragrant flowers 2.5–3.5 cm across. The widely opening flowers are dotted and blotched with cerise or crimson on the basal third, or occasionally more. Arguably the most attractive of the genus, this species is threatened by overcollecting.

It grows best in shallow pots of a well-drained medium such as a mixture of pine bark, charcoal, sandstone or treefern chunks with some added moss. Intermediate to cool conditions with moderate shade suit this species. It should be kept moist all year round. In cultivation plants react very badly to high summer temperatures.

Actual flower size: 2.5–3.5 cm across.

Sarcochilus hartmannii Mueller

Named after its original collector by von Mueller in 1874, this species is closely related to *S. fitzgeraldii*,* but has more deeply channelled falcate leaves. It is also rather easier to manage in cultivation. Its synonym, *S. rubricentrum*, was coined by Fitzgerald in 1884. Native to Australia, it occurs at elevations up to 1,000 m on inland ranges from central New South Wales to southeastern Queensland, growing on exposed cliffs or near creeks in shady positions. It is also occasionally found on the fibrous bases of certain trees. Its distribution is sporadic, and it is found usually in relatively small clumps. Overcollection has made it increasingly rare in the wild.

The branching semi-erect stems bear between four and ten dark green leaves (or sometimes light green in bright light), which are slightly twisted at the base and 5–20 cm long. This species flowers very regularly in cultivation as in the wild, with up to four reddish spikes 6–25 cm long appearing in late winter to spring. Each spike bears up to twenty-five waxy flowers 1–3 cm in diameter which usually open widely. The white sepals and petals have maroon spots at the base, both inside and out. The small lip has red stripes on the side lobes and deep fleshy calli on the mid-lobe.

It is best grown in a fairly deep container with an open medium such as sandstone, brick or bark, with a little added moss or leafmould. Give it intermediate to cool conditions, moderate light and year-round moisture. It tolerates high temperatures better than does *S. fitzgeraldii*.

Actual flower size: 1–3 cm across.

Sarcochilus hillii (Muell.) Mueller

Probably the most diffi-cult of the Australian sarcochilus to cultivate, this species was first described by von Mueller in 1859 as *Den-drobium hillii*. In 1860 he transferred it to the genus *Sarcochilus*. *Thrixspermum hillii* (Reichenbach (f.)) and *Sarcochilus minutiflos* (Bailey) are synonyms, although some botanists consider the latter to be a separate species. It is found from southeastern New South Wales to central Queensland from sea level to 700 m. It grows occasionally in typical rainforest, but more often on small shrubby trees in 'dry scrub' areas away from the coast. It is frequently found on fine twigs in heavily shaded areas, often in large numbers. It also occasionally grows as a lithophyte. The most visible part of the plant is usually the extensive mass of thick, often tangled, roots which anchor the very small pendulous stems that bear between two and ten narrow chan-nelled leaves 1.5–10 cm in length. They are normally dark green spotted with red-purple. The main flowering period is spring, though flowers may occur at other times. The wiry pen-dulous spikes are 3–12 cm long, sometimes branching. They bear two to ten very fragrant flowers 0.6–1.1 cm across, ranging from frosty white to pale pink. The lip has purple stripes and large yellow calli, and the mid-lobe is densely covered with white hairs.

We have had best results with this species by attaching it to small twigs of tea-tree or paper-bark and hanging it in a shady humid position. It should never be allowed to dry out com-pletely. Intermediate temperatures seem best. *Actual flower size: 0.6–1.1 cm across.*

Sarcochilus olivaceus Lindley

First described by Lindley in 1839, and later by Reichenbach (f.) as *Thrix-spermum olivaceum*, this species owes its name to its flower colour — olive-green to gold. It occurs sporadi-cally over a large area of eastern Australia from southeastern New South Wales to Cape York. In its southern range it is found from sea level to 650 m; but it is rarely encountered be-low 900 m in the tropics. It grows mainly as an epiphyte on the mossy bark of small trees and the stems of vines (such as the 'law-yer vine', from which it gets its common name, 'lawyer orchid') in shady humid habitats such as ravines and gullies. Plants found in leaf litter on rocks tend to be thicker and more robust.

The stems, which are up to 8 cm long, do not branch freely. The two to nine leaves are 2.5–12 cm long, mid- to dark green, and sometimes have undulating edges. The pendent spikes are 2–14 cm long with between two and twelve heavy-textured flowers, which have a delicate spicy fragrance. The forward-pointing lip is marked with red and has prominent fleshy calli and a short fleshy spur. This species flowers in late spring in the south, earlier in the tropics.

This is a relatively easy species in cultiva-tion, thriving in suitable conditions. The long aerial roots indicate that it should be mounted. Any material may be used, preferably with a little moss attached. It should be hung in a cool shady position with fairly high humidity and good air movement. It should be watered all year round, except in cold weather, when it may be misted.
Actual flower size: approximately 1.4 cm across.

Schoenorchis pachyrachis (J. J. Sm.) J. J. Smith

A true gem among the miniatures, this species was placed in the genus *Schoenorchis* in 1912 by J. J. Smith. It is very similar to *S. fragrans*, from which it is distinguished by the sharp points on the lateral sepals and by the structure of the anther. It is native to peninsular Thailand, Sumatra and Java, where it grows as an epiphyte.

The stem of this vandaceous monopodial is less than 3 cm long and completely covered by the bases of the closely set, very fleshy, leaves. They are 1.5–2.0 cm long, and minutely dimpled with a single groove above and a rounded undersurface. The simple 2 cm spike rises from the leaf axil, and is usually densely packed with many sparkling flowers (unlike the relatively poorly flowered plant pictured). A well-flowered plant with several spikes may be completely hidden by the flowers. The flowers, which do not open fully, are violet and white, or violet and yellow-white. The sepals and petals are slightly recurved, and the 0.25 cm sepals are almost twice as long as the tiny petals. The three-lobed lip has a distinct slightly swollen spur at the base. The small lateral lobes are erect on either side of the entrance to the spur. The very fleshy mid-lobe is held forward and thickened near the apex.

S. pachyrachis is a subject for mounting, as it does not do well in a pot. It grows well on cork, paperbark or tea-tree, and needs an intermediate to warm environment with moderate light and high humidity. Allow to dry out between waterings.

Actual flower size: approximately 0.5 cm across.

Sedirea japonica (Ldl. & Rchb. (f.)) Garay & Sweet

F ound throughout Japan — including the Ryukyu Islands — and Korea, this species was first described by Lindley and Reichenbach in the mid-19th century as *Aerides japonicum*. It has also been known as *Angraecum japonicum*. It was removed from the genus *Aerides* in 1974 by Garay and Sweet, who created the new genus *Sedirea* (which is actually 'aerides' spelt backwards) specifically for this species. The genus remains monotypic. A feature which differentiates it from the aerides is its unusual column, which is almost as long as the petals.

The plant itself is monopodial, and rather resembles a small phalaenopsis. It has a very short stem with two or three pairs of oval leaves up to 10 cm long. An arching spike to 20 cm long carries several fragrant flowers. The main flowering season is late spring, but flowers may appear occasionally throughout the year. The waxy 3 cm long flowers are quite showy, with their attractive rose markings on the white lip and lateral sepals. First introduced into Europe in about 1862, it has remained justly popular there, as it is in its native countries.

S. japonica will grow and flower well in intermediate to cool conditions with moderate humidity and semi-shade. It may be mounted or grown in pots of coarse well-drained material. However, we have had good results by placing several mounted plants in a suspended pot, with sphagnum moss packed about the base of the mounts. Care should be taken in winter that water does not remain lodged in the crown. Good air movement is essential.

Actual flower size: approximately 3 cm long.

Smitinandia micrantha (Ldl.) Holttum

This monopodial was originally described by Lindley as *Saccolabium micranthum* in 1833, renamed *Cleisostoma micrantha* by King and Pantling in 1898, and transferred to *Ascocentrum* in 1947 by Holttum. In 1969 Holttum created the new genus *Smitinandia*, which he named after Thai botanist Tem Smitinand, to accommodate this and a few other species. It grows as an epiphyte at elevations of 700–1,000 m above sea level, from Sikkim to Indochina and northern peninsular Malaysia.

The erect stems may reach a height of about 8 cm, but are usually shorter. Fleshy roots protrude between the narrow leathery leaves which are about 0.7 cm apart on the stem. The leaves, 6–11 cm long, are yellow-green and deeply and unevenly bilobed at the rounded apex. Up to one hundred and fifty densely packed waxy flowers are borne in summer on a horizontal to arching spike about 7 cm long (occasionally to 15 cm). The round flowers are about 0.7 cm across, faintly fragrant, and last for several weeks. The broadly oval sepals and narrower petals are white, sometimes spotted with purple. The tongue-shaped mauve to purple lip has a small rounded spur at the base, the entrance to which is almost closed by a thick callus. The rounded lateral lobes are erect, while the irregularly indented mid-lobe is held horizontally.

S. micrantha does best when mounted on cork or placed in a small slat basket with a coarse freely draining mixture. It likes plenty of light, high humidity, and intermediate to warm conditions.

Actual flower size: approximately 0.7 cm across.

Sophronitella violacea (Ldl.) Schlechter

Discovered by Gardner in 1837 and described by Lindley in 1840 as *Sophronitis violacea*, this species was separated from that genus in 1925 and placed in Schlechter's newly created genus *Sophronitella*, of which it remains the only species. Distinguishing features include the short-winged column and the lip, which does not enfold the column. This species is common in the cooler mountains of southern Brazil and the drier savannah country of Minas Gerais.

The spindle-shaped pseudobulbs are closely set on a branching rhizome. They are 1.5–3.0 cm long, shallowly ridged, sometimes suffused with purple, and when young are covered with papery bracts. The single grassy leaf is erect to spreading with a prominent keel. The narrow leaf, 3.8–8 cm long, tapers to a sharp point. Spikes from 0.4 cm to 0.9 cm in length carry single starry flowers (occasionally two) in winter and early spring. The violet-purple flowers are paler at the centre, quite long lasting, and about 2 cm long. The acute petals and narrower sepals are 2 cm long, with the edges often curled up. The 1.7 cm lip, which is joined to the column, has a pouch at the base and a sharp point at the curled apex. The fleshy column wings are sickle shaped.

Because *S. violacea* likes a humid atmosphere but resents 'wet feet', it prefers a quick-draining mount such as cork or paperbark. Intermediate conditions are ideal, with moderate light and plenty of water when in active growth. Allow it to dry out completely between waterings and give plants a cool dry winter rest.

Actual flower size: approximately 2 cm long.

Sophronitis brevipedunculata (Cogn.) Fowlie

When Cogniaux described this Brazilian species as *Sophronitis wittigiana* var. *brevipedunculata* at about the end of the 19th century, he suspected that it might be a distinct species. Fowlie confirmed this in 1972. Restricted to the ridges and interior plateaux of Minas Gerais at 1,500–2,000 m above sea level, it grows on vellozia bushes or on rocky outcrops where there is some humus. This area experiences very hot days and cold dewy nights.

The somewhat wrinkled pseudobulbs are globose to cylindrical and 1–2 cm long. They are arranged alternately in two rows on the rhizome and covered with fibrous bracts when young. Each bears a single thick leaf which is very stiff and may be ovate or elongated. From 2.0 cm to 4.5 cm long and up to 2.3 cm wide, the leaves are narrow at the base and rounded or sharply pointed at the apex. From autumn to early winter very short spikes rise from the apex of the pseudobulbs carrying up to three flowers 4.0–7.5 cm across. The sepals and petals are light red to orange-red with darker veins. The lip is yellow-orange, with veining in the tube formed by the lateral lobes. The oblong sepals taper to points, and the rounded petals may be notched on the upper edges. The 2.3–3.0 cm lip is pointed at the apex. Blue, pale yellow and yellow varieties have been reported.

This beautiful and easily grown species does best when mounted on any rough-barked branch or slab. Give it moderate light, intermediate to cool conditions and a dry rest in winter. Drainage must be very good.

Actual flower size: 4–7.5 cm across.

Sophronitis cernua Lindley

Discovered by Harrison near Rio de Janeiro, this species was used by Lindley as the type for the genus *Sophronitis* in 1827. Synonyms include *S. modesta* and *S. hoffmannseggii*. It is quite common throughout eastern Brazil, growing on trees and rocks in the coastal lowlands and inland savannah country.

The flattened pseudobulbs are closely set on a branching rhizome. Arranged alternately in two rows (sometimes in a single row), they are 1–2 cm long and lie flat against the host. The single ovate leaves are 1.5–3.0 cm long, flat or arching. They may be blunt or sharply pointed. Dark green above, they are usually suffused below with purple. The upper leaf edges and mid-vein may have a reddish tinge. Erect to arching spikes 2–5 cm long carry between two and seven flowers 2.2–2.7 cm across in autumn or winter. These do not open flat. They are a sparkling cinnabar-red with white or yellow at the base of the lip and column. The ovate to oblong sepals are pointed, the petals somewhat rhomboid and may be sharply pointed at the apex. The more or less scoop-shaped lip is 0.8–1.0 cm long with upturned sides at the base and an acute apex. A yellow form of this species exists.

S. cernua requires more warmth than other *Sophronitis* species and does better — at least in our experience — on a cork or paperbark mount which dries out quickly after watering. It appreciates a warm to intermediate environment with fairly bright light. Give it year-round watering, with a reduction in colder weather.

Actual flower size: 2.2–2.7 cm across.

Sophronitis coccinea (Ldl.) Reichenbach (f.)

First collected by Descourtilz, this species was described by Lindley in 1836 as *Cattleya coccinea*. Reichenbach transferred it to *Sophronitis* in 1864. *S. grandiflora* and *S. militaris* are synonyms. It inhabits a narrow band from 650 m to 1,500 m above sea level on the coastal mountains in southeastern Brazil, growing in the cool forests on slender moss-covered trees or on rocky ledges in shaded or partly exposed positions.

The clustered, more or less erect pseudobulbs may be egg shaped, cylindrical or spindle shaped. From 1.5 cm to 4.0 cm tall and 0.2–0.6 cm in diameter, they bear a single fleshy leaf with a purple mid-vein and sometimes purple edges. This oblong to elliptic leaf is 3.0–7.5 cm long and up to 2.5 cm wide. An erect to arching spike 3.0–7.5 cm in length carries a single flower 3–7 cm across from autumn to early spring. There are many colour varieties from yellow to bronze or orange, and even variegated forms. But the veined segments are usually bright scarlet with some yellow or orange at the base of the lip. The oblong sepals are 1.7–2.2 cm long. The rounded to diamond-shaped petals are longer and wider. The 1.3–2.0 cm lip has rounded to triangular lateral lobes which enclose the column, and a pointed oblong to triangular mid-lobe.

One of the most attractive and popular miniatures, this species may be mounted or potted in coarse fibrous material. It needs intermediate to cool conditions with moderate light and fairly high humidity. Year-round watering is recommended, with a reduction in winter. *Actual flower size: 3–7 cm across.*

Sophronitis mantiqueirae Fowlie

Originally considered a subspecies of *S. coccinea**, *S. mantiqueirae* was given specific rank by Fowlie in 1972. Few who have grown both would disagree with Fowlie. The pseudobulbs of *S. mantiqueirae* are smaller, it has no red stripe on the leaf reverse, and it flowers in summer, making it unique in the genus. It grows only in the Sierra da Mantiqueira in Brazil, separated from the habitat of *S. coccinea* by about 80 km. In its native habitat this species grows on moss- or lichen-covered saplings in gullies and on exposed ridges. Temperatures range from 9–20°C in summer to 0–15°C in winter. Conditions are often misty and cool, with high humidity, so this is not a species for tropical conditions, under which it will quickly deteriorate.

We grow our plants with a winter minimum of about 7–10°C, and keep them as cool as possible in summer. They are not particular about light levels, and seem to flower equally well in shade or bright light.

This species is well worth cultivating for its small plant size and brilliant scarlet flowers in summer. All sophronitis species are deservedly popular with species growers, and are among the most rewarding of the miniatures. No other genus possesses quite the brilliant and intense reds of the sophronitis. We can often learn much about the cultural requirements of a species by noting the plants with which it shares its habitat. *S. mantiqueirae* grows with *Dryadella lilliputana** and *Oncidium concolor,* O. longicornu* and *O. gardneri*. *Actual flower size: approximately 3 cm across.*

174

Sophronitis species ex Espirito Santo

This unnamed sophronitis is said to come from the mountain ranges of Espirito Santo in Brazil where it grows in the tropical cloudforests at moderate elevations. It may prove to be a variety of *S. mantiqueirae*.*

The terete pseudobulbs, from 2.0 cm to 4.5 cm long, are only 0.5 cm in diameter and clustered on a branching rhizome. Covered with brown papery bracts, they are cylindrical to spindle shaped. Each bears a single only slightly fleshy leaf 4–10 cm in length and about 1.0–1.7 cm wide. These suberect to spreading leaves are dark green with occasional faint purple mottling beneath. They are narrow at the base, tapering to a very acute apex and have a prominent keel. The single 4–6 cm flowers are produced in winter to summer on spikes about 2 cm long. The sepals and petals are apricot-orange with dull red veins, while the three-lobed lip is yellow streaked with red. The sepals are oblong, with the dorsal strongly recurved. The 2–3 cm petals are broadly oval to almost round with slightly recurved margins. The 1.6–2.0 cm long lip has rather large lateral lobes that meet above the column forming a narrow tube, and an oblong mid-lobe with a blunt apex.

Plants of this species grow well in intermediate to cool conditions with high humidity, and moderate light to semi-shade. They may be mounted or potted in a coarse freely draining medium, and require year-round moisture to prevent the pseudobulbs from shrivelling, a condition this species seems rather prone to.
Actual flower size: 4–6 cm across.

Sophronitis wittigiana Barbosa Rodrigues

Very closely related to *S. brevipedunculata*,* this Brazilian species, which was described by Barbosa Rodrigues in 1878, is often known by its synonym, *S. rosea*. It grows on mossy rough-barked trees in the state of Espirito Santo at 700–2,000 m above sea level in deep swampy gorges.

The pseudobulbs, which are arranged in two rows, may be squat and globular or more elongated, especially in cultivation. From 1.5 cm to 2.5 cm tall and up to 1 cm wide, they are covered with fibrous bracts. The stiff fleshy leaves range from broadly ovate (2.5 by 1.5 cm) to oblong (5.0 cm by 2.5 cm) with a sharply pointed apex. They are flat or recurved, and often suffused with purple beneath. The flower spike, produced from late autumn to very early spring, is longer than in other species, continuing to lengthen for several weeks after flowers open. Typically 4.0–6.5 cm across, these flowers are sparkling pink — ranging from very pale to rosy-pink — with darker veins. The tepals are often recurved, especially the dorsal sepal. The oblong sepals are pointed. The large rounded to diamond-shaped petals are 2–3 cm long. The throat of the three-lobed lip is white or yellow with pink veins. The lateral lobes are rounded and enclose the column, and the mid-lobe is acutely pointed. A white variety has been reported.

S. wittigiana does very well when mounted on cork or paperbark and grown in moderately bright light. Intermediate conditions suit it. Give plenty of water when in growth, with a slightly drier winter rest.
Actual flower size: 4.0–6.5 cm across.

Stelis species ex Mexico

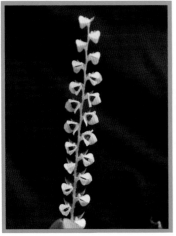

We have been unable to identify the attractive species pictured, which arrived some years ago in a consignment of plants from Mexico. We assume that, like most stelis, it probably comes from the cooler mountain areas at an elevation of 1,000 m or more. We hope that as more taxonomic literature on Mexican species appears we will be able to give it a name.

The erect to arching leaves are closely set on a creeping rhizome. They are 7–10 cm long, including the 2–4 cm stalk, and about 0.8 cm wide. The stalk is covered with papery bracts. The leaves are quite fleshy, have a prominent mid-vein, and are minutely notched at the rounded apex. Spikes up to 10 cm long are produced at the top of the leaf stalk. Over a period of time each stalk produces a number of spikes. They carry twelve to thirty or more 0.5 cm flowers in two rows. These are usually closely set, but may be well spaced. The greenish-white or creamy-yellow sepals open widely, but are always closed in bright light. The sepals are free, rounded at the base, and taper to a blunt point. The minute petals and lip are dark red or maroon.

Like most stelis, this species grows well when mounted or in small pots in a well-drained mixture of treefern fibre, pine bark and sphagnum moss. It requires year-round moisture and high humidity. We grow it in a shady spot with cool to intermediate temperatures and good air movement.

Actual flower size: approximately 0.5 cm across.

Stelis species — *vinosa* alliance

This attractive little species belongs to the *vinosa* alliance, a feature of which is the downy sepals. The alliance, characterised by *S. vinosa* — so-called for its wine-red petals — contains only five species: *S. diaphana, S. guttifera, S. penduliflora, S. plurispicata* and *S. vinosa*. To date we have been unable to determine precisely which of these species it is. It comes from the cool mountain ranges of southern Brazil, where it grows as an epiphyte in the moist forests at moderate elevations.

The clustered leaves are 9–14 cm long, including the long stalks which have a few closely fitting sheaths. The leaf blade is fleshy, elliptic, and minutely three-toothed at the apex. There is a single furrow on the upper surface and a keel beneath. Spikes rise from the stalk late in spring, with several being produced from each stalk over a period of years. From 7 cm to 13 cm long, they carry about thirty well-spaced flowers about 0.3–0.4 cm across and 0.5 cm long. These are arranged in two rows. The sepals are pale green, faintly tinged with pinkish-purple, have three veins and a minutely hairy surface. The 0.3 cm dorsal sepal, which tapers to an acute point, may be held lowermost or perpendicular to the spike, depending on where the flower is situated. The lateral sepals are shorter and rounder. The minute dark purple petals, the purple anther cap and the tiny white lip provide a nice contrast.

Like most other *Stelis*, this species does well in intermediate to cool conditions in light to heavy shade. It may be mounted or potted in treefern, pine bark and sphagnum moss. Plants should be kept moist all year round.

Actual flower size: 0.3–0.4 cm across.

Stenocoryne aureo-fulva (Hook.) Kraenzlin

The genus *Stenocoryne*, created by Lindley in the 19th century, is now regarded by several authors as merely a section of the genus *Bifrenaria*. But this view is not universally accepted, and we feel that stenocoryne flowers are sufficiently differentiated to warrant retention of the original name. The species shown here was first described by Hooker as *Maxillaria aureo-fulva*. Lindley later renamed it *Bifrenaria aureo-fulva*, and Kraenzlin transferred it to *Stenocoryne*. Other synonyms include *Maxillaria stenopetala* and *Stenocoryne secunda*. It comes from the mountains of southern Brazil.

The clustered strongly four-angled pseudobulbs are dark yellow-green or brown-green. From 2.5 cm to 3.5 cm tall, they bear a single 12–20 cm leaf with a prominent mid-vein and acute apex. The erect to pendulous spike, 12–30 cm long, appears from the base of the pseudobulb in late spring. It bears between three and fifteen nodding orange flowers which are tinged with green on the outside. The 1.6 cm sepals and petals are elongated and taper to acute apices. The recurved dorsal sepal and petals are held forward. The lateral sepals join at the base to form a spur. The 1.6 cm long lip is an elongated diamond. The callus at the base is three-lobed at its apex, the mid-lobe short and triangular, the outer ones larger and rounded.

S. aureo-fulva grows well in bright intermediate conditions with plenty of water in the growing season and a drier rest in winter. It may be potted in any well-drained fibrous material, but we grow our plants on treefern slabs. *Actual flower size: approximately 2 cm across.*

Stenocoryne melanopoda (Kl.) Hoehne

Klotzsch originally described this species as *Bifrenaria melanopoda*, the specific name possibly alluding to the darker foot-like projection at the base of the column. Hoehne later transferred the species to the genus *Stenocoryne*. Confined in nature to Brazil, this species comes from cool damp mountain areas in the states of Rio de Janeiro, Sao Paulo and Minas Gerais.

The compressed 2–4 cm tall pseudobulbs are vaguely four-angled, somewhat wrinkled and clustered on a stout rhizome, often lying flat against the host. The single sharply pointed leaf which rises from the apex of each pseudobulb is dark green, broad, and 10–18 cm long, including the short stalk. The arching to pendulous spikes carry between four and ten well-spaced flowers about 2.0–2.5 cm across in spring. The flowers typically do not open widely, but may do so in some plants. They are greenish-yellow suffused with pinkish-brown, and have two bright red spots at the base of the lip. The 1.6 cm dorsal sepal is hooded over the column. The 1.3 cm oval petals are pointed and usually held forward, but sometimes curve outward. The elliptic lateral sepals are widest at the base, where they join to form a small chin. The single-lobed lip is much crisped, with turned-up edges and a yellow callus in the middle.

A charming and easily grown species in intermediate conditions and moderately bright light, it may be potted, but does excellently when mounted on treefern slabs. It appreciates copious water when in growth and a dry winter rest. *Actual flower size: 2–2.5 cm across.*

Stenocoryne racemosa (Hook.) Kraenzlin

Hooker first described this species as *Maxillaria racemosa*, later transferring it to *Bifrenaria*. Kraenzlin then removed it to the genus *Stenocoryne*. It comes from the southern Brazilian states of Rio de Janeiro, Espirito Santo, Parana and Sao Paulo, where it grows in cool mountain habitats.

The clustered pseudobulbs, 2–5 cm tall, are vaguely four-angled, compressed and rather wrinkled. Sometimes slightly curved, they are light to mid-green, often marked with dull brownish-yellow. The single leaf, which is folded at the base to form a short stalk, is 11–15 cm long and up to 2.5 cm wide, tapering to an acute point. It is quite leathery, dark green, and has a prominent mid-vein beneath. In spring suberect to pendulous spikes 8–15 cm long (occasionally to 30 cm) carry between three and ten nodding flowers about 2.5 cm across. The 1.2 cm tepals may be white suffused with pink, greenish-white or green, and have slightly recurved margins with a sharp point at the apex. The dorsal sepal is held forward and the spreading lateral sepals are joined at the base to enclose the 0.3 cm spur formed by the claw of the lip and the base of the column. The petals project forward. The 1.2 cm roundish lip is very wavy, with its sides curved upward at the base, and has a white or yellow three-lobed callus.

We find that this species does well mounted on treefern slabs and hung in moderately bright light. Intermediate temperatures suit it well. Plenty of water should be given when in growth, with a drier winter rest.

Actual flower size: approximately 2.5 cm across.

Stenocoryne vitellina (Ldl.) Kraenzlin

Lindley described this species in 1839 as *Maxillaria vitellina*, and transferred it to the genus *Bifrenaria* in 1843. Kraenzlin placed it in *Stenocoryne*. *Maxillaria barbata* and *Bifrenaria harrisoniae* var. *vitellina* are conspecific. This species occurs in southern Brazil from Espirito Santo and Minas Gerais to Santa Catarina, inhabiting cool mountainous areas.

The strongly four-angled pseudobulbs are clustered, somewhat wrinkled, and covered with papery bracts when young. From 2.5 cm to 5 cm tall and up to 3 cm wide, they are yellow-green to greenish-brown and bear an acute, erect to arching leaf with several prominent veins beneath. The leaf is usually 12–17 cm long, but may occasionally be longer. Spikes 10–20 cm long bear between three and eight yellow flowers about 2.5 cm in diameter with a dark reddish-brown blotch on the mid-lobe and some streaks near the base of the lip. The concave dorsal sepal projects over the column and petals. The latter are narrow at the base, and held forward before curving outward. The more or less triangular lateral sepals are spreading, and form a short spur at the base. The lip is joined to the column by a narrow claw. The large lateral lobes are subtriangular, curling up to meet the column. The wide rounded mid-lobe has wavy edges. In the throat there is a yellow-orange thickened callus with three lobes at the apex.

S. vitellina does well either potted or mounted and grown in intermediate conditions with moderately bright light. Give plenty of water when in growth and a drier rest in winter.

Actual flower size: approximately 2.5 cm across.

Stenoglottis fimbriata Lindley

This species was described by Lindley in 1837 from plants collected by Drège in South Africa. It is widespread in southern Africa from Natal and eastern Cape Province to Tanzania, Zimbabwe and Malawi. It occurs from the coast to 1,800 m above sea level in a variety of habitats, growing in very shallow soil, in decaying vegetation on rocks, even on mossy tree trunks.

The plant comprises a cluster of oblong fleshy tubers with thick white roots. The deciduous leaves, as pictured here, are spotted with purple and lie flat against the ground. They are 2.5–14 cm long and up to 2 cm wide. The flowers, which vary in size and are similar to those of *S. longifolia*,* are borne in summer to autumn on an erect spike which continues to lengthen over several months as flowers open. The sepals and petals are pale to lilac-pink with darker spots toward the recurved apices. The 0.5 cm sepals are spreading, often with some yellow near the base of the laterals. The shorter petals enclose the column. The 0.9 cm lip is three-lobed, whereas that of *S. longifolia* has five lobes. It is pale with purple blotches, and the lobes are long and tapering, the lateral ones shorter and diverging.

With its colourful foliage and ease of cultivation, *S. fimbriata* makes a good companion plant for *S. longifolia* and should be given identical treatment. It is essential that both species are provided with excellent drainage in an open slightly acid medium. Temperatures are not critical provided the plants are given a cool winter rest.

Actual flower size: approximately 1.5 cm long.

Stenoglottis longifolia Hooker (f.)

This easily grown terrestrial first appeared in England in 1888 when Wood, the first curator of the Durban Botanical Gardens in the South African province of Natal, sent some plants from the Ngoye forest to Kew. They first flowered at Kew in September 1889 and Hooker described the species in 1891. It is very closely related to *S. fimbriata*,* but several features distinguish the two species: *S. longifolia* has longer leaves which lack the spotting of *S. fimbriata*; the flower spike has more and larger flowers; the apex of the lip has five feathery lobes rather than three; and, while self-pollination often occurs in *S.fimbriata*, it is unknown in *S. longifolia*. Occurring only in a few inland areas of Natal from 300 m to 700 m above sea level, this species is mainly semi-lithophytic on and around rocky outcrops in the forest.

A rosette of pale green leaves about 20 cm long appears each year in the spring, rising from a cluster of buried tubers. The spike, produced from the leaf rosette, rises to 60 cm or more, and continues to lengthen as the flowers open over a long period in autumn or winter. The pretty flowers are up to 2.5 cm long. After flowering, the deciduous leaves die off and the plant becomes dormant until the next spring.

S. longifolia should be grown in a well-drained medium such as coarse sandy soil and leafmould. It needs a short dry rest when the leaves die down, until the new foliage appears. It does well in cool (even cold) winter conditions in bright indirect light. When in growth it will tolerate quite high temperatures and light levels.

Actual flower size: approximately 1.5–2.5 cm long.

Taeniophyllum glandulosum Blume

There appears to be much confusion regarding the status of many taeniophyllums, particularly in regard to synonymy. This species was first described by Blume in 1825, and is generally regarded as being synonymous with *T. cymbiforme*, *T. wilkianum* (its Australian name) and perhaps *T. retrospiculatum* of the Himalayas. It appears to be very widely distributed, from Sikkim through Sumatra and other parts of Indonesia, Taiwan, Japan, New Guinea and Australia. It inhabits mangrove swamps as well as dry inland areas and damp cloudforests up to 1,700 m elevation, where it grows on the outer twigs and trunks of very slender trees.

Another of the leafless orchids, the species comprises a mass of long fine roots spreading from almost imperceptible stems, and is probably only of interest to the most ardent collectors of miniatures. The greenish-grey roots, which embrace their host closely, carry on the function of photosynthesis. It can form quite extensive colonies, with its capacity for producing new plants from its root tips. This species may flower at any time, producing several spikes up to 5 cm long from the tiny crown. The spike carries up to sixteen pale green or white flowers which turn yellow with age. These short-lived tubular flowers are 0.4 cm long and have a simple boat-shaped lip with a hair-like appendage pointing inward at the tip.

Rather difficult to keep in cultivation, this species should be left on its original host if possible, given moderate shade and year-round water. Intermediate to cool conditions seem to suit it.

Actual flower size: approximately 0.4 cm long.

Trias oblonga Lindley

Lindley used this species as the type for his new genus, describing it in 1829. Its specific epithet refers to the elongated ovary. It has also been described as *Bulbophyllum oblongum*, *Dendrobium tripterum* and *Trias ovata*. It grows as an epiphyte in Burma and Thailand.

The angular to button-like pseudobulbs are closely set on a branching rhizome. About 1 cm across, they bear a single fleshy leaf, which is almost flat or suberect. From 1.7 cm to 3.0 cm long and up to 0.6 cm wide, it is somewhat boat shaped with a prominent keel and a pointed apex. Single flowers are produced on an erect or arching spike up to 2.5 cm long, which comes from the base or side of the pseudobulb in spring. The heavily textured flowers are about 2.5 cm in diameter, and do not last long. The spreading sepals and forward-pointing petals are brownish-green or yellow. The broadly ovate sepals overlap at the base and curve slightly inward, with the laterals forming a broad chin at their base. The small more or less acute petals are three-veined. The maroon or purple lip is joined to the column foot, runs parallel to the column and then turns sharply out and downward. It is trowel shaped with a groove down the middle and tiny erect 'ears' at the base.

T. oblonga likes an intermediate to warm environment, with moderate light and high humidity. It needs year-round moisture, and does best on mounts of cork or paperbark. This species is not difficult to cultivate, and thrives in the same conditions suitable for most Asian bulbophyllums.

Actual flower size: approximately 2.5 cm across.

Trias picta (Par. & Rchb. (f.)) Parish and Hemsley

This charming epiphyte belongs to a small genus whose name refers to the three-pointed star-like flowers. It is closely related to *Bulbophyllum* — indeed, this species was first described by Parish and Reichenbach as *Bulbophyllum pictum,* and transferred to *Trias* in 1882 by Hemsley, using a manuscript supplied by Parish. It is found in Burma and Thailand at about 1,000 m above sea level.

The ovoid to almost round pseudobulbs are 1.2–2.0 cm tall, and up to 2 cm in diameter. Closely set on a creeping rhizome, they bear a single very fleshy leaf to 6 cm long, which tapers at both ends and has a prominent midvein. Flowering may be at any time of the year on short spikes rising from the base of the pseudobulb. The single flower is about 2 cm across and usually pale pink or greenish-white very heavily spotted and blotched with maroon-purple. The spreading sepals are very broad at the base, tapering gently to a more or less acute apex. The lateral sepals are joined to the base of the column, forming a small chin. The small oblong petals, which are darker, point forward. The mobile, blackish-maroon lip is hinged at the base, erect to half its height, then pointing out and downward. It is tongue shaped and has a pair of minute 'ears' at the base.

T. picta should be mounted. We have found cork or paperbark to be best. An intermediate to warm environment suits it very well, with moderate light. It needs year-round moisture, and should be allowed to dry out only if winter temperatures fall below about 10°C.

Actual flower size: approximately 2 cm across.

Tuberolabium kotoense Yamamoto

This species is widely known by its original name of *Saccolabium quisumbingii* (L. O. Williams). Yamamoto renamed it *Tuberolabium kotoense* in 1924; this genus, the name of which refers to the swollen lip, is characterised by its short column. There are only seven members of the genus, occurring from Thailand through Java to the Philippines and Japan. While this is the only species found in Taiwan, where it grows on the trunks of *Ficus* species in mountainous areas, it is one of three found in the Philippines. Here it occurs at 300 m above sea level in Laguna and Rizal provinces of Luzon.

The stems of this vandaceous species are quite short, with thick leathery leaves 6–15 cm long. In winter thick pendulous spikes appear from the leaf axils with numerous long-lasting flowers 1.2 cm across. When the plants are several years old the spike can reach 25 cm in length and carry as many as fifty flowers. The flowers, which are spirally arranged and all open at the same time, are fragrant and waxy. The saccate lip, which is marked with wine-red spots, has a short spur. Although the flowers do not open fully, their crystalline texture makes this a much-admired species.

It should be grown in semi-shade with intermediate to warm temperatures and kept moist all year round. It may be potted in treefern chunks or some other coarse well-drained material, or mounted on treefern, cork or paperbark.

Actual flower size: approximately 1.2 cm across.

Vanda cristata Lindley

Firstcollected in Nepal in 1818 by Wallich, who called it *Aerides cristatum*, this species was renamed *Vanda cristata* by Lindley in 1832. Another synonym is *V. striata* (Reichenbach (f.)). It has recently been reclassified as *Trudelia cristata* by Garay, who transferred it to a new genus he created in 1986. We have retained its old name because of its familiarity with growers. Closely related to *V. alpina* and *V. pumila*,* it is found in Kumaon, Nepal, Sikkim, Bhutan and Meghalaya (India) at elevations of 1,700–2,000 m where it grows as an epiphyte on moss-covered trees. In these habitats there is mist and fog throughout the year with bright light and low temperatures in winter. It is an excellent subject for collectors restricted to cool conditions.

The stem of the plant is usually 10–20 cm tall with leathery leaves up to 15 cm long, but usually shorter in cultivation. The inflorescence rises from the leaf axils and carries one or two flowers up to 5 cm across. Flowering is usually in spring or summer. The fragrant waxy flowers last for up to two months. Flower colour is variable, with sepals and petals usually yellow-green and the lip tawny-yellow with dark maroon markings. The variety *multiflora* grows at lower altitudes in Sikkim and bears between three and five flowers which are smaller than those of the type.

V. cristata is happy in cool to intermediate conditions with bright light and plenty of water when in growth, followed by a dry rest in winter. It may be mounted or grown in well-drained pots or baskets.

Actual flower size: 2.5–5 cm across.

Vanda lilacina Teijsmann & Binnendijk

This monopodial species, which was described by Teijsmann and Binnendijk in 1862, is sometimes known by its synonym, *Vanda loatica*. It is native to Burma, Thailand, Indochina and southwestern China, growing epiphytically from 100 m to 1,000 m above sea level. It is becoming rarer in all areas, suffering from the continuing destruction of its natural habitats.

The stems are quite short, with several pairs of fleshy alternating leaves 9–13 cm long. They are strap shaped, and more or less folded longitudinally, with a notched apex. Erect to suberect spikes appear from the leaf axils in winter, and bear up to twenty well-spaced flowers which nearly all open together. From 2.0 cm to 2.5 cm across, they are strongly fragrant. Colour is white to cream, with or without lavender tips, and with rows of tiny bright lilac-red to amethyst warts on the lip so that it is almost completely covered. The dorsal sepal is more or less erect or curved inward, as are the slightly twisted upward-swept petals. The spreading lateral sepals are broad with recurved edges. The large lateral lobes of the lip are triangular to oblong and held erect. The 0.7 cm tongue-like mid-lobe curves downward, and has a bilobed callus at its base. The funnel-shaped spur is 0.5 cm long with a narrow entrance.

V. lilacina appreciates plenty of bright light and a humid, warm to intermediate environment. It grows well in an open slat basket which allows its extensive root system to ramble. Give plenty of water all year round.

Actual flower size: 2–2.5 cm across.

Vanda pumila Hooker (f.)

Joseph Hooker described this species in 1890, based on material collected by Cathcart in Sikkim. Like *Vanda cristata** and *V. alpina*, this species has recently been transferred to the new genus *Trudelia*. However, some authors believe that differences between these and other vandas do not warrant the creation of a new genus. *V. pumila* is reported from Sikkim, Bhutan, Thailand, Vietnam and southern China from 500 m to 1,000 m above sea level, and may also occur in neighbouring countries.

The short stem is covered on the lower part by the bases of old leaves, and bears several strap-shaped 7–20 cm leaves, which are closely set and strongly folded for much of their length.

They are curved, very fleshy, and appear to be chewed at the apex. Between two and five flowers are usually produced in late spring or summer on an erect spike 10–20 cm long. The heavily textured fragrant flowers are 2.5–5.0 cm wide. The sepals and petals, which curve inward, are white, cream or yellow, with or without a few red-brown spots. The 2.5–3.0 cm sepals are narrower at the base, spreading to a blunt apex. The narrow petals are 1.5–2.8 cm long. The very fleshy lip, from 1.8 cm to 2.3 cm long, is cream to pale yellow with reddish-purple streaks. The triangular lateral lobes are erect, and the concave ovoid mid-lobe has four to six keels. The conical spur is relatively long.

This species prefers a warm to intermediate environment with high humidity and bright light. If cold winters preclude normal watering, then mist on bright days.

Actual flower size: 2.5–5 cm across.

Zygostates lunata Lindley

A member of a small genus of subtropical epiphytes, this species was described in the 19th century by Lindley. The genus is closely related to *Ornithocephalus*, and this species is conspecific with *Dactylostylis fimbriata* and *Ornithocephalus navicularis*. It grows as an epiphyte on mossy trees at moderate altitudes in southern Brazil, where heavy dews are experienced almost every night.

Plants are without pseudobulbs, and comprise fans of between five and seven narrow mid- to dark-green leaves from 4 cm to 9 cm long. They are slightly fleshy with an acute apex and a prominent keel beneath.

Arching to pendent spikes about 10 cm long rise from the leaf axils in late spring to summer and carry thirty or more closely set flowers about 0.8 cm across. The oval sepals, which are often swept back, are greenish-white. The broad fan-shaped petals are greenish-gold to golden-yellow. At their widest point they are 0.4 cm wide, and about the same in length. The edges are deeply and irregularly serrated, and they are covered with tiny glands. The white cup-shaped lip is serrated, and has two thick calli at the base. The column has a long yellow beak-like anther and two 'arms' at the base which end in dark green knobs.

Z. lunata does well mounted on treefern or placed in small pots of well-drained fibrous material. It should be kept moist at all times. It should be grown in semi-shade or full shade in intermediate to cool conditions. A charming species, and an easy grower once established.

Actual flower size: approximately 0.8 cm across.

Glossary

Albino   Lacking in pigmentation, white.

Alliance   A loose grouping, within a genus, of species with similar characteristics.

Anther Cap   Cap which covers the sac at the top of the column which contains the pollinia.

Caatinga   Dry region covered with thorny deciduous scrub (Brazil).

Callus   A hard protuberance or prominence.

Clone   An individual of a species, produced from a single seed, and its vegetatively reproduced progeny.

Column   Specialised formation in orchid flowers resulting from the union of stamen and pistil.

Connate   Joined together.

Conspecific   Synonymous with, identical to.

Deflexed   Turned or bent outward.

Disc   The face or flat portion of a floral segment; in orchids usually the midlobe of the lip.

Endemic   Confined to a distinct area, not found elsewhere.

Epiphyte   A plant which grows on another plant, but which receives no nourishment from its host.

Equitant   Leaves which are set one inside the other in two ranks.

Falcate   Sickle-shaped.

Filiform   Threadlike.

Genus   The grouping of one or more species having similar characteristics and common ancestry.

Gland   A wart-like protuberance.

Homonym   A name unacceptable under the rules of taxonomy, having been previously applied to another species in the same category.

Inorganic   Of mineral origin, containing no carbon in its molecule, not arising from natural growth.

Internode   The portion of a stem or pseudobulb between nodes or joints.

Keel   A projecting ridge.

Labellum   The lip of an orchid flower, a specialised petal.

Lithophyte   A plant growing on stone or rock.

Mentum   Chin-like protuberance formed by the bases of the lateral sepals and the column foot.

Monopodial   A plant which grows only upward from the terminal bud at the apex of the stem.

Monotypic   A genus containing only one species.

Non-resupinate   A flower not turned upside down, i.e., with labellum above column.

Organic   A substance containing carbon in its molecule; resulting from natural growth.

Paperbark   A tree in the genus *Melaleuca*; the bark of such a tree, which comprises many thin papery layers.

Petal   Part of the corolla of a flower, usually coloured, comprising the inner and upper parts of the flower.

Petaloid   Like a petal.

Petiole   Leaf stalk.

Pleurothallid   An orchid of a genus belonging to the subtribe Pleurothallidinae.

Pollinia   The regular granular masses into which orchid pollen is compressed.

Pseudobulb   Thickened bulb-like stem possessed by many orchids; of fibrous constitution and not a true bulb.

Reflexed   Abruptly bent or turned backward or downward.

Resupinate   Inversion of a flower by a

twisting of the ovary (in orchids) so that the lip is lower than the column.

Rhizome   In orchids, a stem which forms a rootstock, either above or below ground.

Rupicolous   Growing on or among rocks or stones.

Sac   A hollow bag-like depression.

Saccate   Sac-like.

Savannah   A dry plain or grassland, only lightly or intermittently wooded.

Sepal   The lower and outer parts of a flower.

Sessile   Lacking a stalk or stem.

Species   A group of plants or animals showing intergrading among its members and having in common one or more significant characteristics which separate it from all other groups. (This is a very conservative definition. Most botanists hesitate to give a definition, as the concept of a species is a very artificial one. All botanical classification is in a sense an attempt to impose a static and abitrary framework upon a dynamic biological situation, and nowhere are the deficiencies of such an attempt made more obvious than in our attempts to arrive at a satisfactory definition of the term 'species'. However, as amateurs of orchidology, we can in practice accept that an orchid species is a representative of a group of plants possessing significant and constant similarities within the group, and distinct differences from other groups; and breeds true from sibling crosses.)

Spur   A hollow tubular extension of a floral organ, often containing nectar-producing glands.

Stolon   Runner.

Substrate   The material on or in which a plant grows.

Symbiosis   A relationship between two dissimilar organisms which benefits both.

Sympodial   A form of growth in which one or more new growths are produced each season at the base of the old growth.

Synanthous   Flowers appearing with new vegetative growth.

Synonym   (In taxonomy) A scientific name rejected in favour of an accepted correct name for a species.

Tepal   Sepal or petal.

Terete   Cylindrical in form.

Terrestrial   Growing in the earth.

Transpiration   Exhalation of water vapour.

Tuber   A specialised thickened stem, usually underground, containing new growth eyes.

Umbel   Inflorescence having usually a flat or convex top, with flower stalks rising from a common point.

Vandaceous   Relating to vandas; used often as a loose synonym for the term monopodial.

Velamen   A layer of tissue containing air cells which covers orchid roots.

Xeric   Extremely dry.

INDEX

Entries in *italics* indicate synonyms.
An asterisk (*) indicates that the
species is mentioned in passing
only.

Acianthus caudatus 33
Acoridium pulcherrimum 73
Acriopsis indica 33
Aerides arachnites* 72
Aerides crassifolium 34
Aerides cristatum 182
Aerides decumbens 91
Aerides difformis* 141
Aerides flabellatum 34
Aerides japonicum 171
Amesiella philippinensis 35
Angraecum caffrum 123
Angraecum chiloschistae 121
Angraecum falcatum 126
Angraecum japonicum 171
Angraecum philippinense 35
Aporum leonis 66
Ascocentrum ampullaceum 35
Ascocentrum ampullaceum v.
  aurantiacum* 35
Ascocentrum curvifolium 36
Ascocentrum curvifolium v.
  citrinum* 36
Ascocentrum micranthum 172
Ascocentrum miniatum 36

Barbosella miersii 37
Barbrodria miersii 37
Barkeria chinensis* 38, 39
Barkeria dorotheae 37
Barkeria halbingeri 38
Barkeria lindleyana* 40
Barkeria naevosa 38
Barkeria palmeri 39
Barkeria shoemakeri 39
Barkeria spectabilis 40
Bifrenaria aureo-fulva 177
Bifrenaria harrisoniae v.
  vitellina 178
Bifrenaria melanopoda 177
Bifrenaria racemosa 178
Bifrenaria tyrianthina* 158, 160
Bifrenaria vitellina 178

Bletia bicolor 102
Brassavola glauca 167
Brassavola nodosa* 40
Brassavola pumilio 88
Broughtonia sanguinea 40
Bulbophyllum aurantiacum 41,
  42*
Bulbophyllum bowkettae 41
Bulbophyllum chlorostachys 48
Bulbophyllum crassulifolium 41*,
  42
Bulbophyllum cummingii* 49
Bulbophyllum dayanum 42
Bulbophyllum dyphoniae 42
Bulbophyllum elisae 43
Bulbophyllum evasum 43
Bulbophyllum gadgarrense 44, 49*
Bulbophyllum globuliforme* 3, 46
Bulbophyllum gracillimum 44
Bulbophyllum inabai 45
Bulbophyllum japonicum 45
Bulbophyllum johnsonii 45
Bulbophyllum kirkwoodii 45
Bulbophyllum lepidum* 49
Bulbophyllum macphersonii 46
Bulbophyllum minutissimum 46
Bulbophyllum negrosianum 47
Bulbophyllum oblongum 180
Bulbophyllum pictum 181
Bulbophyllum picturatum 47
Bulbophyllum planibulbe 48
Bulbophyllum planibulbe v.
  sumatranum* 48
Bulbophyllum prenticei 66
Bulbophyllum propinquum 48
Bulbophyllum psittacoides 44
Bulbophyllum radicans 8
Bulbophyllum schillerianum* 41,
  42
Bulbophyllum serratotruncatum
  49
Bulbophyllum shepherdii* 42
Bulbophyllum taylori 50

Bulbophyllum toressae 71
Bulbophyllum wadsworthii 49
Bulbophyllum waughense 41
Bulbophyllum wendlandianum 50
Bulbophyllum whitei 45

Cadetia taylori 50
Callista bairdiana 60
Callista pachyphylla 69
Callista striolata 71
Camarotis purpurea 122
Capanemia juergensiana 51
Capanemia superflua 51
Capanemia uliginosa 51
Cattleya aclandiae 22*, 51
Cattleya bulbosa 53
Cattleya coccinea 174
Cattleya flavida 52
Cattleya forbesii 52
Cattleya gardneriana 53
Cattleya intermedia 19
Cattleya loddigesii* 53, 90
Cattleya luteola 52
Cattleya marginata 97
Cattleya meyeri 52
Cattleya pinelii 97
Cattleya princeps 53
Cattleya pumila 97
Cattleya spectabilis 97
Cattleya sulphurea 52
Cattleya walkeriana 53
Caularthron bicornutum 53
Chytroglossa marileoniae 54
Cirrhopetalum collettii 50
Cirrhopetalum elisae 43
Cirrhopetalum gracillimum 44
Cirrhopetalum inabai 45
Cirrhopetalum japonicum 45
Cirrhopetalum ochraceum 49
Cirrhopetalum picturatum 47
Cirrhopetalum planibulbe 48
Cirrhopetalum psittacoides 44
Cirrhopetalum wendlandianum 50

Cleisostoma arietinum 54
Cleisostoma beckleri 149
Cleisostoma brevilabre 154
Cleisostoma micrantha 172
Cleisostoma tridentata 155
Cochlioda noezliana 55
Coelogyne confusa 55
Coelogyne cristata v. lemoniana 56
Coelogyne merrillii 56
Coelogyne nitida 57
Coelogyne ochracea 57
Coelogyne uniflora 143
Comparettia coccinea 57
Comparettia falcata 58
Comparettia rosea 58
Constantia cipoensis* 20
Corybas aconitiflorus 58
Cranichis luteola 161
Crytochilus sanguinea 59
Cryptophoranthus acaulis 161
Cryptosanus scriptus 102
Cryptostylis longifolia 59
Cryptostylis subulata 59
Cuitlauzina pendula* 88
Cycnoches chlorochilon* 6
Cymbidium macrorhizon* 7
Cymbidium nitidum 57
Cymbidium speciosissimum 56
Cymbidium stapelioides 163
Cypripedium bellatulum 143
Cypripedium concolor 144
Cypripedium fairrieanum 144
Cypripedium godefroyae 146
Cypripedium javanicum 146
Cypripedium niveum 147
Cypripedium spicerianum 148
Cypripedium tonkinense 144
Cypripedium venustum 148
Cyrtochilum citrinum 130

Dactylostylis fimbriata 183
Dendrobium acrobaticum 62
Dendrobium aemulum 20*, 21, 60
Dendrobium aggregatum 29
Dendrobium agrostophyllum* 60
Dendrobium arachnites* 72
Dendrobium bairdianum 60
Dendrobium bellatulum 61, 68*
Dendrobium braiaense 62
Dendrobium canaliculatum 13, 61
Dendrobium canaliculatum v.
  foelschei* 62
Dendrobium canaliculatum v.
  nigrescens 62
Dendrobium capillipes 62

Dendrobium cariniferum* 61
Dendrobium carronii* 61
Dendrobium chrystianum 68
Dendrobium ciliatum* 64
Dendrobium ciliatum v. breve 64
Dendrobium compactum 63
Dendrobium compressum 65
Dendrobium crassulifolium 42
Dendrobium cucumerinum 63
Dendrobium draconis* 61
Dendrobium delacourii 64
Dendrobium fellowsii 60
Dendrobium flavescens 161
Dendrobium giddinsii 60
Dendrobium hillii 170
Dendrobium kingianum 64
Dendrobium kingianum v.
  album 65
Dendrobium lamellatum 65
Dendrobium leonis 66
Dendrobium lichenastrum* 66, 71
Dendrobium lichenastrum v.
  prenticei 66
Dendrobium lindleyi* 28
Dendrobium linguiforme 67
Dendrobium linguiforme v.
  nugentii 67
Dendrobium margaritaceum 61*,
  68
Dendrobium milliganii 71
Dendrobium minutissimum 46
Dendrobium monophyllum 68,
  70*
Dendrobium pachyphyllum 69
Dendrobium pisibulbum 69
Dendrobium platycaulon 65
Dendrobium prenticei 66
Dendrobium rigidum 69
Dendrobium schoeninum 71
Dendrobium schneiderae 70
Dendrobium senile 70
Dendrobium shepherdii 42
Dendrobium striolatum 71
Dendrobium tattonianum 61
Dendrobium taylori 50
Dendrobium teretifolium* 43
Dendrobium tetragonum 11
Dendrobium toressae 71
Dendrobium trigonopus 72
Dendrobium tripterum 180
Dendrobium unicum 72
Dendrobium uniflos 50
Dendrobium variabile 66
Dendrobium velutinum 72
Dendrobium venustum* 64

Dendrobium wilmsianum* 63
Dendrochilum pulcherrimum 73
Dendrorchis minuta 161
Diacrium amazonicum 53
Diacrium bicornutum 53
Diaphananthe rutila 73
Dinema paleaceum 127
Dinema polybulbon 79
Dipodium punctatum* 7
Dipteranthus duchii 74
Dipteranthus pustulatus 74
Disa grandiflora 75
Disa uniflora 75
Dracula diabola* 105
Dryadella lilliputana 75, 174*
Dryadella zebrina 76

Encyclia amicta 76
Encyclia bicornuta 76
Encyclia boothii 127
Encyclia cyanocolumna 77
Encyclia fausta 77
Encyclia ghiesbreghtiana 78
Encyclia hastata* 78, 80
Encyclia linearifolioides 76
Encyclia mariae 78
Encyclia ochracea 79
Encyclia polybulbon 10, 21*, 79
Encyclia pringlei 80
Encyclia pygmaea* 79
Encyclia tenuissima* 77
Encyclia tripunctata 80
Encyclia vitellina 81
Encyclia widgrenii 81
Epidendrum amictum 76
Epidendrum antenniferum 82
Epidendrum aviculum 98
Epidendrum bicornutum 53
Epidendrum boothii 127
Epidendrum capense 124
Epidendrum cyanocolumnum 77
Epidendrum diguetti 80
Epidendrum discolor 125
Epidendrum faustum 77
Epidendrum ghiesbreghtianum 78
Epidendrum gnomus 126
Epidendrum guttatum* 139
Epidendrum jonquille 163
Epidendrum leucomelanum 90
Epidendrum ligulatum 138
Epidendrum longipetalum 82
Epidendrum luteolum 52
Epidendrum mariae 78
Epidendrum micropus 80
Epidendrum naevosum 38

Epidendrum ochraceum 79
Epidendrum paleaceum 127
Epidendrum palmeri 39
Epidendrum pauper 52
Epidendrum polybulbon 79
Epidendrum porpax 126
Epidendrum porphyrophyllum
  126
Epidendrum pringlei 80
Epidendrum pugioniforme 82
Epidendrum pusillum 164
Epidendrum rowleyi* 82
Epidendrum sanguineum 40
Epidendrum schlechterianum 125
Epidendrum spectabilis 40
Epidendrum tetrapetalum 139
Epidendrum tortipetalum* 82
Epidendrum tribuloides 161
Epidendrum tripunctatum 80
Epidendrum triquetrum 139
Epidendrum triste 79
Epidendrum utricularioides 89
Epidendrum vitellinum 81
Epiphora pubescens 162
Eria dasyphylla 83
Eria pannea 83
Eria queenslandica 84
Erycina echinata 84
Erycina diaphana* 88

Gastrochilus dasypogon 85
Gastrochilus fuscopunctatus 85
Gastrochilus intermedius 86
Gastrochilus japonicus 86
Gastrochilus matsuran 85
Gastrochilus miniatus 36
Gastrochilus somai 86
Grammatophyllum speciosum* 3

Haraella odorata 87
Haraella retrocalla 87
Hartwegia purpurea 125
Holcoglossum kimballianum 87
Homalopetalum pumilio 88
Hymenorchis javieri (?) 88, 123*

Ionopsis utricularioides 89
Isabelia pulchella 89
Isabelia virginalis 90

Jacquiniella leucomelana 90

Kingidium deliciosum 91
Kingiella decumbens 91

Laelia bahiensis 91, 96*
Laelia crispilabia* 158
Laelia dayana 4, 92, 97*
Laelia endsfeldzii 92
Laelia flava* 158
Laelia furfuracea 93
Laelia itambana 93
Laelia jongheana 94
Laelia lilliputana 94
Laelia longipes* 158
Laelia lucasiana 95
Laelia lundii 95
Laelia mantiqueirae 96
Laelia ostermeyeri 95
Laelia pfisteri 91*, 96
Laelia pumila 92*, 97, 98*
Laelia regnellii 95
Laelia regnellii 95
Laelia reichenbachiana 95
Laelia rubescens 97
Laelia sincorana 98
Lanium avicula 98
Lemboglossum cervantesii 99
Lemboglossum cordatum 99
Lemboglossum maculatum* 99
Lemboglossum majale 100
Lemboglossum rossii 100
Lemboglossum stellatum 101
Leochilus carinatus 101
Leochilus major 102
Leochilus powellii 102
Leochilus scriptus 102
Leptorchis coelogynoides 103
Leptotes bicolor 102
Leptotes glaucophylla 102
Leptotes minuta 103
Leptotes pauloensis 103
Leptotes serrulata 102
Leptotes tenuis 103
Limodorum longicorne 124
Liparis coelogynoides 103
Liparis elegans 104
Liparis gracilis 104
Liparis mowbulana 103
Liparis nutans 104
Liparis stricta 104
Lissochilus sylvaticus 162

Malaxis subulata 59
Masdevallia abbreviata 105
Masdevallia aenigma 105
Masdevallia agaster 106
Masdevallia angulifera 106
Masdevallia auropurpurea 105
Masdevallia bicolor 105

Masdevallia calura* 116
Masdevallia campyloglossa 107
Masdevallia caudata 107, 108*,
  115*, 116*
Masdevallia corniculata* 105
Masdevallia decumana 108, 116*
Masdevallia encephala* 105
Masdevallia erinacea 108
Masdevallia estradae 109
Masdevallia floribunda 109
Masdevallia fulvescens* 117
Masdevallia galeottiana 109
Masdevallia gilbertoi 110
Masdevallia herradurae 110
Masdevallia hirtzii 111, 112*
Masdevallia horrida 108
Masdevallia hymenantha 111
Masdevallia infracta* 90
Masdevallia klabochorum 107
Masdevallia lilliputana 75
Masdevallia limax 111*, 112
Masdevallia ludibunda 109
Masdevallia mendozae 111*, 112
Masdevallia myriostigma 109
Masdevallia pallida 118
Masdevallia pandurilabia 113
Masdevallia persicina 113
Masdevallia polysticta 114
Masdevallia prodigiosa 114
Masdevallia pteroglossa 115
Masdevallia purpurella 115
Masdevallia reichenbachiana* 116
Masdevallia replicata* 111
Masdevallia rolfeana 116
Masdevallia sanctae-inesae 116
Masdevallia schroederiana 117
Masdevallia shuttleworthii 107
Masdevallia strobelii 117
Masdevallia triangularis* 115
Masdevallia ventricularia 118
Masdevallia wageneriana v.
  colombiana 115
Masdevallia wageneriana v.
  ecuadorensis 113
Masdevallia wurdackii* 114
Masdevallia xanthina* 118
Masdevallia xanthina ssp. pallida
  118
Masdevallia zebrina 76
Maxillaria aureo-fulva 177
Maxillaria barbata 178
Maxillaria boothii 127
Maxillaria crocea* 119
Maxillaria juergensii 119, 120*
Maxillaria lindleyana 119

Maxillaria meirax 120
Maxillaria notylioglossa 120
Maxillaria parahybunensis 120
Maxillaria racemosa 178
Maxillaria seidelii 121
Maxillaria stapelioides 163
Maxillaria stenopetala 177
Maxillaria vitellina 178
Maxillaria xanthina 163
Meiracyllium wettsteinii 89
Microcoelia exilis 121, 122*
Microcoelia stolzii 122
Micropera rostrata 122
Microsaccus wenzelii 123
Mystacidium caffrum 123
Mystacidium capense 124
Mystacidium filicorne 124
Mystacidium venosum 1, 124

Nageliella purpurea 125
Nanodes discolor 125
Nanodes mathewsii 126
Neofinetia falcata 126
Neolauchia pulchella 89
Neolehmannia porpax 21, 126
Nidema boothii 127
Notylia barkeri 127, 128*
Notylia bipartita 127
Notylia cordiglossa 128
Notylia guatemalensis 127
Notylia hemitricha* 128
*Notylia tridachne** 127
Notylia trisepala 127

Oberonia crassiuscula 153
Oberonia palmicola 128
Oberonia pusilla 153
Oberonia titania* 128
Octomeria decumbens 129
Odontoglossum cervantesii 99
Odontoglossum coerulescens 100
Odontoglossum cordatum 99
Odontoglossum erosum 101
Odontoglossum hookeri 99
Odontoglossum lueddemannii 99
Odontoglossum majale 100
Odontoglossum noezlianum 55
Odontoglossum platycheilum 100
Odontoglossum rossii 100
Odontoglossum rubescens 100
Odontoglossum stellatum 101
Odontoglossum warnerianum 100
Oncidium barbatum 129, 137*
Oncidium bicornutum 137
Oncidium bifolium 130

Oncidium carinatum 101
Oncidium celsium 130
Oncidium ciliatum* 129, 137
Oncidium concolor 130, 131*, 132*, 174*
Oncidium dasystyle 131, 132*
Oncidium dentatum 137
Oncidium echinatum 84
Oncidium echinophorum 134
Oncidium fuscopetalum 131
Oncidium gardneri* 174
Oncidium gracile 132, 134*
Oncidium harrisonianum 132
Oncidium hians 133
Oncidium hookeri 133, 135*
Oncidium hydrophyllum 134
Oncidium iridifolium 164
Oncidium janeirense 135
Oncidium leucostomum 133
Oncidium limminghei 134
Oncidium loefgrenii 133*, 135
Oncidium longicornu* 136, 174
Oncidium longipes 135
Oncidium macronix 136
Oncidium macropetalum 131*, 136
Oncidium macropetalum v. fuscopetalum 131
Oncidium maxilligerum 133
Oncidium mellifluum 135
Oncidium micropogon 129*, 137
Oncidium nanum* 138
Oncidium ottonis 130
Oncidium oxyacanthosmum 135
Oncidium pallidum 132
Oncidium pantherinum 132
Oncidium pentaspilum 132
Oncidium pubes 137
Oncidium pubescens 137
Oncidium pulchellum 138
Oncidium pumilum 138
Oncidium pusillum 164
Oncidium quadricorne 133
Oncidium quadripetalum 139
Oncidium raniferum* 133, 135
Oncidium raniferum v. majus 133
Oncidium sarcodes* 90
Oncidium scriptum 102
Oncidium spilopterum* 160
Oncidium superfluum 51
Oncidium tetrapetalum 139
Oncidium tricolor 139
Oncidium triquetrum 139
Oncidium vexillarium 130
Onychium lamellatum 65

Ornithocephalus elephas 140
Ornithocephalus inflexus 140
Ornithocephalus iridifolius 140
Ornithocephalus mexicanus 140
Ornithocephalus myrticola 141
Ornithocephalus navicularis 183
Ornithocephalus pottsiae 140
Ornithocephalus pustulatus 74
Ornithocephalus pygmaeum 141
Ornithocephalus reitzii 141
Ornithocephalus tonduzii 140
Ornithochilus difformis 141
Ornithochilus fuscus 141
Ornithophora radicans 142

Pabstiella mirabilis 142
Panisea uniflora 143
Paphiopedilum × Ang Thong* 147
Paphiopedilum appletonianum* 16
Paphiopedilum barbatum* 145
Paphiopedilum bellatulum 143, 147*
Paphiopedilum chamberlainianum* 145
Paphiopedilum concolor 144, 146*, 147*
Paphiopedilum fairrieanum 144
Paphiopedilum fowliei 145
Paphiopedilum glaucophyllum 145
Paphiopedilum godefroyae 146, 147*
Paphiopedilum hennisianum* 145
Paphiopedilum javanicum 146
Paphiopedilum lawrenceanum* 145
Paphiopedilum leucochilum 147
Paphiopedilum liemianum* 145
Paphiopedilum moquetteanum 145
Paphiopedilum niveum 146*, 147
Paphiopedilum spicerianum 148
Paphiopedilum venustum 148
Paphiopedilum venustum v. measuresianum 149
Paphiopedilum venustum v. pardinum 149
Paphiopedilum venustum v. rubrum 149
Paphiopedilum venustum v. teestaensis 149
Paphiopedilum victoria-mariae* 145
Paphiopedilum virens* 146

Papillilabium beckleri 149
Parasarcochilus spathulatus 150
Parasarcochilus weinthalii 150
Pelatantheria insectifera 4
Phalaenopsis cornu-cervi 151
Phalaenopsis decumbens 91
Phalaenopsis deliciosa 91
Phalaenopsis devriesiana 151
Phalaenopsis equestris 151
Phalaenopsis riteiwanensis 151
Phalaenopsis rosea 151
Phloeophila pubescens 152
Pholidota species 152
Phreatia baileyana 153
Phreatia crassiuscula 153
Phreatia limenophylax 153
Phreatia pusilla 153
Phyllorchis dayana 42
Physosiphon pubescens 152
Physosiphon loddigesii 154
Physosiphon tubatus 154
Pinalia pannea 83
Plectorrhiza brevilabris 154
Plectorrhiza tridentata 154*, 155
Pleione bulbocodioides* 155
Pleione formosana 155
Pleione speciosissima 56
Pleurothallis bicolor 160
Pleurothallis cuneifolia 157
Pleurothallis fallax 161
Pleurothallis ghiesbreghtiana 156
Pleurothallis grobyi 21, 156, 157*
Pleurothallis hookeri 160
Pleurothallis hypnicola 157
Pleurothallis johnsonii 157
Pleurothallis litophila 158
Pleurothallis marginata 156
Pleurothallis miersii 37
Pleurothallis mirabilis 142
Pleurothallis muscifera 166
Pleurothallis ochracea 158
Pleurothallis pectinata* 158
Pleurothallis prolifera 158
Pleurothallis quadrifida 156
Pleurothallis racemiflora 156
Pleurothallis sarracenia 152
Pleurothallis schiedei 159
Pleurothallis sonderana 157*, 159
Pleurothallis strupifolia 160
Pleurothallis surinamensis 156
Pleurothallis teres 15, 95*, 160
Pleurothallis tribuloides 88*, 161
Pleurothallis tridentata* 158
Polychilos cornu-cervi 151
Polystachya capensis 162

Polystachya glaberrima 162
Polystachya lindleyana 162
Polystachya luteola 161
Polystachya mauritiana 161
Polystachya minuta 161
Polystachya ottoniana 162
Polystachya pisobulbon 162
Polystachya pubescens 162
Promenaea citrina 163
Promenaea stapelioides 163
Promenaea xanthina 163
Psygmorchis pusilla 164
Pteroceras spathulatus 150
Pterostylis nutans 9, 164, 165*
Pterostylis pedunculata 165

Restrepia hemsleyana 165
Restrepia lansbergii 166
Restrepia muscifera 166
Restrepia xanthophthalma 166
Rhinerrhiza divitiflora 166
Rhyncolaelia glauca 167
Robiquetia fuerstenbergiana 167
Rodriguezia anomala 51

Saccolabium ampullaceum 35
Saccolabium arietinum 54
Saccolabium calcaratum 155
Saccolabium curvifolium 36
Saccolabium dasypogon 85
Saccolabium fuerstenbergianum 167
Saccolabium intermedium 86
Saccolabium japonicum 86
Saccolabium micranthum 172
Saccolabium miniatum 36
Saccolabium quisumbingii 181
Saccolabium somai 86
Saccolabium virgatum 149
Sarcanthus beckleri 149
Sarcanthus kunstleri 54
Sarcanthus recurvus 54
Sarcanthus tridentatus 155
Sarcochilus beckleri 149
Sarcochilus ceciliae 168
Sarcochilus divitiflorus 166
Sarcochilus eriochilus 168
Sarcochilus falcatus 86*, 168
Sarcochilus fitzgeraldii 169
Sarcochilus hartmannii 169
Sarcochilus hillii 170
Sarcochilus longmannii 150
Sarcochilus minutiflos 170
Sarcochilus montanus 168
Sarcochilus olivaceus 170

Sarcochilus rubricentrum 169
Sarcochilus spathulatus 150
Sarcochilus tridentatus 155
Sarcochilus weinthalii 150
Sarracenella pubescens 152
Schoenorchis fragrans* 171
Schoenorchis pachyrachis 171
Sedirea japonica 171
Sigmatostalix radicans 142
Smitinandia micrantha 172
Sophronitella violacea 22*, 172
Sophronitis brevipedunculata 173, 175*
Sophronitis cernua 173
Sophronitis coccinea 2, 174
Sophronitis grandiflora 174
Sophronitis hoffmannseggii 173
Sophronitis mantiqueirae 174, 175*
Sophronitis militaris 174
Sophronitis modesta 173
Sophronitis rosea 175
Sophronitis species ex Espirito Santo 175
Sophronitis violacea 172
Sophronitis wittigiana 175
Sophronitis wittigiana v. brevipedunculata 173
Stauroglottis equestris 151
Stelis diaphana* 176
Stelis guttifera* 176
Stelis penduliflora* 176
Stelis plurispicata* 176
Stelis species ex Mexico 176
Stelis species, vinosa alliance 176
Stelis tubata 154
Stelis vinosa* 176
Stenocoryne aureo-fulva 177
Stenocoryne melanopoda 177
Stenocoryne racemosa 178
Stenocoryne secunda 177
Stenocoryne vitellina 178
Stenoglottis fimbriata 179
Stenoglottis longifolia 179
Sturmia coelogynoides 103

Taeniophyllum cymbiforme 180
Taeniophyllum glandulosum 180
Taeniophyllum retrospiculatum 180
Taeniophyllum wilkianum 180
Tetramicra bicolor 102
Thrixspermum ceciliae 168
Thrixspermum falcatum 168
Thrixspermum hillii 170

Thrixspermum olivaceum 170
Thrixspermum tridentatum 155
Trias dayana 42
Trias oblonga 180
Trias ovata 180
Trias picta 181
Trichostosia dasyphylla 83
*Trudelia alpina** 182, 183

Trudelia cristata 182, 183*
Trudelia pumila 182*, 183
Tuberolabium kotoense 181

Vanda alpina* 182, 183
Vanda cristata 182, 183*
Vanda kimballiana 87
Vanda lilacina 182

Vanda laotica 182
Vanda pumila 182*, 183
Vanda striata 182

Zygopetalum stapelioides 163
Zygostates lunata 183
Zygostates pustulatus 74